Everyday Mathematics®

Student Reference Book

The University of Chicago
School Mathematics Project

Everyday Mathematics®

Student Reference Book

The University of Chicago
School Mathematics Project

EVERYDAY LEARNING™

Chicago, Illinois

Authors

Max Bell
Robert Balfanz
William Carroll
Robert Hartfield
James McBride
Peter Saecker

Art

Diana Barrie

Teachers in Residence

Amy Dillard
Kathleen Pitvorec
Denise Porter

Everyday Learning Development Staff

Editorial

John Bretzlauf
Patrick Carroll
Steve Mico

Production / Design

Fran Brown
Héctor Cuadra
Norma Underwood

Cover Design

Curtis Design

Acknowledgments:

Cover Paluan/Art Resource, NY © ARS, NY Knoedler Gallery, New York, N.Y., U.S.A.

Alexander Calder's "Sorel Horse" ©1998 Estate of Alexander Calder / Artists Rights Society (ARS), New York.

© Archive Photos: Ancient astronomical observations at the Observatory at Alexandria, Egypt.

Scala/Art Resource, NY

page 92 Art: Loops from *You Are a Mathematician* by David Wells. Copyright © 1995 by David Wells. Reprinted by permission of John Wiley & Sons, Inc.

page 144 Photo: St. Jerome/Scala/Art Resource, N.Y.

page 145 Photo: Alexander Calder's "Sea Scape, 1947" © 1976 Running Press, Philadelphia, Pennsylvania. Courtesy of Whitney Museum of American Art.

page 255 Photo: Ivory pendant mask from Benin. Courtesy of Corbis-Bettmann.

page 256 Photo: M.C. Escher's "Hand with Reflecting Sphere" © 1997 Cordon Art-Baarn-Holland. All rights reserved.

Photo: M.C. Escher's "Symmetry Drawing E 88" © 1997 Cordon Art-Baarn-Holland. All rights reserved.

page 260 Portrait: A.F. Möbius from The Newberry Library, Chicago.

Photo: M.C. Escher's "Möbius Strip II" © 1997 Cordon Art-Baarn-Holland. All rights reserved.

page 263 Chart: "Vibrations per Second" from *Listeners Guide to Musical Understanding*, 4e by Lean Dallin, Wm. C. Brown Publishers, 1977. Reprinted by permission.

page 268 Music: "America the Beautiful" from *Twenty Tunes to Arrange Set 1* arranged by McGinley. Copyright © 1953 (Renewed) by Shawnee Press, Inc. (ASCAP) International Copyright Secured. All Rights Reserved. Reprinted by Permission.

page 279 Music: Johann Sebastian Bach, *The Six Brandenburg Concertos and the Four Orchestral Suites in Full Score, from the Bach-Gesellschaft Edition*. New York: Dover Publications, 1976.

page 280 Poems: From *A Haiku Menagerie* by Stephen Addiss. New York, Weatherhill, Inc., 1992. Reprinted by permission.

page 283 "Poem" by William Carlos Williams from *Collected Poems 1909–1939, Volume 1*. Copyright 1939 by New Directions Publishing Corporation. Reprinted by permission of New Directions Publishing Corporation and Carcanet Press.

The *Student Reference Book* is based upon work supported by the National Science Foundation under Grant No. ESI-9252984. Any opinions, findings, conclusions, or recommendations expressed in this material are those of the authors and do not necessarily reflect the views of the National Science Foundation.

ISBN 1-57039-163-7

3 4 5 6 7 8 9 CU 02 01 00 99 98

Contents

Measurement 107

Problem Solving 129

Games　　194–195

Projects　　225

A **reference book** is a book that is organized to help people find information quickly and easily. Dictionaries, encyclopedias, atlases, cookbooks, even phone books are examples of reference books. Unlike novels and biographies, which are usually read in sequence from beginning to end, reference books are read in small segments to find specific information at the time it is needed.

You can use this *Student Reference Book* to look up and review information on topics in mathematics. It consists of the following sections:

- A **table of contents** that lists the topics covered and shows how the book is organized.

- Essays on **mathematical topics**, such as whole numbers, fractions, decimals, percents, geometry, measurement, problem solving, and data analysis.

- Descriptions of how to use **calculators** to perform various mathematical operations and functions.

- Directions on how to play some of the **mathematical games** you may have played before.

- Descriptions of **projects** you can do.

- A **glossary** of mathematical terms consisting of brief definitions of important words.

- A set of **quick-reference** pages that summarize information, such as a place-value chart, prefixes for names of large and small numbers, tables of equivalent measures and of equivalent fractions, decimals, and percents.

- An **answer key** for every *Check Your Understanding* problem in the book.

- An **index** to help you locate information quickly.

How to Use the Student Reference Book

Suppose you are asked to write the fraction $\frac{9}{15}$ in simplest terms. You know that you have solved many problems like this before, but at the moment, you are having difficulty remembering how to do it. This is a perfect time to use the *Student Reference Book*.

You can use the index at the back of the book or the table of contents to find the essay on Simplifying Fractions on page 26. Here you will find a definition of *simpler terms* and *simplest terms*, a brief description of how to simplify fractions, a step-by-step sample solution, and a description of how to use a calculator to solve the problem.

Notice the small book symbols shown in the margin. These refer to essays that are related to the topic under discussion. For example, since simplifying fractions involves finding equivalent fractions, there is a reference to page 25, which contains a description of how to find equivalent fractions. There is also a reference to page 31, where two ways of finding the greatest common factor of two numbers are shown, and a reference to page 184, which gives a more detailed description of how to work with fractions on a calculator.

There is also a set of problems at the bottom of the page, labeled *Check Your Understanding*. It is a good idea to solve these problems and then turn to the answer key at the back of the book to check your answers to make sure that you understand the information presented on the page.

Always read mathematical text with paper and pencil in hand. Take notes, draw pictures and diagrams to help you understand what you are reading. Work the examples. If you get a wrong answer in the *Check Your Understanding* problems, try to find your mistake by working back from the correct answer given in the answer key.

It is not always easy to read text about mathematics, but the more you use the *Student Reference Book,* the better you will become at understanding this kind of material. You may find that your skills as an independent problem-solver are improving. We are confident that these skills will serve you well as you undertake more advanced mathematics courses.

The numbers you have used in *Everyday Mathematics* include **counting numbers, whole numbers** (counting numbers and zero), **positive rational numbers** expressed as fractions, decimals, and percents, and the full set of **rational numbers**, consisting of all the positive rational numbers, their opposites, and zero.

These numbers were not invented all at once. The earliest civilizations knew only the numbers used for counting. These counting systems were based on various body parts. Some used fingers for counting, resulting in base-10 systems similar to our modern system. Others involved counting knuckles on one finger (base 3), knuckles on the fingers of one hand (base 12), fingers and toes (base 20), or spaces between fingers (base 4 or base 8). At first, there were no symbols for expressing counting numbers in written form.

Written symbols (**numerals**) were invented because people needed a permanent record of their transactions. At first, these numeration systems were very simple. For example, tally marks may have been used to keep track of the number of cattle being bartered. More sophisticated numeration systems, using place value, were invented in India before 5000 B.C. In time, zero was added to existing symbols to hold places in numerals. (Without zero or some other placeholder, 53 could mean 53, 503, 5003, 530, or many other numbers.) These numeration systems eventually evolved into our present-day, base-10 place-value system that allows recording both the relatively small counts of everyday life and very large numbers—in the millions, trillions, and beyond.

Counting numbers are useful for counting, but they do not work for measures, most of which fall between two consecutive whole numbers. Fraction and decimal notation were invented to keep track of such measures. For example, measures expressed as fractions are common in carpentry and other building trades; decimal notation is used for almost all measures in science and industry. Fractions are used almost exclusively in stock market quotations, while decimals are standard in all other financial applications.

Finally, negative numbers were invented to express quantities with reference to a zero point. For example, a temperature of 10 degrees below zero can be written as −10° and a depth of 2356 feet below sea level as −2356 feet. Positive and negative numbers are also used to express changes in quantities. For example, we can record a weight gain of $4\frac{1}{2}$ pounds as $+4\frac{1}{2}$ pounds and a decrease in income of 1000 dollars as −$1000.

Both the idea of negative numbers and the symbols for recording them were probably invented in India and used there in a systematic way by about 650 A.D.

Check Your Understanding

Write two sentences containing each kind of number.

1. a counting number   **2.** a fraction or a decimal   **3.** a negative number

Notation

With our present-day base-10 place-value system, any whole number, no matter how large, can be written using the ten digits 0 through 9. The value of each digit depends on its place in the numeral. For example, in the numeral 5,367,048 the digit 7 is in the thousands place and has a value of 7000, the digit 3 is in the hundred thousands place and has a value of 300,000. The digit 0, although it has a value of zero, does serve a purpose; without it, the number would be written as 536,748; the value of the digit 7 would be 700 instead of 7000; and the value of the digit 3 would be 30,000 instead of 300,000. The digit zero is in the hundreds place and has a value of zero.

Very large numbers—millions, trillions, and beyond, are often expressed with words (for example, 5 quintillion) or in scientific notation. One advantage of scientific notation is that computation with large numbers is easier. Scientific notation also makes it possible to work with numbers on a calculator consisting of more digits than can be shown on the calculator display.

Relations

When comparing whole numbers written in standard notation, the value of the digits in the places of the numerals tells you which numbers are largest and which are smallest. For example, 45,011 is greater than 39,999 because the value of the digit in the ten thousands place of 45,011 is 40,000, which is greater than the value of the corresponding digit in 39,999 (30,000). Numbers expressed in words give the same information. For numbers written in scientific notation, the larger the power of ten, the larger the number. For example, $1.006 * 10^9 = 1,006,000,000$ is greater than $9.99 * 10^6 = 9,990,000$ because 10^9 is greater than 10^6. On a number line, the greater the distance from 0, the greater the whole number.

> The following relation symbols are used:
>
> $<$ means "is less than"
> $=$ means "is equal to"
> $>$ means "is greater than"
>
> Examples:
>
> $39,999 < 45,011$
> $9,990,000 > 1,006,000$

Operations

Basic Facts, Fact Families, and Extended Facts: All procedures (algorithms) for doing operations with whole numbers depend on the basic facts for addition and multiplication of the numbers 0 through 9 and on the "extended facts" that are derived from the basic facts. The basic facts for addition and multiplication are linked with the operations of subtraction and division to form "fact families," which you first encountered in first grade.

> **Fact Families**
>
> | | |
> |---|---|
> | $3 + 5 = 8$ | $4 * 6 = 24$ |
> | $5 + 3 = 8$ | $6 * 4 = 24$ |
> | $8 - 5 = 3$ | $24/4 = 6$ |
> | $8 - 3 = 5$ | $24/6 = 4$ |

The extended facts are also very useful for estimating the size of answers.

Examples of Extended Facts

$200 + 300 = 500$	$6000 - 4000 = 2000$	$40 * 500 = 20,000$	$15,000/3000 = 5$
$7000 + 2000 = 9000$	$15,000 - 8000 = 7000$	$9 * 7000 = 63,000$	$8000/200 = 40$

Algorithms for Addition, Subtraction, Multiplication, and Division of Whole Numbers: In today's world, we can use calculators and computers to do almost any calculation we wish. Still, it is worthwhile to know some easy ways to do calculations mentally or with pencil and paper.

- Inventing or learning such procedures teaches us about how each operation works and the basic meanings of and relationships among operations.

- It is often quicker to do easy calculations mentally or on paper than to find and then use a calculator.

- Knowing at least one algorithm for each standard operation with whole numbers often helps in making good estimates, which are often all one needs to solve a problem.

By now, you probably have a favorite algorithm for each of the operations. Here is an example of each of our favorites.

Addition	**Subtraction**	**Multiplication**	**Division**	
4792	7016	365	27)7364	100
+ 5069	− 2593	* 72	−2700	
9000	5000	21000	4664	100
700	− 500	4200	−2700	
150	− 80	350	1964	50
11	3	600	−1350	
9861	4423	120	614	20
		10	− 540	
		26280	74	
			− 54	2
			20	
			272 R20	

If you know how to solve any of these problems another way, try it to see if you get the same answer.

Dozens of other algorithms exist; a few of them are shown, beginning on page 9.

Any number, no matter how large or small, can be written using the **digits** 0, 1, 2, 3, 4, 5, 6, 7, 8, and 9. The **value** of a digit depends on its **place** in the numeral. As you move from right to left in a numeral, the value of each place becomes 10 times greater, as shown in the following **place-value chart**.

10 thousands	thousands	hundreds	tens	ones
10 * 1000	10 * 100	10 * 10	10 * 1	1
8	2	7	0	3

Example:

In the numeral 82,703 shown in the place-value chart above, the value of the 8 is 80,000 (8 * 10,000); the value of the 2 is 2000 (2 * 1000); the value of the 7 is 700 (7 * 100); and so on.

82,703 is read as "eighty-two thousand, seven hundred three."

In numerals for larger numbers, groups of 3 digits are separated by commas. This helps identify the thousands, millions, billions, and trillions, as shown in the following place-value chart.

trillions			billions			millions			thousands			ones		
100	10	1	100	10	1	100	10	1	100	10	1	100	10	1

• Digits followed by **3** whole-number places name **thousands**.

• Digits followed by **6** whole-number places name **millions**.

• Digits followed by **9** whole-number places name **billions**.

• Digits followed by **12** whole-number places name **trillions**.

The next group of 3 places to the left name **quadrillions**, then **quintillions**, **sextillions**, **septillions**, **octillions**, and so on.

Note that 1 thousand is the same as 1000 ones; 1 million is the same as 1000 thousands; 1 billion is the same as 1000 millions; and 1 trillion is the same as 1000 billions.

Check Your Understanding

How would you read the following numbers?

1. 27,308   2. 91,672,450   3. 675,000,000,000   4. 7,000,420

5. What is the value of the 7 in each of the numerals in Problems 1–4?

Exponential Notation

A **square array** is a special rectangular array consisting of the same number of rows and columns. A whole number that can be represented by a square array is called a **square number**. Any square number can be written as the product of a number multiplied by itself.

Example:

> 16 is a square number because it can be represented by an array consisting of 4 rows and 4 columns. 16 can be written as 4 * 4.

16

There is a shorthand way of writing square numbers:

$$16 = 4 * 4 = 4^2$$

4^2 can be read as "4 times 4," "4 squared," or "4 to the second power." The raised 2 is called the **exponent**. It tells that 4 is used as a factor two times. The 4 is called the **base**. Numbers written with an exponent are said to be in **exponential notation**.

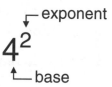

Exponents can also be used to write products that result from a factor being used more than twice.

Examples:

> $2^3 = 2 * 2 * 2$. The number 2 is used as a factor 3 times. It may be read as "2 cubed" or "2 to the third power."
>
> $9^5 = 9 * 9 * 9 * 9 * 9$. The number 9 is used as a factor 5 times. It is read as "9 to the fifth power."
>
> Any number raised to the first power is equal to itself. For example, $5^1 = 5$, since 5 is used as a factor once.

Some calculators have special keys for renaming numbers written in exponential notation as standard numerals.

- The $[x^2]$ key can be used for finding the *square* of a number.
- The $[y^x]$ key can be used for finding *any power* of a number.

190

Examples:

> To rename 15^2, press 15 $[x^2]$. The display shows 225.
>
> To rename 8^6, press 8 $[y^x]$ 6 [=]. The display shows 262,144, so $8^6 = 262,144$. You can verify this by keying in 8 [×] 8 [×] 8 [×] 8 [×] 8 [×] 8 [=].

Check Your Understanding

Write each number without exponents. Do not use a calculator to solve Problems 1–4.

1. 5^2 **2.** 3^3 **3.** 10^5 **4.** 8^1 **5.** 345^2 **6.** 12^4

Scientific Notation for Big Numbers

In the statement "The population of the world is about $6 * 10^9$ people," $6 * 10^9$ is written in **scientific notation**. It is read as "six times ten to the ninth power."

Scientific notation is a way to represent big and small numbers with only a few symbols. A number in scientific notation is written as the product of two factors. **The first factor is at least 1 but less than 10. The second factor is a power of ten.**

Example:

> Write $6 * 10^9$ in **standard notation.**
>
> First, look at the power of 10. It is 10 to the ninth power, so it is the product of 10 used as a factor 9 times:
>
> $$10^9 = 10 * 10 * 10 * 10 * 10 * 10 * 10 * 10 * 10$$
> $$= 1,000,000,000 = 1 \text{ billion}$$
>
> So $6 * 10^9 = 6 * 1,000,000,000$
> $$= 6,000,000,000 = 6 \text{ billion}$$

5 | 6

Often the first factor of a number in scientific notation has digits to the right of the decimal point.

Examples:

> The nearest star after the Sun is about $2.5 * 10^{13}$ miles away. In standard notation, $2.5 * 10^{13} = 2.5 * 10,000,000,000,000 = 25,000,000,000,000$. $2.5 * 10^{13}$ is best read as "two and five tenths times ten to the thirteenth power." It can be read more briefly as "two point five times ten to the thirteenth."
>
> There are about $8.07 * 10^{67}$ different ways to arrange a deck of 52 playing cards. In standard notation, $8.07 * 10^{67}$ can be written as 807 followed by 65 zeros.

50 | 51

Scientific Notation for Small Numbers

Small numbers (positive numbers less than 1) are written in scientific notation with negative powers of 10.

39

Example:

> The smallest virus has a diameter of about $2 * 10^{-5}$ millimeter. In standard notation,
>
> $$2 * 10^{-5} = 2 * \left(\tfrac{1}{10}\right)^5 = 2 * \tfrac{1}{10} * \tfrac{1}{10} * \tfrac{1}{10} * \tfrac{1}{10} * \tfrac{1}{10}$$
> $$= 2 * \tfrac{1}{100,000}$$
> $$= 0.00002$$
>
> $2 * 10^{-5}$ is read as "two times ten to the negative five power."

Scientific Notation (continued)

Converting Notations

From Scientific Notation to Standard Notation

Examples:

Convert $8.7 * 10^6$ and $5.6 * 10^{-4}$ to standard notation.

1. Note the exponent in the power of 10. $\qquad$ $8.7 * 10^6$ $\qquad\qquad$ $5.6 * 10^{-4}$

2. If the exponent is *positive*, as in $8.7 * 10^6$, move the decimal point in the other factor that many places to the *right*. (Insert the decimal point if necessary, and attach 0's as you move it.)

8 . 7 0 0 0 0 0 .
(6 places)
$8.7 * 10^6 = 8,700,000$

3. If the exponent is *negative*, as in $5.6 * 10^{-4}$, move the decimal point in the other factor that many places to the *left*. (Insert the decimal point if necessary, and attach 0's as you move it.)

0 . 0 0 0 5 . 6
(4 places)
$5.6 * 10^{-4} = 0.00056$

From Standard Notation to Scientific Notation

Examples:

Convert 8,700,000 and 0.00056 from standard notation to scientific notation.

1. Locate the decimal point. Write or imagine the decimal point if it isn't there.

8,700,000. $\qquad\qquad$ 0.00056

2. Move the decimal point so that you get a number with only one digit (not 0) to the left of the decimal point (in the ones place). Count the number of places you moved the decimal point.

8 . 7 0 0 0 0 0 . $\qquad$ 0 . 0 0 0 5 . 6
(6 places) $\qquad\qquad$ (4 places)

3. The number of places you moved the decimal point tells which power of 10 to use. If the original number was between 0 and 1, the power is negative.

10^6 $\qquad\qquad$ 10^{-4}

4. Use the number you got in Step 2 and the power of 10 you got in Step 3 to write the number in scientific notation. Omit any 0's you don't need.

$8,700,000 = 8.7 * 10^6$ $\qquad$ $0.00056 = 5.6 * 10^{-4}$

Check Your Understanding

1. Write in scientific notation.

    a. 500,000 $\qquad$ **b.** 10 billion $\qquad$ **c.** 750,000,000 $\qquad$ **d.** 0.00008 $\qquad$ **e.** 0.045

2. Write in standard notation.

    a. $3 * 10^8$ $\qquad$ **b.** $4.1 * 10^7$ $\qquad$ **c.** $7.09 * 10^{10}$ $\qquad$ **d.** $4 * 10^{-3}$ $\qquad$ **e.** $9.06 * 10^{-2}$

The Opposite-Change Rule

When a number is added to one addend and **the same number** is subtracted from the other addend, the sum is the same.

You can use this rule to make the problem easier by changing **either of the addends** to a number with zero in the ones place.

Example: 59 + 26 = ?

One way: Add and subtract 1.			Another way: Subtract and add 4.		
59	(add 1)	60	59	(subtract 4)	55
+ 26	(subtract 1)	+ 25	+ 26	(add 4)	+ 30
		85			85

The Partial-Sums Method

Add from left to right, one column at a time. Then add the partial sums.

Example: 496 + 229 + 347 = ?

$$\begin{array}{r} 496 \\ 229 \\ + 347 \end{array}$$

Add the hundreds: 400 + 200 + 300 =   900
Add the tens: 90 + 20 + 40 =   150
Add the ones: 6 + 9 + 7 =   22
Find the total: 900 + 150 + 22 =   1072

A Short Algorithm

Add from right to left, one column at a time, without displaying partial sums.

Example: 275 + 98 = ?

Step 1
Add the ones.

$$\begin{array}{r} \overset{1}{2}75 \\ + 98 \\ \hline 3 \end{array}$$

(5 ones + 8 ones = 13 ones
= 1 ten + 3 ones)

Step 2
Add the tens.

$$\begin{array}{r} \overset{11}{2}75 \\ + 98 \\ \hline 73 \end{array}$$

(1 ten + 7 tens + 9 tens =
17 tens = 1 hundred + 7 tens)

Step 3
Add the hundreds.

$$\begin{array}{r} \overset{11}{2}75 \\ + 98 \\ \hline 373 \end{array}$$

(1 hundred + 2 hundreds =
3 hundreds)

Check Your Understanding

1. 75 + 38   **2.** 68 + 296   **3.** 538 + 427   **4.** 769 + 348 + 692   **5.** 3942 + 5781

Subtraction Algorithms

The Same-Change Rule

In a subtraction problem, if **the same number** is added to or subtracted from both numbers in the problem, the answer is the same.

You can use this rule to make the problem easier by changing the **second number** in the problem to a number with zero in the ones place.

Example: 92 – 36 = ?

One way: Add 4.

$$\begin{array}{r} 92 \\ - 36 \\ \hline \end{array} \quad \begin{array}{l} \text{(add 4)} \\ \text{(add 4)} \end{array} \quad \begin{array}{r} 96 \\ - 40 \\ \hline 56 \end{array}$$

Another way: Subtract 6.

$$\begin{array}{r} 92 \\ - 36 \\ \hline \end{array} \quad \begin{array}{l} \text{(subtract 6)} \\ \text{(subtract 6)} \end{array} \quad \begin{array}{r} 86 \\ - 30 \\ \hline 56 \end{array}$$

The Partial-Differences Method

Subtract from left to right, one column at a time. Then add the partial differences.

Example: 8520 – 2364 = ?

$$\begin{array}{r} 8520 \\ - 2364 \\ \hline \end{array}$$

Subtract the thousands: 8000 – 2000 = 6000
Subtract the hundreds: 500 – 300 = 200   (6000 + 200 = 6200)
Subtract the tens: 20 – 60 = – 40   (6200 – 40 = 6160)
Subtract the ones: 0 – 4 = – 4   (6160 – 4 = 6156)
Find the total: 6000 + 200 – 40 – 4 = 6156

A Short Algorithm

Subtract from right to left, one column at a time, without displaying partial differences.

Example: 592 – 297 = ?

Step 1
Rename the tens and ones and subtract the ones.

$$\begin{array}{r} {}^{8}\;\; \\ 5\,\overset{1}{9}\,2 \\ -2\,9\,7 \\ \hline 5 \end{array}$$

(9 tens + 2 ones =
8 tens + 12 ones)

Step 2
Rename the hundreds and tens and subtract the tens.

$$\begin{array}{r} {}^{4}{}^{1}8\; \\ 5\,\overset{1}{9}\,2 \\ -2\,9\,7 \\ \hline 9\,5 \end{array}$$

(5 hundreds + 8 tens =
4 hundreds + 18 tens)

Step 3
Subtract the hundreds.

$$\begin{array}{r} {}^{4}{}^{1}8\; \\ 5\,\overset{1}{9}\,2 \\ -2\,9\,7 \\ \hline 2\,9\,5 \end{array}$$

Check Your Understanding

1. 76 – 39   **2.** 81 – 47   **3.** 635 – 275   **4.** 307 – 292   **5.** 700 – 361

Numbers such as 10, 100, and 1000 are called **powers of 10**. To multiply a whole number *n* by a power of 10, simply attach as many zeros to the right of the number *n* as there are zeros in the power of 10.

Examples:

10 * 64 = 640	**10** * 30 = 300	**100** * 270 = 27,000
100 * 64 = 6400	**100** * 30 = 3000	**10,000** * 61 = 610,000
1000 * 64 = 64,000	**1000** * 30 = 30,000	**1,000,000** * 8 = 8,000,000

If you have memorized the multiplication facts, you can solve problems such as 8 * 60 and 4000 * 3 in your head.

Examples:

8 * 60 = ?	4000 * 3 = ?
Think: 8 [6's] = 48	Think: 4 [3's] = 12
Since 8 [60's] is 10 times as much, 8 * 60 = 480.	Since 4000 [3's] is 1000 times as much, 4000 * 3 = 12,000.

You can use a similar method to solve problems such as 30 * 50 and 200 * 90 in your head.

Examples:

30 * 50 = ?	200 * 90 = ?
Think: 3 [50's] = 150	Think: 2 [90's] = 180
Since 30 [50's] is 10 times as much, 30 * 50 = 1500.	Since 200 [90's] is 100 times as much, 200 * 90 = 18,000.

Check Your Understanding

Solve these problems in your head.

1. 1000 * 37   2. 6 * 400   3. 3000 * 8   4. 70 * 30   5. 600 * 50

Multiplication Algorithms

Example: 73 * 46 = ?

The Partial-Products Method

Multiply each part of one factor by each part of the other factor. Then add the partial products.

$$
\begin{array}{r}
73 \\
*\;\; 46 \\
\hline
\end{array}
$$

40 * 70 =	2800
40 * 3 =	120
6 * 70 =	420
6 * 3 =	+ 18
	3358

A Short Algorithm

Multiply each part of the second factor by the first factor.

$$
\begin{array}{r}
73 \\
*\;\; 46 \\
\hline
\end{array}
$$

6 * 73 =	438
40 * 73 =	+ 2920
	3358

The Lattice Method

Step 1
Write the factors on the outside of the lattice.

Step 2
Multiply each digit in one factor by each digit in the other factor.

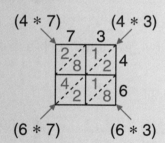

(4 * 7)   (4 * 3)

(6 * 7)   (6 * 3)

Step 3
Add the numbers inside the lattice along each diagonal.

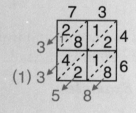

The Egyptian Method

Step 1
Start with 1 in the first column and 46 in the second column. Double the numbers in each column. It is not necessary to go past 73 in the first column.

Step 2
Check off the numbers in the first column whose sum is 73 (1 + 8 + 64 = 73). Cross out the numbers in the unchecked rows.

Step 3
Add the remaining numbers in the second column. (46 + 368 + 2944 = 3358)

73 * 46

✓	1	46
	2	92
	4	184
✓	8	368
	16	736
	32	1472
✓	64	+ 2944
		3358

Check Your Understanding

Multiply.

1. 7 * 461   **2.** 9 * 3795   **3.** 54 * 97   **4.** 78 * 43   **5.** 23 * 217

Numbers such as 10, 100, and 1000 are called **powers of 10**. To divide a whole number n by a power of 10, simply cross out as many zeros in the number n, starting in the ones place, as there are zeros in the power of 10.

11

Examples:

$48{,}000/\mathbf{10} = 4800\cancel{0}$	$70{,}000/\mathbf{10} = 7000\cancel{0}$	$46{,}000/\mathbf{100} = 460\cancel{00}$
$48{,}000/\mathbf{100} = 480\cancel{00}$	$70{,}000/\mathbf{100} = 700\cancel{00}$	$830{,}000/\mathbf{10{,}000} = 83\cancel{0000}$
$48{,}000/\mathbf{1000} = 48\cancel{000}$	$70{,}000/\mathbf{1000} = 70\cancel{000}$	$3{,}000{,}000/\mathbf{100{,}000} = 30\cancel{00000}$

If you know the division facts, you can solve problems such as $540/9$ and $\frac{15{,}000}{5}$ in your head.

Examples:

$540/9 = ?$	$\frac{15{,}000}{5} = ?$
Think: $54/9 = 6$	Think: $15/5 = 3$
Since $540/9$ is 10 times as much, $540/9 = 10 * 6 = 60$.	Since $15{,}000/5$ is 1000 times as much, $15{,}000/5 = 1000 * 3 = 3000$.

You can use a similar method to solve problems such as $\frac{18{,}000}{30}$ and $32{,}000/400$ in your head.

Examples:

$\frac{18{,}000}{30} = ?$	$32{,}000/400 = ?$
Think: $18{,}000/3 = 6000$	Think: $32{,}000/4 = 8000$
Since $18{,}000/30$ is $\frac{1}{10}$ as much, $18{,}000/30 = \frac{1}{10}$ of $6000 = 600$.	Since $32{,}000/400$ is $\frac{1}{100}$ as much, $32{,}000/400 = \frac{1}{100}$ of $8000 = 80$.

Check Your Understanding

Solve these problems in your head.

1. $53{,}000/1000$ 2. $3600/4$ 3. $\frac{24{,}000}{8}$ 4. $4200/70$ 5. $\frac{45{,}000}{900}$

Example: 95/6 = ?

Estimate. How many [6's] in 95?		
Calculate 10 * 6.		
Subtract. Estimate again.		
Calculate 5 * 6.		
Subtract.		

$$6\overline{)95}$$ | 10 (10 [6's] in 95)
− 60
35 | 5 (5 [6's] in 35)
− 30
5 |

Add the estimates. 15

The **quotient** is 15 with a **remainder** of 5. We can write the answer as 15 R5.

Example: 371/4 = ?

One way:

$$4\overline{)371}$$ | 50
− 200
171 | 30
− 120
51 | 10
− 40
11 | 2
− 8
3

92 R3

Another way:

$$4\overline{)371}$$ | 50
− 200
171 | 40
− 160
11 | 2
− 8
3

92 R3

Another way:

$$4\overline{)371}$$ | 90
− 360
11 | 2
− 8
3

92 R3

Example: $\frac{788}{3}$ = ?

One way:

$$3\overline{)788}$$ | 100
− 300
488 | 100
− 300
188 | 50
− 150
38 | 10
− 30
8 | 2
− 6
2

262 R2

Another way:

$$3\overline{)788}$$ | 200
− 600
188 | 60
− 180
8 | 2
− 6
2

262 R2

On a calculator:
Key in:

788 [INT÷] 3 [=]

The display shows:

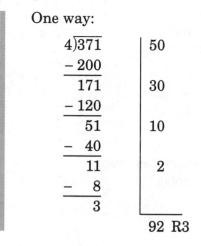

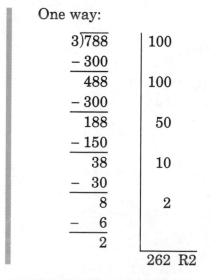

Check Your Understanding

Divide.

1. 85/2   2. 130/7   3. $\frac{166}{3}$ 4. 694/5   5. $\frac{921}{4}$

Division Algorithm—2-Digit Divisors

Example: 575/22 = ?

9 11 14

Estimate. How many [22's] in 575?	22)575	10	(10 [22's] in 575)
Calculate 10 * 22.	– 220		
Subtract. Estimate again.	355	10	(10 [22's] in 355)
Calculate 10 * 22.	– 220		
Subtract. Estimate again.	135	5	(5 [22's] in 135)
Calculate 5 * 22.	– 110		
Calculate 1 * 22.	25	1	(1 [22] in 25)
Subtract.	– 22		
Add the estimates.	3		
		26 R3	

It takes fewer steps if you use better estimates, as shown below.

Estimate. How many [22's] in 575?	22)575	20	(20 [22's] in 575)
Calculate 20 * 22.	– 440		
Subtract. Estimate again.	135	6	(6 [22's] in 135)
Calculate 6 * 22.	– 132		
Subtract.	3		
Add the estimates.		26 R3	

Example: $\frac{891}{18}$ = ?

One way:

18)891	20
– 360	
531	20
– 360	
171	5
– 90	
81	3
– 54	
27	
– 18	1
9	
	49 R9

Another way:

18)891	40
– 720	
171	9
– 162	
9	
	49 R9

On a calculator:

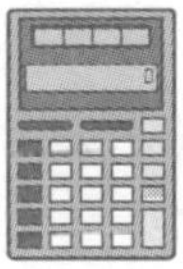

Key in:

891 [INT÷] 18 [=]

The display shows:

Q 49, R 9

183

Check Your Understanding

Divide.

1. 544/8
2. $\frac{195}{12}$
3. 782/35
4. $\frac{1853}{26}$

Factors

A **rectangular array** is an arrangement of objects in rows and columns. Each row has the same number of objects and each column also has the same number of objects. A rectangular array can be represented by a multiplication **number model**.

6

Example:

> This rectangular array has 15 dots.
> It has 3 rows with 5 dots in each row.
> 3 * 5 = 15 is a number model for this array.
> 3 and 5 are whole-number **factors** of 15.
> 15 is the **product** of 3 and 5.
> 3 and 5 are a **factor pair** for 15.

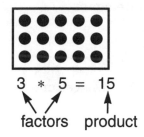

$$3 \quad * \quad 5 \quad = \quad 15$$

factors   product

Numbers can have more than one factor pair.

- 1 and 15 are also factors of 15 because 1 * 15 = 15.

- 1 and 15 is another factor pair for 15.

To test whether a number f is a whole-number factor of a number p, divide p by f. If the result is a whole number and the remainder is 0, then f is a factor of p.

17

Examples:

> 4 is a factor of 12 because 12/4 gives 3 with a remainder of 0.
> The number 12 is said to be **divisible by** 4.
>
> 6 is not a factor of 14 because 14/6 gives 2 with a remainder of 2.
> The number 14 is *not* divisible by 6.

One way to find all the factors of a number is to find all the factor pairs for that number.

Example: Find all the whole-number factors of the number 24.

Number Models	Factor Pairs	
24 = 1 * 24	1, 24	
24 = 2 * 12	2, 12	The whole-number factors of 24 are
24 = 3 * 8	3, 8	1, 2, 3, 4, 6, 8, 12, and 24.
24 = 4 * 6	4, 6	

Check Your Understanding

List all the whole-number factors of each number.

1. 8   **2.** 27   **3.** 49   **4.** 36   **5.** 13   **6.** 100

When a whole number is divided by a whole number and the quotient is a whole number with a remainder of 0, then the first number is **divisible by** the second number.

Example:

| 124/4 → 31 R0 The remainder is 0, so 124 is divisible by 4.

When a whole number is divided by a whole number and the quotient is a whole number with a non-zero remainder, then the first number is *not divisible* by the second number.

Example:

| 88/5 → 17 R3 The remainder is not 0, so 88 is not divisible by 5.

For some numbers, even large ones, it is possible to test for divisibility without dividing. Here are a few **divisibility tests** that make it unnecessary to divide:

- All numbers are **divisible by 1**.
- All even numbers, numbers with 0, 2, 4, 6, or 8 in the ones place, are **divisible by 2**.
- Any whole number with 0 in the ones place is **divisible by 10**.
- Any whole number with 0 or 5 in the ones place is **divisible by 5**.
- If the sum of the digits in a whole number is divisible by 3, then the number is **divisible by 3**.
- If the sum of the digits in a whole number is divisible by 9, then the number is **divisible by 9**.
- If a whole number is divisible by both 2 and by 3, it is **divisible by 6**.

Examples:

| 216 is divisible by
| 2 because 6 in the ones place is an even number;
| 3 because the sum of its digits is 9, which is divisible by 3;
| 9 because the sum of its digits is 9, which is divisible by 9;
| 6 because it is divisible both by 2 and by 3.
| 216 is not divisible by 10 or by 5 because it does not have 0 or 5 in the ones place.

| 340 is divisible by 2, 5, and 10 because it has 0 in the ones place.
| 340 is not divisible by 3 or 9 because the sum of its digits is 7, and 7 is not
| divisible by 3 or 9.
| 340 is not divisible by 6 because it is not divisible by both 2 and 3.

Check Your Understanding

Which numbers are divisible by 2? By 3? By 5? By 6? By 9? By 10?

| 105 | 6270 | 526 | 711 | 13,680 |

Prime and Composite Numbers

A **prime number** is a whole number greater than 1 that has exactly two whole-number factors: 1 and the number itself. A prime number is divisible only by 1 and itself.

A **composite number** is a whole number that has more than two whole-number factors. A composite number is divisible by at least three whole numbers.

Examples:

> 11 is a prime number because its only whole-number factors are 1 and 11.
>
> 20 is a composite number because it has more than two whole-number factors. Its factors are 1, 2, 4, 5, 10, and 20.
>
> The number 1 is neither prime nor composite.

Every composite number can be renamed as a product of prime numbers.

Example:

> The number 48 can be renamed as the product 2 * 2 * 2 * 2 * 3. This is called the **prime factorization** of 48. Using exponential notation, the prime factorization of 48 is written as $2^4 * 3$.

One way to find the prime factorization of a number is to make a **factor tree**. First, write the number. Then, underneath, write any two factors whose product is that number. Repeat the process for these two factors. Continue until all the factors are prime numbers.

Example:

> Find the prime factorization of 24. No matter which two factors are used to start the tree, the tree will always end with the same prime factors.

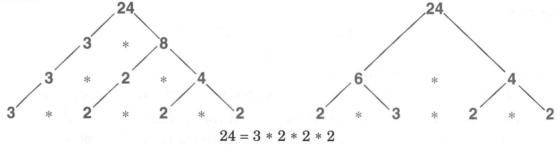

$$24 = 3 * 2 * 2 * 2$$

> The prime factorization of 24 is 2 * 2 * 2 * 3.

Check Your Understanding

Make a factor tree to find the prime factorization of each number.

1. 12   2. 28   3. 50   4. 36   5. 32   6. 60

Whole numbers work fine for counts, but there are many other situations for which **positive rational numbers**—numbers which fall between consecutive whole numbers—are needed.

Notation

Positive rational numbers can be written in any of three forms: as fractions, as decimals, and as percents. Even though fraction, decimal, and percent forms are interchangeable, each form has its own special characteristics, and the ways of doing standard operations with the three notations are very different.

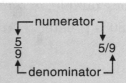

A fraction consists of a pair of numbers (numerator and denominator) separated by either a slash or a horizontal segment. (This separator is called a *vinculum*.) In simple cases, the denominator indicates the number of equal divisions, or parts, of some ONE or whole. The denominator may be any whole number except zero. The numerator indicates the number of parts named by the fraction. The numerator may be any whole number.

$$\frac{\text{numerator}}{} \qquad \frac{5}{9} \qquad 5/9 \qquad \frac{}{\text{denominator}}$$

A fraction may be used to indicate division of *any* two numbers (except division by zero), not just whole numbers. The numerator or denominator of a fraction might be a decimal or even a fraction or mixed number.

$$\frac{2.3}{6.5} \qquad \frac{1\frac{4}{5}}{12} \qquad \frac{\frac{3}{4}}{\frac{5}{8}}$$

If you look in any high school mathematics book, you will see fractions such as $\frac{\sqrt{2}}{2}$ or $\frac{4\pi}{3}$; these are called **irrational numbers**. One way in which irrational numbers differ from rational numbers is that they cannot be written as decimals that terminate, such as 2.25, or that have one or more repeating digits, such as 0.66666.... Decimals that name irrational numbers go on without end, without any repeating pattern in the digits.

In this book, all fractions represent rational numbers, unless you are specifically told otherwise.

Relations

Fraction notation has two powerful properties:

- Any rational number can be represented by an unlimited number of fraction names.

$$\frac{2}{3}, \frac{4}{6}, \frac{6}{9}, \frac{8}{12}, \cdots$$

- Any two (or more) fractions can be written with the same (common) denominator.

$$\frac{2}{3}, \frac{1}{2} \rightarrow \frac{4}{6}, \frac{3}{6}$$

Fractions that name the same rational number are called **equivalent fractions**. You can rename a fraction as an equivalent fraction by multiplying or dividing its numerator and denominator by the same number.

$$\frac{2}{3} = \frac{2*2}{3*2} = \frac{4}{6}$$

$$\frac{9}{12} = \frac{9/3}{12/3} = \frac{3}{4}$$

The common denominator property can be used to determine which of two fractions is greater (or whether two fractions are equivalent). Simply rename one or both fractions as equivalent fractions with a common denominator and compare the numerators. For example, to compare $\frac{2}{3}$ and $\frac{3}{4}$, rename each fraction as an equivalent fraction whose denominator is 12:

$$\frac{2}{3} = \frac{2*4}{3*4} = \frac{8}{12} \text{ and } \frac{3*3}{4*3} = \frac{9}{12}$$

Since $\frac{9}{12}$ is greater than $\frac{8}{12}$, $\frac{3}{4}$ is greater than $\frac{2}{3}$.

Another way to compare two fractions is to convert both to decimal form. For example, to compare $\frac{3}{4}$ and $\frac{4}{5}$, rename $\frac{3}{4}$ as 0.75 and $\frac{4}{5}$ as 0.80. Since 0.80 is greater than 0.75, $\frac{4}{5}$ is greater than $\frac{3}{4}$.

Operations

Inverse, reciprocal: One advantage of rational numbers is illustrated by these examples:

$$2 * \frac{1}{2} = 1;\ 10 * \frac{1}{10} = 1;\ \frac{1}{3} * 3 = 1;\ \frac{3}{4} * \frac{4}{3} = 1;\ \frac{1}{1000} * 1000 = 1$$

That is, for any rational number except 0, you can find another rational number so that the product of the two rational numbers is 1. Each of these numbers is called the **multiplicative inverse** or **reciprocal** of the other. Reciprocals are useful when dividing fractions and in simplifying fairly complicated fractions.

The reciprocal of any fraction $\frac{a}{b}$ is the fraction $\frac{b}{a}$. For example, the reciprocal of $\frac{3}{4}$ is $\frac{4}{3}$, since $\frac{3}{4} * \frac{4}{3} = 1$.

Since any whole number can be written as a fraction with a denominator of 1, the reciprocal of a whole number (except 0) is a fraction with 1 in the numerator and the whole number in the denominator. For example, $5 = \frac{5}{1}$ and the reciprocal of $\frac{5}{1}$ is $\frac{1}{5}$. Similarly, the reciprocal of any fraction $\frac{1}{a}$ is the number a. For example, the reciprocal of $\frac{1}{4}$ is $\frac{4}{1}$, or simply 4.

Addition and subtraction: Simply rename the fractions as fractions with a common denominator and add or subtract the numerators. Write the result over the common denominator.

Multiplication: Multiply the numerators and multiply the denominators.

Division: Multiply the first fraction by the reciprocal of the second fraction. Another way to divide two fractions is to rename the fractions as fractions with a common denominator and divide the numerators.

Procedures for operations with fractions and mixed numbers are described in greater detail beginning on page 32.

$$\frac{2}{3} + \frac{1}{4} = \frac{8}{12} + \frac{3}{12} = \frac{11}{12}$$

$$\frac{5}{8} - \frac{1}{2} = \frac{5}{8} - \frac{4}{8} = \frac{1}{8}$$

$$\frac{2}{5} * \frac{1}{3} = \frac{2*1}{5*3} = \frac{2}{15}$$

$$\frac{3}{8} \div \frac{1}{4} = \frac{3}{8} * \frac{4}{1}$$

$$= \frac{12}{8} = 1\frac{4}{8}, \text{ or } 1\frac{1}{2}$$

Notation	$\frac{a}{b}$ or a/b, where the **numerator** a can be any number at all and the **denominator** b is any number *except zero*.

$\frac{a}{b}$ ← numerator
← denominator $b \neq 0$

Many Names	A number can be written as a fraction in infinitely many ways by multiplying or dividing both numerator and denominator by the same number. That number also has a decimal name and a percent name, which can be found by dividing numerator by denominator.

															0.5	50%
$\frac{1}{2}$,	$\frac{2}{4}$,	$\frac{3}{6}$,	$\frac{4}{8}$,	$\frac{5}{10}$,	$\frac{6}{12}$,	$\frac{7}{14}$,	$\frac{8}{16}$,	$\frac{9}{18}$,	$\frac{10}{20}$,	$\frac{11}{22}$,	$\frac{12}{24}$,	$\frac{13}{26}$,	$\frac{14}{28}$,	$\frac{15}{30}$	0.5	50%
$\frac{1}{3}$,	$\frac{2}{6}$,	$\frac{3}{9}$,	$\frac{4}{12}$,	$\frac{5}{15}$,	$\frac{6}{18}$,	$\frac{7}{21}$,	$\frac{8}{24}$,	$\frac{9}{27}$,	$\frac{10}{30}$,	$\frac{11}{33}$,	$\frac{12}{36}$,	$\frac{13}{39}$,	$\frac{14}{42}$,	$\frac{15}{45}$	$0.\overline{3}$	$33\frac{1}{3}\%$

Using Equivalent Names	Two fractions can be compared, added, or subtracted by using  fractions with the same denominator. You can also use the decimal names to decide which is bigger or smaller, or to add and subtract.

$\frac{2}{3} < \frac{3}{4}$ since $\frac{8}{12} < \frac{9}{12}$ and $0.\overline{6} < 0.75$

$\frac{2}{3} + \frac{1}{6} = \frac{4}{6} + \frac{1}{6} = \frac{5}{6}$ $\frac{3}{4} - \frac{3}{5} = 0.75 - 0.60 = 0.15$

Uses	**Parts of Wholes** 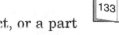

Fractions are used to name a part of a whole object, or a part of a collection of objects.

$\frac{5}{6}$ of the hexagon is shaded. $\frac{6}{10}$ of the dimes are circled.

Points on Number Lines

Fractions can name points on a number line that are "in-between" points named with whole numbers.

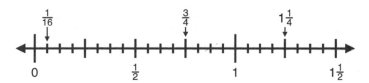

Uses

"In-Between" Measures

Fractions can name measures that are "in-between" whole measures.

Division Notation

A fraction $\frac{a}{b}$ is another way of saying a divided by b.

$$\frac{a}{b} \qquad a/b$$
$$a \div b \qquad b\overline{)a}$$

Ratios

Fractions are used to compare quantities with the same unit.

Curie won 7 out of 17 ($\frac{7}{17}$ or about 41%) games during last year's basketball season.

PUBLIC-RED CENTRAL		
	Conf.	Overall
Dunbar	4-0	9-6
King	4-1	14-4
Robeson	3-2	8-9
Gage Park	2-3	8-10
Harper	2-4	8-7
Curie	1-3	7-10
Hubbard	1-4	8-9

Rates

Fractions are used to compare quantities with different units.

Bill's car can travel about 35 miles on 1 gallon of gasoline. At this rate, it can travel about 245 miles on 7 gallons of gasoline.

$$\frac{35 \text{ mi}}{1 \text{ gal}} = \frac{245 \text{ mi}}{7 \text{ gal}}$$

Scales

Fractions are used to compare a drawing or a model to the actual size of the object.

A scale on a map given as 1:100,000 (another way of expressing 1/100,000), means that each inch on the map represents 100,000 inches or about $1\frac{1}{2}$ miles.

Probabilities

Fractions are a way to describe the chance that an event will happen.

In a well shuffled playing card deck (52 cards), the chance of selecting the ace of spades on a given draw is $\frac{1}{52}$ or about 2%. The chance of drawing any ace is $\frac{4}{52}$ or about 8%.

Miscellaneous

People use fractions in a variety of ways every day.

The critic gave the new movie $3\frac{1}{2}$ stars.

The stock closed at $14\frac{5}{8}$ — down $1\frac{1}{2}$ dollars from yesterday.

It was a half-baked idea — I'm not surprised that it didn't work.

Renaming a Mixed Number or Whole Number as a Fraction

A **mixed number**, such as $2\frac{3}{4}$, names a number of wholes and a part of a whole.

Example:

This shows the mixed number $2\frac{3}{4}$.

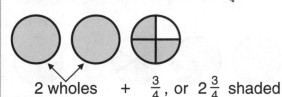

2 wholes   + $\frac{3}{4}$, or $2\frac{3}{4}$ shaded

A mixed number can be renamed as a fraction.

Example:

$$1 \ + \ 1 \ + \ \frac{3}{4} \ = \ \frac{4}{4} \ + \ \frac{4}{4} \ + \ \frac{3}{4}$$

$$2\frac{3}{4} \ = \ \frac{11}{4}$$

Shortcut for renaming $2\frac{3}{4}$ as a fraction:

Step 1
Multiply the whole-number part, 2, by the denominator, 4: $2 * 4 = 8$. This is the number of fourths in 2 wholes.

Step 2
Add the numerator of the fraction part, 3, to the result, 8: $8 + 3 = 11$. This is the number of fourths in the mixed number, $2\frac{3}{4}$.

Thus, $2\frac{3}{4} = \dfrac{(2 * 4) + 3}{4} = \dfrac{8 + 3}{4} = \dfrac{11}{4}$

Check Your Understanding

Rename as a fraction.

1. $1\frac{2}{3}$ 2. $4\frac{1}{2}$ 3. $3\frac{3}{4}$ 4. $2\frac{1}{2}$ 5. $3\frac{2}{5}$ 6. 4

Renaming a Fraction as a Mixed Number or Whole Number

A fraction greater than or equal to 1 can be renamed as a mixed number or whole number.

Example:

Rename $\frac{23}{6}$ as a mixed number.

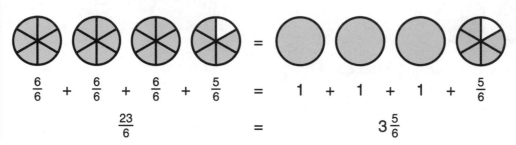

$$\frac{6}{6} + \frac{6}{6} + \frac{6}{6} + \frac{5}{6} = 1 + 1 + 1 + \frac{5}{6}$$

$$\frac{23}{6} = 3\frac{5}{6}$$

Whole

Shortcut for renaming $\frac{23}{6}$ as a mixed number:

Divide the numerator, 23, by the denominator, 6: 23/6 gives 3 R5.

- The quotient, 3, is the whole-number part of the mixed number. It tells how many wholes there are in $\frac{23}{6}$.

- The remainder, 5, is the numerator of the fraction part. It tells how many sixths there are left that cannot be made into wholes.

$$\begin{array}{r} 3 \\ 6\overline{)23} \\ -18 \\ \hline 5 \end{array}$$

$$\frac{23}{6} = 3\frac{5}{6}$$

Some calculators have a special key for renaming fractions as whole numbers or mixed numbers.

Example:

To rename $\frac{23}{6}$ as a mixed number, key in:

23 [/] 6 [Ab/c]

The display shows "3u5/6." The "u" stands for the word "unit," so "3u5/6" stands for the mixed number $3\frac{5}{6}$. See if you can do this on your calculator.

Check Your Understanding

Rename each fraction as a mixed number or a whole number.

1. $\frac{6}{5}$
2. $\frac{21}{8}$
3. $\frac{24}{6}$
4. $\frac{11}{2}$
5. $\frac{15}{4}$
6. $\frac{20}{3}$

Two fractions that name the same number are called **equivalent fractions**.

One way to rename a fraction as an equivalent fraction is to *multiply* the numerator and denominator of the fraction by the same number.

Example:

The rectangular region is divided into 4 equal parts. 3 of the parts are shaded. $\frac{3}{4}$ of the region is shaded.

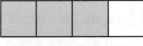

If each of the 4 parts is split into 2 equal parts, there are now 8 equal parts and 6 of them are shaded. $\frac{6}{8}$ of the region is shaded.

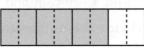

$\frac{3}{4}$ and $\frac{6}{8}$ both name the same amount of shaded part. $\frac{3}{4}$ and $\frac{6}{8}$ are equivalent fractions.

$$\frac{3}{4} = \frac{6}{8}$$

The number of parts in the region was doubled. We can show this by multiplying the numerator and denominator of $\frac{3}{4}$ by 2.

$$\frac{3 * 2}{4 * 2} = \frac{6}{8}$$

If each part in the region is divided into 3 equal parts, the number of parts is tripled. We can show this by multiplying the numerator and denominator of $\frac{3}{4}$ by 3. $\frac{9}{12}$ is equivalent to $\frac{3}{4}$.

$$\frac{3 * 3}{4 * 3} = \frac{9}{12}$$

Another way to rename a fraction as an equivalent fraction is to *divide* the numerator and denominator of the fraction by the same number.

Example:

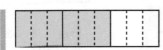

$\frac{6}{9}$ is shaded.

$$\frac{6/3}{9/3} = \frac{2}{3}$$

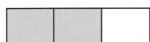

$\frac{2}{3}$ is shaded.

$\frac{2}{3}$ is equivalent to $\frac{6}{9}$.

Check Your Understanding

Rename each fraction as an equivalent fraction. Use multiplication in Problems 1–3 and division in Problems 4–6.

1. $\frac{1}{4}$ 　　　2. $\frac{4}{8}$ 　　　3. $\frac{3}{2}$ 　　　4. $\frac{9}{12}$ 　　　5. $\frac{8}{10}$ 　　　6. $\frac{12}{15}$

Simplifying Fractions

When a fraction is renamed as an equivalent fraction with a smaller numerator and denominator, the new fraction is in **simpler terms**. You can simplify a fraction by dividing its numerator and denominator by a common whole-number factor greater than 1.

25

Example:

Rename $\frac{8}{12}$ in simpler terms.

Step 1: 2 and 4 are common whole-number factors of 8 and 12.

Step 2: Divide the numerator and denominator of $\frac{8}{12}$ by 2 or 4.

$\frac{8/2}{12/2} = \frac{4}{6}$ $\frac{4}{6}$ is equivalent to $\frac{8}{12}$, and is in simpler terms.   or $\frac{8/4}{12/4} = \frac{2}{3}$ $\frac{2}{3}$ is equivalent to $\frac{8}{12}$, and is in simpler terms.

A fraction is in **simplest terms** if it cannot be renamed in simpler terms. You can rename a fraction in simplest terms by dividing its numerator and denominator by the **greatest common factor** of the numerator and denominator.

31

In the example above, 4 is the greatest common factor of 8 and 12. Therefore, $\frac{2}{3}$ is equivalent to $\frac{8}{12}$, in simplest terms.

A fraction is in simplest terms if the greatest common factor of the numerator and denominator is 1.

Some calculators have a special key for renaming fractions in simpler terms.

Example:

To rename $\frac{8}{12}$ in simpler terms, key in:

     8 [/] 12 [SIMP] [=]

184

The display shows 4/6. If, without clearing the display, you key in [SIMP] [=] again, the display will show 2/3. If you key in [SIMP] [=] one more time, the display will show 2/3 again. Therefore, $\frac{2}{3}$ is in simplest terms. See if you can do this on your calculator.

Check Your Understanding

Write each fraction in Problems 1–3 in simpler terms. Write each fraction in Problems 4–6 in simplest terms.

1. $\frac{4}{8}$ 2. $\frac{12}{16}$ 3. $\frac{20}{24}$ 4. $\frac{9}{12}$ 5. $\frac{12}{18}$ 6. $\frac{20}{24}$

Each stick on the Fraction-Stick Chart represents 1 whole. Each stick (except the 1-stick) is divided equally into pieces. Each piece represents a fraction of 1 whole.

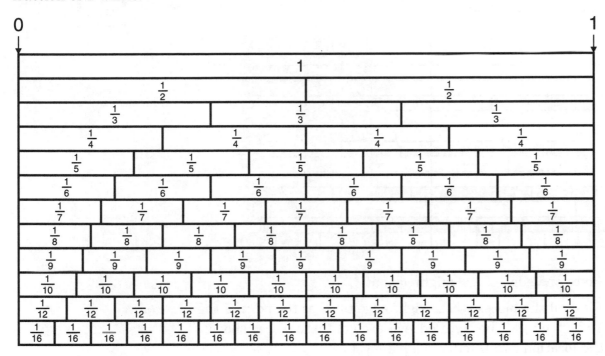

How to Locate a Fraction on the Fraction-Stick Chart

1. Select the stick shown by the denominator of the fraction.

2. Count the number of pieces shown by the numerator, starting at the left edge of the chart.

   Example:

   The "fourths" stick is divided into 4 pieces, each labeled $\frac{1}{4}$. It can be used to locate fractions whose denominator is 4. To locate the fraction $\frac{3}{4}$, count 3 pieces, starting at the left. $\frac{3}{4}$ is located at the right edge of the third piece.

   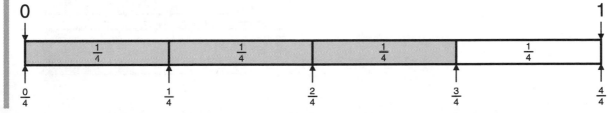

Check Your Understanding

Locate the fractions on the Fraction-Stick Chart.

1. $\frac{1}{3}$ 2. $\frac{5}{8}$ 3. $\frac{5}{5}$ 4. $\frac{10}{12}$ 5. $\frac{0}{6}$ 6. $\frac{4}{9}$

How to Use the Fraction-Stick Chart to Find Equivalent Fractions

Example:

Find fractions equivalent to $\frac{2}{3}$.

25

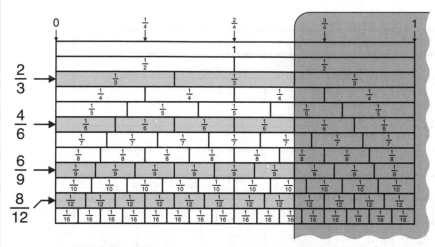

Step 1: Place one edge of a straightedge at $\frac{2}{3}$.

Step 2: Find all the pieces whose right edge touches the edge of the straightedge. The right edge of each of these pieces shows the location of a fraction equivalent to $\frac{2}{3}$.

$\frac{4}{6}$, $\frac{6}{9}$, and $\frac{8}{12}$ are equivalent to $\frac{2}{3}$.

How to Use the Fraction-Stick Chart to Compare Two Fractions

Example:

Compare $\frac{4}{9}$ and $\frac{3}{8}$. Which is less?

Step 1: Place one edge of a straightedge at $\frac{4}{9}$.

Step 2: Locate $\frac{3}{8}$ on the "eighths" stick.

Step 3: Since $\frac{3}{8}$ is to the left of $\frac{4}{9}$, $\frac{3}{8}$ is less than $\frac{4}{9}$.

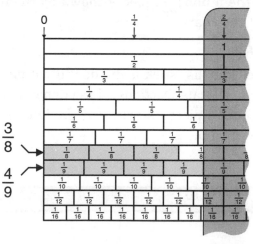

Check Your Understanding

1. Use the Fraction-Stick Chart to find an equivalent fraction.

   a. $\frac{2}{4}$
   b. $\frac{4}{12}$
   c. $\frac{3}{4}$
   d. $\frac{10}{16}$
   e. $\frac{4}{6}$

2. Which fraction is less? Use the Fraction-Stick Chart to decide.

   a. $\frac{1}{10}$ or $\frac{1}{8}$
   b. $\frac{3}{5}$ or $\frac{3}{7}$
   c. $\frac{11}{12}$ or $\frac{15}{16}$
   d. $\frac{5}{9}$ or $\frac{6}{10}$

When solving problems that involve fractions that do not have like denominators, we can rename the fractions so that the new fractions have the same denominator. The following example illustrates several methods for renaming fractions as fractions with a common denominator.

Example: Rename $\frac{3}{4}$ and $\frac{1}{6}$ as fractions with a common denominator.

Method 1: The Equivalent Fractions Method

Step 1: List equivalent fractions for $\frac{3}{4}$ and $\frac{1}{6}$.

$\frac{3}{4} = \frac{6}{8} = \frac{9}{12} = \frac{12}{16} = \dots$

$\frac{1}{6} = \frac{2}{12} = \frac{3}{18} = \frac{4}{24} = \dots$

Step 2: Both $\frac{3}{4}$ and $\frac{1}{6}$ can be renamed as fractions with the common denominator 12.

$\frac{3}{4} = \frac{9}{12}$ and $\frac{1}{6} = \frac{2}{12}$

Method 2: The Multiplication Method

Step 1: Multiply the numerator and denominator of the first fraction by the denominator of the second fraction.

$\frac{3 * 6}{4 * 6} = \frac{18}{24}$

Step 2: Multiply the numerator and denominator of the second fraction by the denominator of the first fraction.

$\frac{1 * 4}{6 * 4} = \frac{4}{24}$

Step 3: Both $\frac{3}{4}$ and $\frac{1}{6}$ can be renamed as fractions with the common denominator 24.

$\frac{3}{4} = \frac{18}{24}$ and $\frac{1}{6} = \frac{4}{24}$

Method 3: The Least Common Multiple Method

Step 1: Find the least common multiple of the denominators. The least common multiple of 4 and 6 is 12.

Step 2: Rename the fractions so that their denominator is the least common multiple.

$\frac{3}{4} = \frac{9}{12}$ and $\frac{1}{6} = \frac{2}{12}$

12 is the **least common denominator** of $\frac{3}{4}$ and $\frac{1}{6}$.

Check Your Understanding

Rename each pair of fractions as fractions with a common denominator.

1. $\frac{2}{3}$ and $\frac{1}{6}$
2. $\frac{1}{4}$ and $\frac{2}{5}$
3. $\frac{3}{10}$ and $\frac{1}{2}$
4. $\frac{3}{4}$ and $\frac{7}{10}$
5. $\frac{3}{6}$ and $\frac{6}{8}$

Least Common Multiples and Least Common Denominators

A **multiple of a number** n is the product of any whole number by the number n. A multiple of n is always divisible by n.

16

Examples:

> 6 is a multiple of 3, because $3 * 2 = 6$ and 6 is divisible by 3.
>
> 24 is a multiple of 4, because $4 * 6 = 24$ and 24 is divisible by 4.

The **least common multiple** of two whole numbers is the smallest number that is a multiple of both numbers.

Example:

> Find the least common multiple of 4 and 6.
>
> Step 1: List a few multiples of 4: 4, 8, 12, 16, 20, 24, and so on.
>
> Step 2: List a few multiples of 6: 6, 12, 18, 24, 30, and so on.
>
> 12 and 24 are on both lists. They are common multiples.
>
> 12 is the smallest. It is the least common multiple of 4 and 6.

Another way to find the least common multiple of two numbers is to use prime factorization.

18

Example:

> Find the least common multiple of 4 and 6.
>
> | Step 1 | Step 2 | Step 3 | Step 4 |
> |---|---|---|---|
> | Write the prime factorization of each. | Circle pairs of common prime factors. | Cross out one factor in each circled pair. | Multiply the factors that have not been crossed out. |
>
>
>
> The least common multiple of 4 and 6 is 12.

The least common multiple of the denominators of two fractions in simplest form is the **least common denominator** of the fractions. For example, 24 is the least common denominator of $\frac{3}{8}$ and $\frac{5}{12}$, because 24 is the least common multiple of 8 and 12.

32

Check Your Understanding

Find the least common multiple of each pair of numbers.

1. 6 and 12   **2.** 4 and 10   **3.** 3 and 4   **4.** 6 and 8   **5.** 6 and 9   **6.** 9 and 15

The **greatest common factor** of two whole numbers is the largest number that is a factor of both numbers.

Example:

> Find the greatest common factor of 20 and 24.
>
> Step 1: List all the factors of 20: 1, 2, 4, 5, 10, and 20.
>
> Step 2: List all the factors of 24: 1, 2, 3, 4, 6, 8, 12, and 24.
>
> 1, 2, and 4 are on both lists. They are common factors.
>
> 4 is the largest. It is the greatest common factor of 20 and 24.

Another way to find the greatest common factor of two numbers is to use prime factorization.

Example:

> Find the greatest common factor of 20 and 24.

Step 1	Step 2	Step 3	Step 4
Write the prime factorization of each.	Circle pairs of common prime factors.	Cross out the factors that are not circled.	Multiply one factor in each pair of circled factors.
$20 = 2 * 2 * 5$	$20 = \boxed{2} * \boxed{2} * 5$	$20 = \boxed{2} * \boxed{2} * \cancel{5}$	$2 * 2 = 4$
$24 = 2 * 2 * 2 * 3$	$24 = \boxed{2} * \boxed{2} * 2 * 3$	$24 = \boxed{2} * \boxed{2} * \cancel{2} * \cancel{3}$	

> The greatest common factor of 20 and 24 is 4.

An Interesting Fact

The product of the least common multiple and the greatest common factor of two numbers is the same as the product of the two numbers.

Example:

> The least common multiple of 4 and 6 is 12.
>
> The greatest common factor of 4 and 6 is 2.
>
> The product of the least common multiple and the greatest common factor of 4 and 6 is 12 * 2, or 24.
>
> The product of 4 and 6 is 24.

Check Your Understanding

Find the greatest common factor of each pair of numbers.

1. 3 and 5   **2.** 4 and 10   **3.** 8 and 24   **4.** 35 and 28   **5.** 18 and 12   **6.** 9 and 15

Addition and Subtraction of Fractions

To find the sum of fractions that have the same denominator, you add the numerators, but not the denominators. The denominator does not change. Subtraction of fractions with like denominators is done in the same way.

Example: $\frac{1}{4} + \frac{2}{4} = ?$

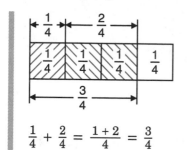

$$\frac{1}{4} + \frac{2}{4} = \frac{1+2}{4} = \frac{3}{4}$$

Example: $\frac{4}{5} - \frac{3}{5} = ?$

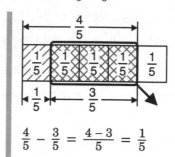

$$\frac{4}{5} - \frac{3}{5} = \frac{4-3}{5} = \frac{1}{5}$$

To find the sum of fractions that do not have the same denominator, you must first rename the fractions as fractions with a common denominator. Subtraction of fractions with unlike denominators is done in the same way.

Example: $\frac{3}{4} + \frac{1}{8} = ?$

Different Denominators		Common Denominator
$\frac{3}{4}$	$\left(\frac{3}{4} = \frac{6}{8}\right)$	$\frac{6}{8}$
$+ \frac{1}{8}$		$+ \frac{1}{8}$
		$\frac{7}{8}$

Example: $\frac{5}{6} - \frac{1}{4} = ?$

Different Denominators		Common Denominator
$\frac{5}{6}$	$\left(\frac{5}{6} = \frac{10}{12}\right)$	$\frac{10}{12}$
$- \frac{1}{4}$	$\left(\frac{1}{4} = \frac{2}{8} = \frac{3}{12}\right)$	$- \frac{3}{12}$
		$\frac{7}{12}$

It is possible to add and subtract fractions on some calculators.

Example: $\frac{3}{8} + \frac{1}{3} = ?$

Key in: 3 [/] 8 [+] 1 [/] 3 [=]

The display will show 17/24.

Example: $\frac{7}{8} - \frac{3}{5} = ?$

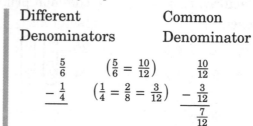

Key in: 7 [/] 8 [−] 3 [/] 5 [=]

The display will show 11/40.

184

See if you can do this on your calculator.

Check Your Understanding

Solve.

1. $\frac{2}{9} + \frac{4}{9}$

2. $\frac{3}{2} - \frac{3}{4}$

3. $\frac{1}{4} + \frac{1}{3}$

4. $\frac{5}{4} - \frac{7}{6}$

5. $\frac{5}{8} + \frac{1}{6}$

One way to add mixed numbers is to add the fractions that are part of the mixed numbers and add the whole-number parts. This may require renaming the sum.

Example: $4\frac{5}{8} + 2\frac{7}{8} = ?$

Step 1	Step 2	Step 3
Add the fractions.	Add the whole numbers.	Rename the sum.

$$4\frac{5}{8}$$
$$+\ 2\frac{7}{8}$$
$$\overline{\quad \frac{12}{8}}$$

$$4\frac{5}{8}$$
$$+\ 2\frac{7}{8}$$
$$\overline{\quad 6\frac{12}{8}}$$

$$6\frac{12}{8} = 6 + \frac{8}{8} + \frac{4}{8}$$
$$= 6 + 1 + \frac{4}{8}$$
$$= 7\frac{4}{8}$$
$$= 7\frac{1}{2}$$

If the fractions in the mixed numbers do not have the same denominator, you must first rename the fractions so that the fractions have a common denominator.

Example: $3\frac{3}{4} + 5\frac{2}{3} = ?$

Step 1	Step 2	Step 3
Rename the fractions with a common denominator; add them.	Add the whole numbers.	Rename the sum.

$3\frac{3}{4}$ $(3\frac{3}{4} = 3\frac{9}{12})$ $\quad 3\frac{9}{12}$
$+5\frac{2}{3}$ $(5\frac{2}{3} = 5\frac{8}{12})$ $\ +5\frac{8}{12}$
$\qquad\qquad\qquad\qquad\quad\ \overline{\quad \frac{17}{12}}$

$3\frac{3}{4}$ $(3\frac{3}{4} = 3\frac{9}{12})$ $\quad 3\frac{9}{12}$
$+5\frac{2}{3}$ $(5\frac{2}{3} = 5\frac{8}{12})$ $\ +5\frac{8}{12}$
$\qquad\qquad\qquad\qquad\quad\ \overline{\quad 8\frac{17}{12}}$

$8\frac{17}{12} = 8 + \frac{12}{12} + \frac{5}{12}$
$= 8 + 1 \ + \frac{5}{12}$
$= 9\frac{5}{12}$

Some calculators have special keys for entering and renaming mixed numbers.

Example:

To solve $3\frac{3}{4} + 5\frac{2}{3}$ on a calculator, key in:

3 [UNIT] 3 [/] 4 [+] 5 [UNIT] 2 [/] 3 [=]

The display will show 8u17/12. To rename the sum, press [Ab/c].
The display will show 9u5/12.

Check Your Understanding

Solve Problems 1–3 without a calculator. Solve Problem 4 with a calculator.

1. $6\frac{1}{8} + 4\frac{7}{8}$ **2.** $1\frac{1}{2} + 4\frac{2}{5}$ **3.** $7\frac{5}{6} + 2\frac{1}{4}$ **4.** $12\frac{4}{7} + 9\frac{7}{9}$

Subtraction of Mixed Numbers

Here is one way to subtract a mixed number from a mixed number:

- Subtract the fraction parts of the mixed numbers.
- Then subtract the whole-number parts.

If the fraction parts do not have the same denominator, you must first rename the fractions as fractions with a common denominator.

Example: $3\frac{7}{8} - 1\frac{3}{4} = ?$

Step 1
Rename the fractions as fractions with a common denominator.

$$3\frac{7}{8} \qquad\qquad 3\frac{7}{8}$$
$$-1\frac{3}{4} \;\;(1\frac{3}{4}=1\frac{6}{8}) \;\; -1\frac{6}{8}$$

Step 2
Subtract the fractions.

$$3\frac{7}{8} \qquad\qquad 3\frac{7}{8}$$
$$-1\frac{3}{4} \;\;(1\frac{3}{4}=1\frac{6}{8}) \;\; -1\frac{6}{8}$$
$$\frac{1}{8}$$

Step 3
Subtract the whole numbers.

$$3\frac{7}{8} \qquad\qquad \mathbf{3\frac{7}{8}}$$
$$-1\frac{3}{4} \;\;(1\frac{3}{4}=1\frac{6}{8}) \;\; \mathbf{-1\frac{6}{8}}$$
$$\mathbf{2\frac{1}{8}}$$

To subtract a mixed number from a whole number, you must first rename the whole number as the sum of a whole number and a fraction that is equivalent to 1.

Example: $5 - 2\frac{2}{3} = ?$

Step 1
Rename the whole number.

$$5 = 4 + 1 = 4 + \frac{3}{3} = 4\frac{3}{3}$$

$$\mathbf{5} \;\;(5=4\frac{3}{3}) \;\; 4\frac{3}{3}$$
$$-2\frac{2}{3} \qquad\qquad -2\frac{2}{3}$$

Step 2
Subtract the fractions.

$$5 \;\;(5=4\frac{3}{3}) \;\; 4\frac{3}{3}$$
$$-2\frac{2}{3} \qquad\qquad -2\frac{2}{3}$$
$$\frac{1}{3}$$

Step 3
Subtract the whole numbers.

$$5 \;\;(5=4\frac{3}{3}) \;\; \mathbf{4\frac{3}{3}}$$
$$-2\frac{2}{3} \qquad\qquad \mathbf{-2\frac{2}{3}}$$
$$\mathbf{2\frac{1}{3}}$$

When subtracting mixed numbers, you must rename the first mixed number if it contains a fraction that is less than the fraction in the second mixed number.

Example: $7\frac{1}{5} - 3\frac{3}{5} = ?$

Step 1
Rename the first mixed number.

$$7\frac{1}{5} = 6 + 1 + \frac{1}{5}$$
$$= 6 + \frac{5}{5} + \frac{1}{5} = 6\frac{6}{5}$$

$$\mathbf{7\frac{1}{5}} \;\;(7\frac{1}{5}=6\frac{6}{5}) \;\; \mathbf{6\frac{6}{5}}$$
$$-3\frac{3}{5} \qquad\qquad -3\frac{3}{5}$$

Step 2
Subtract the fractions.

$$7\frac{1}{5} \;\;(7\frac{1}{5}=6\frac{6}{5}) \;\; 6\frac{6}{5}$$
$$-3\frac{3}{5} \qquad\qquad -3\frac{3}{5}$$
$$\frac{3}{5}$$

Step 3
Subtract the whole numbers.

$$7\frac{1}{5} \;\;(7\frac{1}{5}=6\frac{6}{5}) \;\; \mathbf{6\frac{6}{5}}$$
$$-3\frac{3}{5} \qquad\qquad \mathbf{-3\frac{3}{5}}$$
$$\mathbf{3\frac{3}{5}}$$

The examples below illustrate three methods of solving the problem $4\frac{1}{6} - 2\frac{2}{3} = ?$

Method 1: This is the method shown on page 34.

Step 1
Rename the fractions as fractions with a common denominator.

$$4\frac{1}{6}$$
$$-2\frac{2}{3} \quad (2\frac{2}{3} = 2\frac{4}{6}) \quad \begin{array}{r} 4\frac{1}{6} \\ -2\frac{4}{6} \end{array}$$

Step 2
Rename the first mixed number.

$$4\frac{1}{6} = 3 + 1 + \frac{1}{6} = 3 + \frac{6}{6} + \frac{1}{6}$$
$$= 3 + \frac{7}{6} = 3\frac{7}{6}$$

$$\begin{array}{cc} 4\frac{1}{6} \quad (4\frac{1}{6} = 3\frac{7}{6}) & 3\frac{7}{6} \\ -2\frac{2}{3} & -2\frac{4}{6} \end{array}$$

Step 3
Subtract.

$$\begin{array}{rll} 4\frac{1}{6} & (4\frac{1}{6} = 3\frac{7}{6}) & 3\frac{7}{6} \\ -2\frac{2}{3} & (2\frac{2}{3} = 2\frac{4}{6}) & -2\frac{4}{6} \\ & & \overline{1\frac{3}{6} = 1\frac{1}{2}} \end{array}$$

[23 | 24]

Method 2: Work with the fraction names for the mixed numbers.

Step 1
Rename the mixed numbers as fractions.

$$4\frac{1}{6} = \frac{25}{6}$$
$$2\frac{2}{3} = \frac{8}{3}$$

Step 2
Subtract.

$$\begin{array}{rll} \frac{25}{6} & & \frac{25}{6} \\ -\frac{8}{3} & (\frac{8}{3} = \frac{16}{6}) & -\frac{16}{6} \\ & & \overline{\frac{9}{6}} \end{array}$$

Step 3
Rename the result as a mixed number.

$$\frac{9}{6} = 1\frac{3}{6} = 1\frac{1}{2}$$

Method 3: Find partial differences and add.

$$\begin{array}{r} 4\frac{1}{6} \\ -2\frac{2}{3} \end{array}$$

$$\begin{array}{rl} 4 - 2 = & +2 \\ \frac{1}{6} - \frac{2}{3} = \frac{1}{6} - \frac{4}{6} = & -\frac{3}{6} \\ 2 - \frac{3}{6} = & \overline{1\frac{3}{6} = 1\frac{1}{2}} \end{array}$$

You can also subtract mixed numbers on calculators that have the [/] and [UNIT] keys for entering mixed numbers. Try it.

[184]

Subtract.

1. $4\frac{3}{5} - 2\frac{1}{3}$

2. $7 - 3\frac{5}{8}$

3. $3\frac{2}{9} - \frac{8}{9}$

4. $6\frac{1}{2} - 2\frac{5}{6}$

Multiplication of Fractions

One way to find the product of two fractions is to use an **area model**.

Example: $\frac{3}{4} * \frac{2}{3} = ?$

Step 1

Think: How much is $\frac{3}{4}$ of $\frac{2}{3}$ of this rectangular region?

Step 2

Shade $\frac{2}{3}$ of the region this way:

Step 3

Shade $\frac{3}{4}$ of the region this way: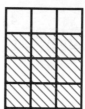

$\frac{3}{4}$ of $\frac{2}{3}$ of the region is shaded both ways:

That's $\frac{6}{12}$ or $\frac{1}{2}$ of the whole region.

$\frac{3}{4}$ of $\frac{2}{3} = \frac{6}{12} = \frac{1}{2}$

$\frac{3}{4} * \frac{2}{3} = \frac{6}{12} = \frac{1}{2}$

Another way is to use the **Multiplication of Fractions Property**.

To find the product of two fractions:

- Multiply the numerator of one fraction by the numerator of the other fraction; and

- Multiply the denominator of one fraction by the denominator of the other fraction.

$$\frac{a}{b} * \frac{c}{d} = \frac{a * c}{b * d}$$

b and d may not be 0.

Example:

$$\frac{3}{4} * \frac{2}{3} = \frac{3 * 2}{4 * 3} = \frac{6}{12} = \frac{1}{2}$$

You can multiply fractions on calculators that have a [/] key.
For example, to find the product of $\frac{3}{4}$ and $\frac{2}{3}$, key in 3 [/] 4 [×] 2 [/] 3 [=].
The display will show 6/12.

To rename the product in simpler form, press [SIMP] [=]. The display will show 3/6. Press [SIMP] [=] again. The display will show 1/2.

184

Check Your Understanding

Multiply.

1. $\frac{1}{3} * \frac{1}{2}$ **2.** $\frac{3}{5} * \frac{1}{4}$ **3.** $\frac{5}{6} * \frac{3}{10}$ **4.** $\frac{5}{8} * \frac{0}{8}$ **5.** $\frac{9}{4} * \frac{2}{3}$

Multiplication by Whole Numbers and Mixed Numbers

To **multiply a whole number and a fraction**, you can rename the whole number as a fraction with 1 in the denominator. Then multiply the two fractions.

Example: $5 * \frac{2}{3} = ?$ $\left(5 = \frac{5}{1}\right)$

$$5 * \frac{2}{3} = \frac{5}{1} * \frac{2}{3} = \frac{5*2}{1*3} = \frac{10}{3} = 3\frac{1}{3}$$

You can **multiply a whole number and a mixed number** by multiplying the whole number by each part of the mixed number and adding the products. This method uses the distributive property.

Example: $7 * 2\frac{3}{5} = ?$

Step 1	Step 2	Step 3
Multiply the whole number by the whole-number part of the mixed number.	Multiply the whole number by the fraction part of the mixed number.	Add the partial products. $14 + 4\frac{1}{5} = 18\frac{1}{5}$
$7 * 2 = 14$	$7 * \frac{3}{5} = \frac{7}{1} * \frac{3}{5} = \frac{21}{5} = 4\frac{1}{5}$	

$$7 * 2\frac{3}{5} = (7 * 2) + (7 * \frac{3}{5}) = 14 + 4\frac{1}{5} = 18\frac{1}{5}$$

A good way to **multiply two mixed numbers** is to rename each mixed number as a fraction, multiply the fractions, and rename the product as a mixed number. You can multiply a whole number by a mixed number in the same way.

Example: $3\frac{1}{4} * 1\frac{5}{6} = ?$

Step 1	Step 2	Step 3
Rename the mixed numbers as fractions.	Multiply the fractions.	Rename the product as a mixed number.
$3\frac{1}{4} = \frac{13}{4}$	$\frac{13}{4} * \frac{11}{6} = \frac{13*11}{4*6}$	$\frac{143}{24} = 5\frac{23}{24}$
$1\frac{5}{6} = \frac{11}{6}$	$= \frac{143}{24}$	

$$3\frac{1}{4} * 1\frac{5}{6} = \frac{13}{4} * \frac{11}{6} = \frac{143}{24} = 5\frac{23}{24}$$

$$24\overline{)143} \quad\begin{array}{r} 5 \\ -120 \\ \hline 23 \end{array}\bigg|_{5}$$

You can solve this problem on a calculator that has keys for entering mixed numbers. Key in 3 [UNIT] 1 [/] 4 [×] 1 [UNIT] 5 [/] 6 [=]. The display will show 143/24. To rename the product as a mixed number, press the [Ab/c key]. The display will show 5u23/24.

Check Your Understanding

Solve Problems 1–3 without a calculator. Use a calculator to solve Problem 4.

1. $6 * \frac{1}{4}$

2. $2\frac{2}{3} * 9$

3. $3\frac{3}{5} * 4\frac{1}{2}$

4. $3\frac{5}{6} * 2\frac{3}{8}$

Division of Fractions and Mixed Numbers

Division of Fractions Property

To find the quotient of two fractions, multiply the first fraction by the reciprocal of the second fraction.

$$\frac{a}{b} \div \frac{c}{d} = \frac{a}{b} * \frac{d}{c}$$

Example 1:

$$\frac{4}{5} \div \frac{2}{3} = \frac{4}{5} * \frac{3}{2}$$

$$= \frac{12}{10}$$

$$= 1\frac{2}{10}, \text{ or } 1\frac{1}{5}$$

Example 2:

$$2\frac{3}{4} \div 1\frac{1}{3} = \frac{11}{4} \div \frac{4}{3}$$

$$= \frac{11}{4} * \frac{3}{4}$$

$$= \frac{33}{16}, \text{ or } 2\frac{1}{16}$$

23 36 37

The Division of Fractions Property is based on the following rules.

Rule 1: A fraction can have any number in its numerator and any number, except 0, in its denominator.

Examples:

27/55 can be written as the fraction $\frac{27}{55}$.

6.3/π can be written as $\frac{6.3}{\pi}$.

$\frac{2}{3} \div \frac{3}{4}$ can be written as $\dfrac{\frac{2}{3}}{\frac{3}{4}}$

Rule 2: $\frac{a}{b} * \frac{c}{d} = \frac{a * c}{b * d}$; a and c may be any numbers; b and d may be any numbers except 0.

Examples :

$$\frac{5}{8} * \frac{3}{2} = \frac{5 * 3}{8 * 2} = \frac{15}{16}$$

$$\frac{3}{5} * 7 = \frac{3}{5} * \frac{7}{1} = \frac{3 * 7}{5 * 1} = \frac{21}{5}, \text{ or } 4\frac{1}{5}$$

Rule 3: If the product of two numbers is 1, then the numbers are called **reciprocals** of each other. If a number is written as a fraction, then its reciprocal is the fraction written "upside down."

Examples:

5 and $\frac{1}{5}$ are reciprocals of each other because $5 * \frac{1}{5} = 1$.

$\frac{3}{4}$ and $\frac{4}{3}$ are reciprocals of each other because $\frac{3}{4} * \frac{4}{3} = 1$.

$2\frac{3}{5}$ and $\frac{5}{13}$ are reciprocals of each other because $2\frac{3}{5} = \frac{13}{5}$ and $\frac{13}{5} * \frac{5}{13} = 1$.

Rule 4: If the numerator and denominator of a fraction are multiplied by the same number, then the result is equivalent to the original fraction.

Example:

$$\frac{3}{5} = \frac{3 * 4}{5 * 4} = \frac{12}{20}$$

Rule 5: Any number a, divided by 1, is equal to a. That is, $a/1 = \frac{a}{1} = a$.

Examples:

$23 \div 1 = \frac{23}{1} = 23$

$46.3 \div 1 = \frac{46.3}{1} = 46.3$

$\frac{3}{8} \div 1 = \frac{\frac{3}{8}}{1} = \frac{3}{8}$

The following example shows why the Division of Fractions Property works.

Divide $\frac{3}{4}$ by $\frac{2}{5}$.

Step 1: Write the problem as a fraction. (Rule 1)

$$\frac{3}{4} \div \frac{2}{5} = \frac{\frac{3}{4} \leftarrow \text{numerator}}{\frac{2}{5} \leftarrow \text{denominator}}$$

Step 2: Multiply the numerator and denominator of the fraction by the reciprocal of the denominator. (Rules 3 and 4)

$$\frac{\frac{3}{4}}{\frac{2}{5}} = \frac{\frac{3}{4} * \frac{5}{2}}{\frac{2}{5} * \frac{5}{2}}$$

Step 3: Simplify the denominator. (Rule 3)

$$\frac{\frac{3}{4} * \frac{5}{2}}{\frac{2}{5} * \frac{5}{2}} = \frac{\frac{3}{4} * \frac{5}{2}}{1}$$

Step 4: Divide by 1. (Rule 5)

$$\frac{\frac{3}{4} * \frac{5}{2}}{1} = \frac{3}{4} * \frac{5}{2}$$

Step 5: Multiply. (Rule 2)

$$\frac{3}{4} * \frac{5}{2} = \frac{3 * 5}{4 * 2} = \frac{15}{8}, \text{ or } 1\frac{7}{8}$$

You can see from Step 5 that $\frac{3}{4} \div \frac{2}{5} = \frac{3}{4} * \frac{5}{2}$; that is, the first fraction is being multiplied by the reciprocal of the second fraction.

Check Your Understanding

Divide.

1. $\frac{3}{5} \div \frac{1}{4}$　　　**2.** $5 \div \frac{5}{3}$　　　**3.** $\frac{1}{7} \div \frac{3}{7}$　　　**4.** $2\frac{2}{3} \div 4$　　　**5.** $3\frac{1}{2} \div 1\frac{1}{4}$

When sharing a pizza equally, you are more likely to refer to each share in fraction form rather than in decimal form. On the other hand, when measuring an object using metric units, it makes more sense to express the measurement in decimal form. This is because a measurement in one metric unit can be converted to another metric unit by multiplying or dividing it by 10, 100, 1000, and so on; this is consistent with the base-10 place-value system.

Notation

Rational numbers are written in decimal form by extending the place-value system used for expressing whole numbers.

Hundreds	Tens	Ones		Tenths	Hundredths	Thousandths
2	2	2	.	2	2	2

In the base-10 place-value system, the value of each place is $\frac{1}{10}$ of the value of the place to its left. Thus, in the numeral 222.222, the 2 in the hundreds place has a value of 200 and the 2 in the tens place has a value of 20, which is $\frac{1}{10}$ of 200. Similarly, the 2 in the tenths place has a value of 2 tenths which is $\frac{1}{10}$ of 2, and the 2 in the hundredths place has a value of 2 hundredths, which is $\frac{1}{10}$ of 2 tenths.

Percent notation is simply another way of naming a fraction whose denominator is 100 or the number of hundredths in a decimal. Just as we might write "3 billion" instead of "3,000,000,000," we write a decimal like "0.25" as "25%" (or "25 percent"), meaning "25 parts per hundred."

Relations

The same rules for comparing whole numbers are used for comparing decimals. When decimals are written in standard notation, the value of the digits in the places of the numeral tell you which numbers are largest and which are smallest. For example, 0.35 is greater than 0.288 because the value of the digit in the tenths place of 0.35 is 3 tenths, which is greater than the value of the corresponding digit in 0.288 (2 tenths).

Percent notation is particularly useful when comparing ratios. When such ratios are renamed as percents, they are given 100 as their common denominator. For example, if Cindy got 14 out of 25 votes in the 5th-grade class election, this is the same as getting 56 out of 100 votes, or 56% of the votes. If Bruce got 18 out of 30 votes in the 6th-grade election, this is the same as getting 60 out of 100 votes, or 60% of the votes. Once each ratio has been renamed in percent form, it is easy to see that Bruce got a larger portion of votes than Cindy.

Operations

When doing operations with decimals, you can proceed as if the numbers were whole numbers and then place the decimal point in the result to make it the proper size.

Study the place-value chart.

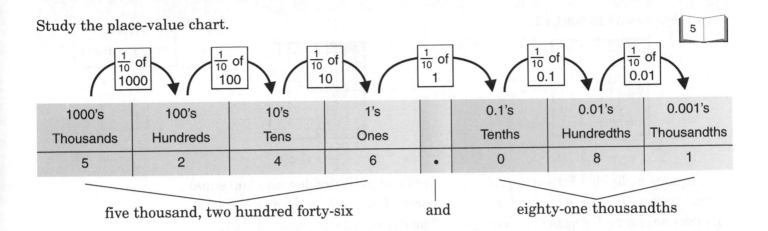

1000's	100's	10's	1's		0.1's	0.01's	0.001's
Thousands	Hundreds	Tens	Ones		Tenths	Hundredths	Thousandths
5	2	4	6	•	0	8	1

five thousand, two hundred forty-six   and   eighty-one thousandths

Notice that the value of each place is $\frac{1}{10}$ of the value of the place to its left. This is true both for whole-number places and decimal places.

Whole Numbers	Decimals
$\frac{1}{10}$ of 1000 = 100	$\frac{1}{10}$ of 1 = 0.1
$\frac{1}{10}$ of 100 = 10	$\frac{1}{10}$ of 0.1 = 0.01
$\frac{1}{10}$ of 10 = 1	$\frac{1}{10}$ of 0.01 = 0.001

A whole number that can be written using only 10's as factors is called a **power of 10**. A power of 10 can be written in exponential notation.

Powers of 10		
100	10 * 10	10^2
1000	10 * 10 * 10	10^3
10,000	10 * 10 * 10 * 10	10^4
100,000	10 * 10 * 10 * 10 * 10	10^5

Decimals that can be written using only 0.1's as factors are also powers of 10. They can be written in exponential notation with negative exponents.

Powers of 10 (less than 1)		
0.01	0.1 * 0.1	10^{-2}
0.001	0.1 * 0.1 * 0.1	10^{-3}
0.0001	0.1 * 0.1 * 0.1 * 0.1	10^{-4}
0.00001	0.1 * 0.1 * 0.1 * 0.1 * 0.1	10^{-5}

The value of each place in a place-value chart is a power of 10.

100,000's	10,000's	1000's	100's	10's	1's		0.1's	0.01's	0.001's	0.0001's	0.00001's
10^5	10^4	10^3	10^2	10^1	10^0	•	10^{-1}	10^{-2}	10^{-3}	10^{-4}	10^{-5}

Note the pattern in the exponents: Each exponent is 1 less than the exponent in the place to its left. According to this pattern:

$$10^1 = 10 \qquad 10^0 = 1 \qquad 10^{-1} = 0.1$$

Decimal Names

Each large square is worth 1.

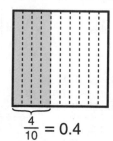

$\frac{4}{10} = 0.4$

This square is divided into 10 equal parts. Each part is $\frac{1}{10}$ of the square. The decimal name for $\frac{1}{10}$ is 0.1. The decimal 0.1 is read as *one-tenth* or *zero point one*.

$\frac{4}{10}$ of the square is shaded. The decimal name for $\frac{4}{10}$ is 0.4.

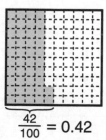

$\frac{42}{100} = 0.42$

This square is divided into 100 equal parts. Each part is $\frac{1}{100}$ of the square. The decimal name for $\frac{1}{100}$ is 0.01. The decimal 0.01 is read as *one-hundredth* or *zero point zero one*.

$\frac{42}{100}$ of the square is shaded. The decimal name for $\frac{42}{100}$ is 0.42.

Whole
large square

41

The decimal name for $\frac{1}{1000}$ is 0.001. It is read as *one-thousandth* or *zero point zero zero one*.

This number line shows tenths.

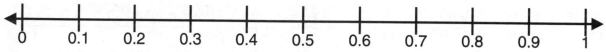

Whole
unit segment

This number line shows hundredths. Each tenth is divided into 10 equal parts, each worth $\frac{1}{100}$, or 0.01.

0.01

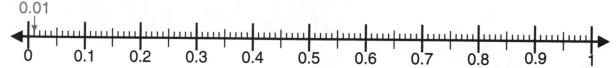

In a decimal numeral, the whole-number part is separated from the decimal part by a **decimal point**. 56.8 is read as *fifty-six **and** eight-tenths* or *fifty-six **point** eight*.

The decimal...	is read as...
0.17	17 hundredths or 0 point 17
2.061	2 and 61 thousandths or 2 point 061
23.4	23 and 4 tenths or 23 point 4
0.09	9 hundredths or 0 point 09
55.005	55 and 5 thousandths or 55 point 005
6.50	6 and 50 hundredths or 6 point 50

Check Your Understanding

Read each decimal to yourself.

1. 0.2 **2.** 1.36 **3.** 0.948 **4.** 19.07 **5.** 0.006 **6.** 74.082

Fractions, decimals, and percents are different ways of naming numbers. Often, they are used to name quantities that are less than 1 whole, or 100%. For example, $\frac{1}{2}$ cup is less than 1 cup, $0.25 is less than $1, and 42% of registered voters is less than 100% of registered voters. But they can also name numbers that are greater than 1 whole, or 100%.

If a fraction, a decimal, or a percent name the same number, we say that they are equivalent. For example, each large square below represents 1 whole or 100%. $\frac{3}{10}$, 0.3, $\frac{6}{20}$, $\frac{30}{100}$, and 30% are all equivalent names for the shaded part of the squares.

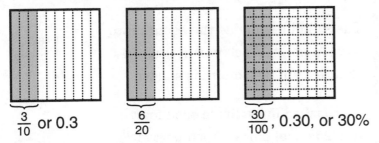

$\frac{3}{10}$ or 0.3 $\frac{6}{20}$ $\frac{30}{100}$, 0.30, or 30%

Fractions and decimals can be shown on a number line. Use your fraction sense to estimate what fraction and decimal name point A on the number line below.

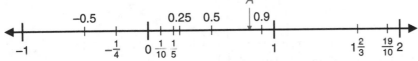

Even percents can be shown on a number line. For example, you can think of $\frac{1}{5}$ or 0.2 as 20% of the distance from 0 to 1. The Probability Meter, which you may remember from your work in fifth grade, is an example of a number line that shows percents.

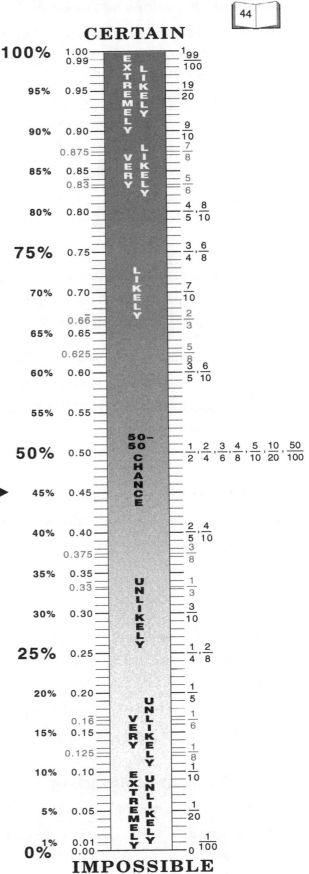

Converting Between Fractions and Decimals

Renaming Fractions as Decimals

One way to rename a fraction as a decimal is to find an equivalent fraction whose denominator is a power of 10, that is, 10, 100, 1000, and so on. This method works only for some fractions.

25

Examples:

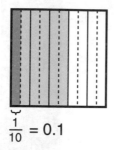

$$\frac{1}{10} = 0.1$$

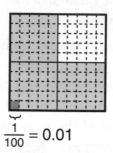

Whole
large square

$$\frac{1}{100} = 0.01$$

The solid lines divide the square into 5 equal parts. Each part is $\frac{1}{5}$ of the square. $\frac{3}{5}$ of the square is shaded.

The dashed lines divide each fifth into 2 equal parts. Each part is $\frac{1}{10}$, or 0.1 of the square. $\frac{6}{10}$, or 0.6 of the square is shaded.

$$\frac{3}{5} = \frac{6}{10} = 0.6$$

46

The solid lines divide the square into 4 equal parts. Each part is $\frac{1}{4}$ of the square. $\frac{3}{4}$ of the square is shaded.

The dashed lines divide each fourth into 25 equal parts. Each part is $\frac{1}{100}$, or 0.01 of the square. $\frac{75}{100}$, or 0.75 of the square is shaded.

$$\frac{3}{4} = \frac{75}{100} = 0.75$$

Renaming Decimals as Fractions

A decimal is a name for a fraction whose denominator is a power of 10.

Examples:

$$0.4 = \frac{4}{10} = \frac{2}{5}$$

$$0.08 = \frac{8}{100} = \frac{4}{50} = \frac{2}{25}$$

$$0.25 = \frac{25}{100} = \frac{5}{20} = \frac{1}{4}$$

$$0.124 = \frac{124}{1000} = \frac{62}{500} = \frac{31}{250}$$

Renaming Decimals with a Calculator

Some calculators have a special key for renaming decimals as fractions.

185

Example:

To rename 0.48 as a fraction, key in [.] 48 [F⇄D]. The display shows 48/100.

To simplify the fraction, key in [SIMP] [=] [SIMP] [=]. The display shows 12/25.

Check Your Understanding

1. Rename as a decimal.   **a.** $\frac{1}{4}$ **b.** $\frac{4}{5}$ **c.** $\frac{5}{2}$ **d.** $\frac{13}{20}$ **e.** $\frac{4}{25}$

2. Rename as a fraction or mixed number. Check your answers on your calculator.
   a. 0.8   **b.** 0.25   **c.** 3.32   **d.** 0.028

The Fraction-Stick Chart, along with a number line for decimals, can be used to rename fractions as decimals. Note that the result is usually only an approximation. You can use a calculator to obtain better approximations.

27	44
28	46

Example:

Rename $\frac{2}{3}$ as a decimal.

1. Locate $\frac{2}{3}$ on the "thirds" stick.

2. Place one edge of a straightedge at $\frac{2}{3}$. $\frac{2}{3} \rightarrow$

3. Find where the straightedge crosses the number line.

The straightedge crosses the number line between 0.66 and 0.67, so $\frac{2}{3}$ is equivalent to about 0.66 or 0.67.

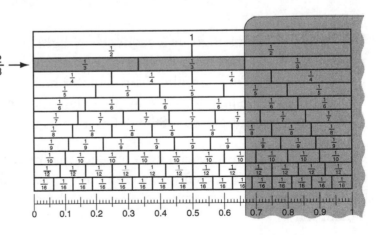

Check Your Understanding

Use the chart above to find an approximate decimal name for each fraction or mixed number.

1. $\frac{3}{10}$ 2. $\frac{7}{8}$ 3. $4\frac{1}{3}$ 4. $\frac{12}{16}$ 5. $1\frac{7}{9}$ 6. $\frac{2}{7}$

Renaming Fractions as Decimals with a Calculator

One way to rename a fraction as a decimal is to divide the numerator of the fraction by its denominator. This can be done easily on a calculator.

Examples:

To rename $\frac{3}{4}$ as a decimal, key in:

3 [÷] 4 [=]

The display shows 0.75. $\frac{3}{4} = 0.75$

To rename $\frac{7}{8}$ as a decimal, key in:

7 [÷] 8 [=]

The display shows 0.875. $\frac{7}{8} = 0.875$

In some cases, the decimal takes up the entire calculator display. If a digit or a sequence of digits is repeated the decimal can be written in a simple way by writing the repeating digit or digits just once and putting a bar over each.

Examples:

Fraction	Key in:	Calculator Display	Decimal
$\frac{1}{3}$	1 [÷] 3 [=]	0.333333333	$0.\overline{3}$
$\frac{2}{3}$	2 [÷] 3 [=]	0.666666666 or 0.666666667 (depending on the calculator)	$0.\overline{6}$
$\frac{1}{6}$	1 [÷] 6 [=]	0.166666666 or 0.166666667 (depending on the calculator)	$0.1\overline{6}$
$\frac{4}{9}$	4 [÷] 9 [=]	0.444444444	$0.\overline{4}$
$\frac{6}{11}$	6 [÷] 11 [=]	0.545454545	$0.\overline{54}$
$\frac{7}{12}$	7 [÷] 12 [=]	0.583333333	$0.58\overline{3}$

Decimals in which a digit or a sequence of digits is repeated are called **repeating decimals**. In a repeating decimal, the pattern of repeating digits goes on forever. For example, if a calculator had a display that could show 1000 digits, the display would show 0. followed by 999 sixes for the fraction $\frac{2}{3}$. A calculator that shows 0.666666667 rounds the last digit in the display.

Some calculators have special keys for entering fractions and renaming them as decimals. For example, to rename $\frac{3}{5}$, you could key in 3 [/] 5 [F⇄D]. The result would be the same as if you had divided the numerator by the denominator.

Check Your Understanding

Use a calculator to rename each fraction as a decimal.

1. $\frac{1}{8}$ 2. $\frac{8}{12}$ 3. $\frac{5}{12}$ 4. $\frac{5}{6}$ 5. $\frac{7}{9}$ 6. $\frac{3}{16}$

The word *percent* comes from the Latin *per centum*: *per* means *for* and *centum* means *one hundred*. For example, the statement "60% of registered voters went to the polls" means that 60 out of 100 registered voters voted. This does not mean that there were exactly 100 registered voters and that 60 of them voted. It does mean that *for every 100* registered voters, 60 of them voted.

A percent always represents a *percent of something*. The "something" is the whole (or unit, or 100%). In the example above, the whole is the total number of registered voters, that is, 100% of the registered voters.

Renaming Fractions as Percents

One way to rename a fraction as a percent is to find an equivalent fraction whose denominator is 100 and then write the fraction as a percent. This method works only with some fractions.

Example:

The solid lines divide the square into 4 equal parts. Each part is $\frac{1}{4}$ of the square. $\frac{3}{4}$ of the square is shaded.

The dashed lines divide each fourth into 25 equal parts. Each part is $\frac{1}{100}$, or 1% of the square. $\frac{75}{100}$, or 75% of the square is shaded.

$$\frac{3}{4} = \frac{75}{100} = 75\%$$

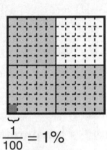

100%
large square

$\frac{1}{100} = 1\%$

Another way to rename a fraction as a percent is to divide the numerator by the denominator of the fraction and multiply the result by 100. You may want to do this on a calculator.

Example:

To rename $\frac{3}{8}$ as a percent, key in 3 [÷] 8 [×] 100 [=]. The display shows 37.5. Therefore, $\frac{3}{8} = 37.5\%$.

Renaming Percents as Fractions

A percent can always be written as a fraction whose denominator is 100.

Examples:

$40\% = \frac{40}{100} = \frac{2}{5}$ $85\% = \frac{85}{100} = \frac{17}{20}$ $150\% = \frac{150}{100} = \frac{3}{2} = 1\frac{1}{2}$

Check Your Understanding

1. Rename as a percent. **a.** $\frac{1}{5}$ **b.** $\frac{7}{10}$ **c.** $\frac{5}{8}$ **d.** $1\frac{1}{4}$ **e.** $\frac{1}{3}$

2. Rename as a fraction or mixed number.   **a.** 60%   **b.** 35%   **c.** 250%

Addition and Subtraction of Decimals

When adding or subtracting whole numbers, we always add or subtract the values of digits in like places–hundreds and hundreds, tens and tens, and so on. The same principle applies to decimals—we add or subtract tenths and tenths, hundredths and hundredths, thousandths and thousandths, and so on. You can do this, no matter which addition or subtraction algorithms you use, as long as you are careful to keep track of the place values—both whole-number and decimal place values.

The following examples use the Partial-Sums and Partial-Differences Algorithms. When adding and subtracting decimals, adapt your favorite whole-number algorithms to these operations with decimals.

Examples:

$32.5 + 19.6 = ?$	32.5	$5.67 - 1.84 = ?$	5.67
	$+ 19.6$		$- 1.84$
Add the tens: $30 + 10 =$	40.0	Subtract the ones: $5 - 1 =$	4.00
Add the ones: $2 + 9 =$	11.0	Subtract the tenths: $0.6 - 0.8 =$ $- 0.20$ $(= 3.80)$	
Add the tenths: $0.5 + 0.6 =$	1.1	Subtract the hundredths:	
Find the total:	52.1	$0.07 - 0.04 =$	0.03 $(= 3.83)$
		Find the total:	3.83

Counts and measures always have units. For addition or subtraction, all the numbers must have the same unit. If they do not have the same units, you will have to convert at least one of the numbers so that all of the numbers have the same unit.

Example:

Find the perimeter of the triangle.

One way: Convert the centimeter measures to millimeters. Then add.

5 cm = 50 mm
3 cm = 30 mm
Perimeter = 50 mm + 30 mm + 65 mm = 145 mm

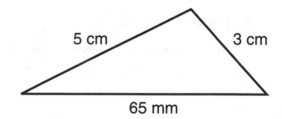

Another way: Convert the millimeter measure to centimeters. Then add.

65 mm = 6.5 cm
Perimeter = 5 cm + 3 cm + 6.5 cm = 14.5 cm

At times, you will encounter a situation in which the numbers to be added or subtracted do not have the same number of decimal places. When this happens, you need to rename at least one of the numbers so that all numerals have the same number of decimal places.

Example: Solve $6.5 - 3.105 = ?$

> Step 1
>
> 3.105 has 3 decimal places. Add 2 zeros to the right of 6.5 so that it also has 3 decimal places.
>
> $6.5 = 6.500$

> Step 2
>
> Subtract.
>
> $6.500 - 3.105 = 3.395$

In most practical situations, all the measures have the same precision. For example, in a 100-meter race, all the times might be measured to the nearest tenth of a second. If the measures do not have the same precision, you need to convert at least one of the measures so that all measures have the same precision—that of the least precise measure.

Example:

> The 1994 *Information Please Almanac* gives the following winning times in the men's 100-meter dash in the 1968 and 1972 Olympic Games:
>
> | Year | Winner | Time |
> | --- | --- | --- |
> | 1968 | James Hines, U.S.A. | 9.9 seconds |
> | 1972 | Valery Borzow, U.S.S.R. | 10.14 seconds |
>
> How much faster did James Hines run the race than Valery Borzow?
>
> Valery Borzow was timed to a greater degree of precision, since his time was measured to the nearest hundredth of a second while James Hines' time was measured to the nearest tenth of a second. Before we can find the difference between their times, we round the more precise measure, 10.14 seconds, to match the less precise measure, 9.9 seconds, that is, to the nearest tenth of a second: 10.14 seconds is rounded to 10.1 seconds.
>
> Since $10.1 - 9.9 = 0.2$, James Hines ran the 100-meter dash about 0.2 second faster than Valery Borzow.

Check Your Understanding

1. Which measurement is more precise: 7.3 meters or 2.58 meters?
2. Solve.

   a. $3.78 + 5.24$ b. $27.3 - 5.7$ c. $9.6 + 2.06$ d. $7.3 \text{ m} - 2.58 \text{ m}$

Multiplying by Powers of 10

		10^4	10^3	10^2	10^1	10^0	.	10^{-1}	10^{-2}	10^{-3}	10^{-4}	
. . .		10,000	1000	100	10	1	.	0.1	0.01	0.001	0.0001	. . .

Some Powers of 10

Multiplying by a **power of 10** is easy. Here is one method.

	$1000 * 45.6 = ?$	$0.001 * 45.6 = ?$
Step 1 Locate the decimal point in the power of 10.	$1000 = 1000.$	0.001
Step 2 Move the decimal point LEFT or RIGHT until you get the number 1.	1.000.	0.001.
Step 3 Count the number of places you moved the decimal point.	3 places	3 places
Step 4* Move the decimal point in the other factor the same number of places, but in the OPPOSITE direction. Insert 0's as needed.	4 5.6 0 0.	0.0 4 5.6
Step 5 That's the answer.	$1000 * 45.6 = 45,600$	$0.001 * 45.6 = 0.0456$

* To help you decide whether to move the decimal point right or left,
    think: "Is the answer greater than or less than the other factor?"

Some Powers of 10											
. . .	10^4	10^3	10^2	10^1	10^0	.	10^{-1}	10^{-2}	10^{-3}	10^{-4}	. . .
. . .	10,000	1000	100	10	1	.	0.1	0.01	0.001	0.0001	. . .

Here is another method.

	$1000 * 45.6 = ?$	$0.001 * 45.6 = ?$
Step 1 Think of the power of 10 in exponential notation.	$1000 = 10^3$	$0.001 = 10^{-3}$
Step 2 Note the number in the exponent.	10^3	10^{-3}
Step 3* If the exponent is POSITIVE, move the decimal point in the other factor that number of places to the RIGHT. Insert 0's as needed.	4 5.6 0 0.	
Step 4* If the exponent is NEGATIVE, move the decimal point in the other factor that number of places to the LEFT. Insert 0's as needed.		0.0 4 5.6
Step 5 That's the answer.	$1000 * 45.6 = 45,600$	$0.001 * 45.6 = 0.0456$

* To help you decide whether to move the decimal point right or left,
  think: "Is the answer greater than or less than the other factor?"

Check Your Understanding

1. $100 * 3.45 = ?$
2. $0.01 * 3.45 = ?$
3. $? = 0.16 * 10,000$
4. $5.09 * 0.1 = ?$
5. $0.55 * 0.001 = ?$
6. $? = 1000 * \$5.50$
7. $1.08 * 10 = ?$
8. $0.01 * 32.7 = ?$

Multiplication of Decimals

Because the base-10 place-value system works in the same way for whole numbers and for rational numbers expressed as decimals, you can use the same procedures for multiplying whole numbers when multiplying with decimals. The only difference is that the size of the answers will not be the same.

Here is one way to multiply with decimals:

Step 1: Ignore any decimal points in the factors, that is, treat them as if they were whole numbers. Use the multiplication algorithm you would use for whole numbers. The answer will be a whole number.

Step 2: Estimate the proper size of the product and place the decimal point in the product accordingly.

> *Example:* 15.2 * 3.6 = ?

Step 1	Step 2
Multiply, ignoring the decimal points.	Estimate the size of the product.

Step 1
Multiply, ignoring the decimal points.

$$
\begin{array}{rr}
 & 152 \\
 & *\ 36 \\
30 * 100 = & 3000 \\
30 * 50 = & 1500 \\
30 * 2 = & 60 \\
6 * 100 = & 600 \\
6 * 50 = & 300 \\
6 * 2 = & \underline{\ 12} \\
 & 5472 \\
\end{array}
$$

Step 2
Estimate the size of the product.

15.2 is a little more than 15 and 3.6 is between 3 and 4.

Therefore, 15.2 * 3.6 is between 45 (3 * 15) and 60 (4 * 15).

54.72 is between 45 and 60, so 15.2 * 3.6 = 54.72.

Step 2 shortcut: To find where to put the decimal point in the product:

- Count the total number of decimal places in both factors.

- Place the decimal point in the product so that there are as many decimal places in the product as there are in both factors.

This method is especially useful when the factors are less than 1 and have many decimal places.

> *Example:* 0.05 * 0.0062 = ?

0.0062	(4 decimal places)
* 0.05	(2 decimal places)
0.000310	(6 decimal places)

Note that when these two numbers are multiplied as if they were whole numbers, there are only 3 digits in the product (5 * 62 = 310). It is necessary to insert 3 zeros after the decimal point and in front of 310 in order to obtain 6 decimal places in the product, since ten-thousandths times hundredths give millionths.

Check Your Understanding

Multiply.

1. 2.8 * 4.6   **2.** 1.44 * 9.3   **3.** 0.52 * 3.03   **4.** 0.2 * 0.016

					Some Powers of 10						
	10^4	10^3	10^2	10^1	10^0	.	10^{-1}	10^{-2}	10^{-3}	10^{-4}	. . .
. . .	10,000	1000	100	10	1	.	0.1	0.01	0.001	0.0001	. . .

Dividing by a power of 10 is easy. Here is one method.

	45.6/1000 = ?	$\frac{45.6}{0.001}$ = ?
Step 1 Locate the decimal point in the power of 10.	1000 = 1000.	0.001
Step 2 Move the decimal point LEFT or RIGHT until you get the number 1.	1 0 0 0	0 0 0 1
Step 3 Count the number of places you moved the decimal point.	3 places	3 places
Step 4* Move the decimal point in the other factor the same number of places, in the SAME direction. Insert 0's as needed.	0 0 4 5 6	4 5 6 0 0
Step 5 That's the answer.	45.6/1000 = 0.0456	$\frac{45.6}{0.001}$ = 45,600

* To help you decide whether to move the decimal point right or left, think: "Is the answer greater than or less than the other factor?"

Dividing by Powers of 10 (continued)

Here is another method.

	45.6/1000 = ?	$\frac{45.6}{0.001}$ = ?
Step 1 Think of the power of 10 in exponential notation.	$1000 = 10^3$	$0.001 = 10^{-3}$
Step 2 Note the number in the exponent.	10^3	10^{-3}
Step 3* If the exponent is POSITIVE, move the decimal point in the other factor that number of places to the LEFT. Insert 0's as needed.	0.0 4 5.6	
Step 4* If the exponent is NEGATIVE, move the decimal point in the other factor that number of places to the RIGHT. Insert 0's as needed.		
Step 5 That's the answer.	45.6/1000 = 0.0456	$\frac{45.6}{0.001}$ = 45,600

* To help you decide whether to move the decimal point right or left, think: "Is the answer greater than or less than the other factor?"

Check Your Understanding

1. 67.8/10 = ?
2. $\frac{67.8}{0.1}$ = ?
3. ? = 0.54/100
4. $290/1000 = ?
5. ? = 7.75/0.001
6. ? = $\frac{40}{10,000}$
7. 37.5/0.01 = ?
8. $\frac{0.02}{0.001}$ = ?

The basic procedure is the same as for multiplication:

14 | 15

- Divide as if the divisor and dividend were whole numbers.

- Use estimation to determine the size of the answer and place the decimal point in the answer accordingly.

Example: 97.24/2.6 = ?

Step 1
Divide, ignoring the decimal points.

```
26)9724    │ 300
  − 7800   │
    1924   │ 70
  − 1820   │
     104   │ 4
   − 104   │
       0   │
           └─────
             374
```

Step 2
Estimate the size of the quotient.

Ask yourself: "What number, times 2.6, equals 97.24?"

Suppose the quotient is 37.4. Could 37.4 * 2.6 = 97.24? 37.4 is almost 40. 40 * 2.6 is about 100, so 37.4 * 2.6 is a little less than 100. Therefore, the quotient is 37.4.

When a number greater than 1 (the dividend) is divided by a number less than 1 (the divisor), the quotient will always be greater than the dividend.

For example, if you divide each of 4 pies in half, you end up with 8 pieces, that is, $4/\frac{1}{2} = 4/0.5 = 8$. The quotient, 8, is greater than the dividend, 4, because the dividend, 4, is greater than 1 and the divisor, 0.5, is less than 1.

dividend/divisor = quotient
4/0.5 = 8

Example: 8.25/0.3 = ?

Step 1
Divide, ignoring the decimal points.

```
3)825    │ 200
 − 600   │
   225   │ 70
 − 210   │
    15   │ 5
  − 15   │
     0   │
         └─────
           275
```

Step 2
Estimate the size of the quotient.

Since 8.25, which is greater than 1, is being divided by 0.3, which is less than 1, the answer must be greater than 8.25. Therefore, the quotient cannot be 2.75.

0.3 is almost $\frac{1}{3}$ and 8.25 is a little more than 8. If each of 8 pieces is divided into thirds, there will be 24 pieces, that is, $8/\frac{1}{3} = 24$. Therefore, it makes sense that 8.25/0.3 = 27.5.

Check Your Understanding

Divide.

1. 9.6/3.2

2. 7.68/2.4

3. $\frac{56.8}{0.1}$

4. 3.825/0.25

Positive and Negative Rational Numbers

You have seen positive and negative numbers on a temperature scale. They express temperatures with reference to a zero point (0 degrees). There are many other situations in which positive and negative numbers are used. For example:

Situation	Negative	Zero	Positive
bank account	withdrawal	no change	deposit
weight	loss	no change	gain
time	before	now	after
games	behind	even	ahead
business	loss	break even	profit
elevation	below sea level	sea level	above sea level

Just as withdrawal/deposit, loss/gain, before/after, behind/ahead, profit/loss, and below/above are opposites of each other, so a negative number is the opposite of a positive number and a positive number is the opposite of a negative number.

Notation

The symbol "–" is written before a numeral to denote that it represents a negative number. For example, –5 is read as "negative 5," –12.3 as "negative 12.3," and $-\frac{5}{8}$ as "negative $\frac{5}{8}$."

When a negative number follows an operation symbol in a number sentence, the negative number appears in parentheses; for example, $8 - (-7) = 15$.

Relations

When two positive rational numbers are shown on a number line, the number that is the greater distance to the right of zero on a horizontal number line or above zero on a vertical number line is the larger number. For example, on the vertical number line at the right, 6 is greater than 2. The same rule is applied to positive and negative rational numbers. Thus, 4 is greater than –7, and –2.435 is greater than –3.627.

Operations

The **absolute value** of a positive number is the number itself; the absolute value of a negative number is the opposite of the number. The rules for adding and subtracting positive and negative numbers depend on the sign of the numbers and on their absolute values. The procedures for multiplying and dividing positive and negative numbers are the same as for the operations with whole numbers. The sign of the factors determines whether the product is a positive or negative number.

The procedures for these operations are described in more detail starting on page 57.

When adding two positive or negative numbers, you can think of the first addend as a starting point on a number line, the second addend as a move away from the starting point, and the sum as the ending point after the move. If the second addend is a positive number, the move is made in the positive direction, that is, to the right on a horizontal number line. If the second addend is a negative number, the move is made in the negative direction, that is, to the left on a horizontal number line.

56

No matter where you start, adding a positive number results in a sum that is greater than the first addend and adding a negative number results in a sum that is less than the first addend.

Examples:

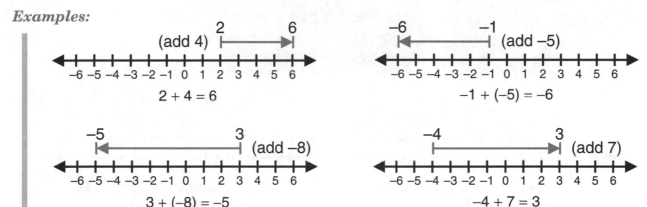

$2 + 4 = 6$

$-1 + (-5) = -6$

$3 + (-8) = -5$

$-4 + 7 = 3$

Here is another way to think about addition of rational numbers.

- The **absolute value** of a positive number is the number itself. For example, the absolute value of 3 is 3. The absolute value of a negative number is the opposite of the number. For example, the absolute value of −6 is 6.

- The sum of two positive numbers is a positive number. For example, $3 + 5 = 8$.

- To find the sum of two negative numbers, add the absolute values of the addends. The sum is the opposite of the result. For example, $-3 + (-5) = (op)(3 + 5) = -8$.

- To find the sum of a positive and a negative number, subtract the smaller absolute value from the larger absolute value. The sum takes on the sign of the addend with the larger absolute value. For example, $-7 + 3 = -(7 - 3) = -4$ and $-2 + 8 = 8 - 2 = 6$

- The sum of two opposites is zero. For example, $-5 + 5 = 0$.

Check Your Understanding

Add.

1. $-9 + (-6)$ **2.** $-14 + 38$ **3.** $5.2 + (-5.6)$ **4.** $7 + 12$ **5.** $9 + (-27)$

Subtraction of Positive and Negative Rational Numbers

57

You can picture addition of positive and negative numbers on the number line. The first addend is the starting point, the second addend is a move away from the starting point, and the sum is the ending point after the move.

Addition and subtraction work in opposite ways. Therefore, if the move is in one direction for addition, it is in the opposite direction for subtraction.

Addition	Subtraction
If the second addend is positive, move in the positive direction. If the second addend is negative, move in the negative direction.	If the number that is being subtracted is positive, move in the negative direction. If the number that is being subtracted is negative, move in the positive direction.

Examples:

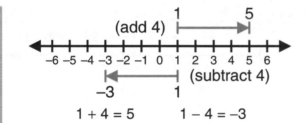

$$1 + 4 = 5 \qquad 1 - 4 = -3$$

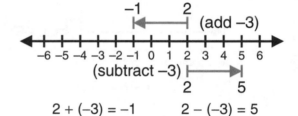

$$2 + (-3) = -1 \qquad 2 - (-3) = 5$$

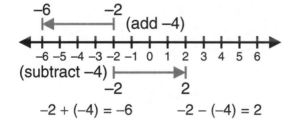

$$-2 + (-4) = -6 \qquad -2 - (-4) = 2$$

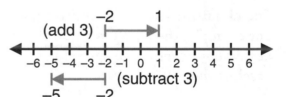

$$-2 + 3 = 1 \qquad -2 - 3 = -5$$

Another way to think about subtraction of rational numbers is to change the subtraction problem into an addition problem.

To subtract a number b from a number a, add the *opposite* of b to a. Thus, for any numbers a and b, $a - b = a +$ (opposite) of b, or $a - b = a + (-b)$.

Examples:

$$1 - 4 = 1 + (-4) = -3 \qquad\qquad 2 - (-3) = 2 + 3 = 5$$
$$-2 - (-4) = -2 + 4 = 2 \qquad\qquad -2 - 3 = -2 + (-3) = -5$$

Check Your Understanding

Subtract.

1. $3 - 7$ **2.** $-5 - (-2)$ **3.** $-6 - 4$ **4.** $8 - (-9)$

Multiplication and Division of Positive and Negative Rational Numbers

To multiply or divide two (nonzero) positive or negative rational numbers, calculate the answer as if both numbers in the problem were positive. Then use one of the following rules to decide whether the answer is a positive or negative rational number.

- If the numbers are both positive or both negative, the result is a positive number.

- If one of the numbers is negative and the other is positive, the result is a negative number.

	Multiplication Examples	Division Examples	Result
both positive	$8.2 * 3.6 = 29.52$	$51.3/19 = 2.7$	positive
both negative	$-\frac{3}{4} * (-1\frac{2}{5}) = 1\frac{1}{20}$	$-81/(-3) = 27$	positive
one positive and one negative	$12 * (-6) = -72$ $-25 * 8 = -200$	$-275/25 = -11$ $102.432/(-4.8) = -21.34$	negative

- If one of the factors in a multiplication problem is zero, then the product is zero.

Example:

$-38.65 * 0 = 0$

- If the number that is being divided (the dividend) in a division problem is zero, then the quotient is zero.

Example:

$0/(-25\frac{3}{7}) = 0$

The number the dividend is being divided by (the divisor) may never be zero.

Example:

$38/0$ is not allowed.

Check Your Understanding

1. Multiply.
   a. $-15 * 6$
   b. $0 * (-234)$
   c. $10 * (-27)$
   d. $9 * (-8)$

2. Divide.
   a. $72/(-6)$
   b. $\frac{-54}{9}$
   c. $0/99$
   d. $-100/(-20)$

Our Number System

Counting is almost as old as the human race and has been used in some form by every human society. But people soon found that the **counting numbers** did not meet all their needs.

- Counting numbers could not be used to express measures between two consecutive whole numbers, such as $2\frac{1}{2}$ inches and 5.3 kilometers.
- With the counting numbers, division problems such as 8/5 and 3/7 did not have an answer.

The **positive rational numbers** were invented to meet these needs. These are the numbers that can be expressed as fractions and decimals. With the invention of the positive rational numbers, it became possible to express rates and ratio comparisons, to name many more points on the number line, and to solve any division problems.

Even the positive rational numbers did not meet every need. For example, problems such as $5 - 7$ and $2\frac{3}{4} - 5\frac{1}{4}$ did not have an answer. This led to the invention of the **negative rational numbers**. Negative numbers serve several purposes in mathematics and in everyday life.

- They can be used to express locations in opposite directions from a specific starting point, such as temperatures above and below zero, elevations above and below sea level, and years before or after the birth of Christ.
- They may be used to express changes, such as profits and losses, yards gained and lost in a football game, and increases and decreases in weight.
- They allow the number line to be extended from zero in the opposite direction of the positive rational numbers.
- Without them, many subtraction problems have no answer.

The **rational numbers** are made up of every positive and negative rational number and zero. **Integers** are a special kind of rational number. The set of integers consists of all counting numbers, all the opposites of counting numbers, and zero. You can find a summary of the properties of the rational numbers, beginning on page 64.

There are still more numbers, some of which, like the number π, you have used before. These are called **irrational numbers**. Others, with which you are not familiar, such as $\sqrt{2}$ and tan 30°, are shown on the Real Number Line Poster on page 62. You will learn more about irrational numbers when you study algebra.

All the rational numbers and irrational numbers are called the **real numbers**. Between any two real numbers, no matter how close together, you can always find another real number.

Counting Numbers:

1, 2, 3, 4, 5, ...

Positive Rational Numbers:

$5, \frac{1}{2}, 2, 7.08, 40\%$

Negative Rational Numbers:

$-6, -\left(\frac{3}{8}\right), -0.006, -1\frac{1}{2}$

Integers:

12, 0, –37

Irrational Numbers:

$\sqrt{2}$, tan 30°

Real Numbers:

All of the examples on pages 60 and 61.

There are infinitely many rational numbers. You could count them and not miss any, but it would take forever. The number of rational numbers is represented by the symbol $\aleph_0$, which is read "aleph null." There are even more irrational numbers than rational numbers. You couldn't count them, even if you counted forever.

Notation

A rational number is any number that can be written in the form $\frac{a}{b}$, where a and b are integers and b is not 0. A rational number can also be written as a **terminating decimal**, for which all the digits can be written, or as a **repeating decimal**, in which a pattern of one or more digits repeats endlessly.

Examples:

$\frac{5}{8} = 0.625$

$\frac{1}{3} = 0.\overline{3} = 0.3333...$

$\frac{1}{7} = 0.\overline{142857} = 0.142857142857...$

An irrational number can be written as a decimal, but not as a terminating or repeating decimal. It cannot be written in the form $\frac{a}{b}$, where a and b are integers.

Examples:

$\pi = 3.141592653...$	The decimal continues without a repeating pattern.
$\sqrt{2} = 1.414213653...$	The decimal continues without a repeating pattern.
$1.010010001...$	There is a pattern in the decimal, but it does not repeat.

Check Your Understanding

Refer to the Real Number Line on page 62 to answer the questions.

1. a. Which counting numbers are shown on the real number line?
   b. Which integers are shown on the number line?

2. a. Can 0.2 be written as a fraction?
   b. Can 1.1666... be written as a fraction?

3. a. Is 10^{-1} a positive rational number?
   b. Is 1.333... a rational number?
   c. Which rational numbers are shown between 1 and 2?

4. Is $\sqrt{16}$ a rational number?

5. Which numbers, shown on the Real Number Line cannot be written as either terminating or repeating decimals?

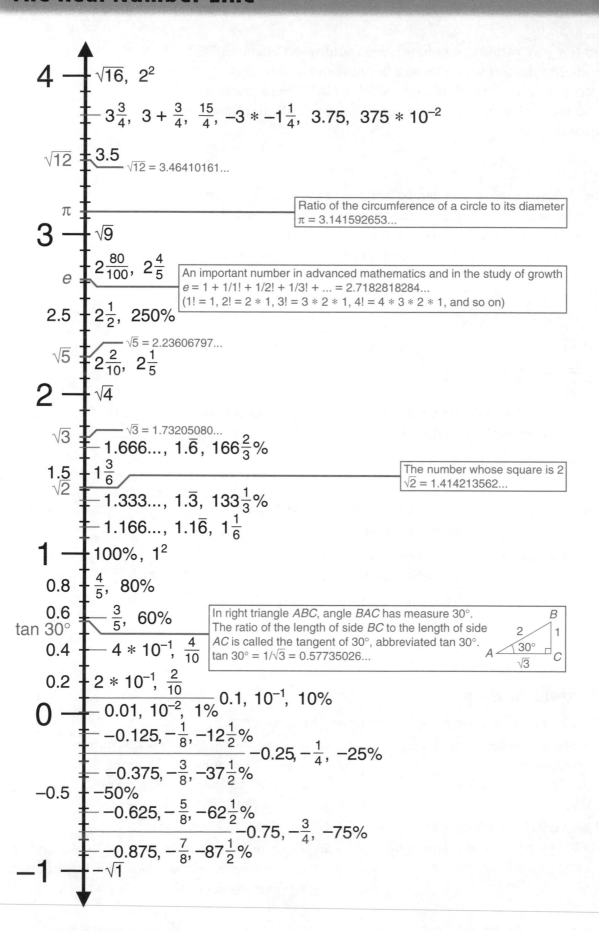

4 — $\sqrt{16}$, 2^2

$3\frac{3}{4}$, $3 + \frac{3}{4}$, $\frac{15}{4}$, $-3 * -1\frac{1}{4}$, 3.75, $375 * 10^{-2}$

$\sqrt{12}$ 3.5
$\sqrt{12} = 3.46410161...$

π —
Ratio of the circumference of a circle to its diameter
$\pi = 3.141592653...$

3 — $\sqrt{9}$

e — $2\frac{80}{100}$, $2\frac{4}{5}$
An important number in advanced mathematics and in the study of growth
$e = 1 + 1/1! + 1/2! + 1/3! + ... = 2.7182818284...$
$(1! = 1, 2! = 2 * 1, 3! = 3 * 2 * 1, 4! = 4 * 3 * 2 * 1$, and so on$)$

2.5 — $2\frac{1}{2}$, 250%

$\sqrt{5}$ $\sqrt{5} = 2.23606797...$
$2\frac{2}{10}$, $2\frac{1}{5}$

2 — $\sqrt{4}$

$\sqrt{3}$ $\sqrt{3} = 1.73205080...$
$1.666...$, $1.\overline{6}$, $166\frac{2}{3}\%$

1.5 $1\frac{3}{6}$
$\sqrt{2}$
The number whose square is 2
$\sqrt{2} = 1.414213562...$
$1.333...$, $1.\overline{3}$, $133\frac{1}{3}\%$

$1.166...$, $1.1\overline{6}$, $1\frac{1}{6}$

1 — 100%, 1^2

0.8 — $\frac{4}{5}$, 80%

0.6 — $\frac{3}{5}$, 60%
$\tan 30°$
In right triangle ABC, angle BAC has measure 30°.
The ratio of the length of side BC to the length of side
AC is called the tangent of 30°, abbreviated $\tan 30°$.
$\tan 30° = 1/\sqrt{3} = 0.57735026...$

0.4 — $4 * 10^{-1}$, $\frac{4}{10}$

0.2 — $2 * 10^{-1}$, $\frac{2}{10}$
0.1, 10^{-1}, 10%

0 — 0.01, 10^{-2}, 1%

-0.125, $-\frac{1}{8}$, $-12\frac{1}{2}\%$

-0.25, $-\frac{1}{4}$, -25%

-0.375, $-\frac{3}{8}$, $-37\frac{1}{2}\%$

-0.5 — -50%

-0.625, $-\frac{5}{8}$, $-62\frac{1}{2}\%$

-0.75, $-\frac{3}{4}$, -75%

-0.875, $-\frac{7}{8}$, $-87\frac{1}{2}\%$

-1 — $-\sqrt{1}$

Many rules involving numbers can be described with the help of variables, such as n, A, or $\square$. For example, the rule "The sum of a number and its opposite is 0" can be expressed as $a + (-a) = 0$, where a stands for any number. This is sometimes called a **general pattern**. A **special case** of this general pattern can be given by replacing the variable a with any number. For example, $5 + (-5) = 0$ and $27\frac{1}{2} + (-27\frac{1}{2}) = 0$ are special cases of the general pattern $a + (-a) = 0$.

Example 1:

Express the rule "The square of a number is the number multiplied by itself" with variables. Give three special cases of the general pattern.

General pattern: $n^2 = n * n$

Special cases:

For $n = 3$: $3^2 = 3 * 3$

For $n = -7$: $-7^2 = -7 * (-7)$

For $n = \frac{2}{3}$: $\left(\frac{2}{3}\right)^2 = \frac{2}{3} * \frac{2}{3}$

Example 2:

Use variables to describe the general pattern for the following special cases.

Special cases: $8/8 = 1$ $0.5/0.5 = 1$ $2\frac{3}{4}/2\frac{3}{4} = 1$

Step 1
Write everything that is the same for all the special cases and use blanks for the parts that change.

$$\underline{}/\underline{} = 1$$

Step 2
Fill in the blanks. Use a variable for the number that varies.

$$\underline{x} / \underline{x} = 1$$

Note: x may not be 0.

Check Your Understanding

1. Write three special cases for each general pattern.

   a. $2 * r + r = 3 * r$

   b. $b + (b + 1) + (b + 2) = 3 * (b + 1)$

2. Use variables to express the general pattern for these special cases.

   a. $4 + 8 = 8 + 4$

      $0.25 + 0.75 = 0.75 + 0.25$

      $\frac{3}{5} + \frac{1}{5} = \frac{1}{5} + \frac{3}{5}$

   b. $\frac{3}{4} * \frac{4}{3} = 1$

      $\frac{2}{1} * \frac{1}{2} = 1$

      $\frac{3}{8} * \frac{8}{3} = 1$

Properties of Rational Numbers

The following properties are true for all rational numbers. The variables a, b, c, and d stand for any rational numbers (except 0, if the variable stands for a divisor).

Properties	Examples
Binary Operations Property When any two numbers are added, subtracted, multiplied, or divided, the result is a single number. $a + b$, $a - b$, $a * b$, and a/b are equal to single numbers.	$5 + 7 = 12$ $-3 - \frac{8}{3} = -5\frac{2}{3}$ $0.5 * (-4) = -2$ $2\frac{3}{5} \div \frac{8}{3} = \frac{39}{40}$
Commutative Properties The sum or product of two numbers is the same, regardless of the order of the numbers. $a + b = b + a$ $a * b = b * a$	$7 + 8 = 8 + 7 = 15$ $-5 * (-6) = -6 * (-5) = 30$ $\frac{3}{4} * \left(-\frac{4}{5}\right) = -\frac{4}{5} * \frac{3}{4}$ $\qquad = -\frac{12}{20}$, or $-\frac{3}{5}$
Associative Properties The sum or product of three or more numbers is the same, regardless of how the numbers are paired. $a + (b + c) = (a + b) + c$ $a * (b * c) = (a * b) * c$	$(7 + 5) + 8 = 7 + (5 + 8)$ $\quad 12 \quad + 8 = 7 + \quad 13$ $\qquad 20 = 20$ $2\frac{1}{2} * (2 * 3) = (2\frac{1}{2} * 2) * 3$ $2\frac{1}{2} * \quad 6 \quad = \quad 5 \quad * 3$ $\qquad 15 = 15$
Distributive Property When a number is multiplied by the sum or difference of two or more numbers, the number is "distributed" over the numbers that are added or subtracted. $a * (b + c) = (a * b) + (a * c)$ $a * (b - c) = (a * b) - (a * c)$	$5 * (8 + 2) = (5 * 8) + (5 * 2)$ $5 * \quad 10 \quad = \quad 40 + \quad 10$ $\qquad 50 = 50$ $-2 * (8 - 3) = (-2 * 8) - (-2 * 3)$ $-2 * \quad 5 \quad = -16 \quad - \quad (-6)$ $\qquad -10 = -10$
Addition Property of Zero The sum of any number and 0 is equal to the original number. $a + 0 = 0 + a = a$	$5.37 + 0 = 5.37$ $0 + (-6) = -6$
Multiplication Property of One The product of any number and 1 is equal to the original number. $a * 1 = 1 * a = a$	$\frac{2}{3} * 1 = \frac{2}{3}$ $1 * 19 = 19$

Opposites Properties The opposite of a number a may be written as $-a$ or (op)a. If a is a positive number, then (op)a is a negative number. If a is a negative number, then (op)a is a positive number. If $a = 0$, then (op)$a = 0$ The opposite of a number is the product of (-1) and the number. $-a = -1 * a$	$(\text{op})8 = -8$ $(\text{op})-\frac{3}{4} = \frac{3}{4}$ $(\text{op})-7 = 7$ $(\text{op})0 = 0$ $\begin{aligned}-(x + 2) &= -1 * (x + 2)\\ &= (-1 * x) + (-1 * 2)\\ &= -x + (-2)\\ &= -x - 2\end{aligned}$
Opposite of Opposites Property The opposite of the opposite of a number is equal to the original number. $(\text{op})(\text{op})a = (\text{op})(-a) = a$	$(\text{op})(\text{op})\frac{2}{3} = (\text{op})-\frac{2}{3} = \frac{2}{3}$ $(\text{op})(\text{op})(-9) = (\text{op})9 = -9$
Sum of Opposites Property The sum of any number and its opposite is 0. $a + (-a) = (-a) + a = 0$	$15 + (-15) = 0$ $-2 + 2 = 0$
Multiplication of Reciprocals Property The product of any number and its reciprocal is 1. $a * \frac{1}{a} = \frac{1}{a} * a = 1$	$20 * \frac{1}{20} = 1$ $-\frac{2}{5} * \left(-\frac{5}{2}\right) = 1$
Addition Property of Positive and Negative Numbers The sum of two positive numbers is a positive number. The sum of two negative numbers is the opposite of the sum of the "number parts" of the addends. To find the sum of a positive and negative number, subtract the smaller from the larger "number part." The sum takes on the sign of the addend with the larger "number part."	$7 + 8 = 15$ $-7 + (-8) = (\text{op})(7 + 8) = -15$ $-2.5 + 1.5 = -(2.5 - 1.5) = -1$ $\frac{3}{4} + \left(-\frac{1}{4}\right) = \frac{3}{4} - \frac{1}{4} = \frac{2}{4}, \text{ or } \frac{1}{2}$
Multiplication Property of Positive and Negative Numbers The product of two positive numbers or of two negative numbers is a positive number. The product of a positive and a negative number is a negative number.	$6 * 3 = 18$ $-6 * (-3) = 18$ $\frac{1}{3} * \left(-\frac{4}{5}\right) = -\frac{4}{15}$

Properties of Rational Numbers (continued)

Subtraction and Division Properties All subtraction problems can be solved by addition, and all division problems can be solved by multiplication. $a - b = a + (-b)$ $\frac{a}{b} = a * \frac{1}{b}$	$15 - 7 = 15 + (-7) = 8$ $-9 - (-6) = -9 + (\text{op})-6$ $\qquad\quad = -9 + 6$ $\qquad\quad = -3$ $12/4 = 12 * \frac{1}{4} = \frac{12}{4} = 3$ $25/(-5) = 25 * \left(-\frac{1}{5}\right)$ $\qquad\quad = -\frac{25}{5} = -5$
Equivalent Fractions Properties If the numerator and denominator of a fraction are multiplied or divided by the same number, the resulting fraction is equivalent to the original fraction. $\frac{a}{b} = \frac{a * c}{b * c} \qquad \frac{a}{b} = \frac{a/c}{b/c}$	$\frac{2}{3} = \frac{2 * 5}{3 * 5} = \frac{10}{15}$ $\frac{6}{8} = \frac{6/2}{8/2} = \frac{3}{4}$
Addition and Subtraction of Fractions Properties The sum or difference of fractions with like denominators is the sum or difference of the numerators over the denominator. To add or subtract fractions with unlike denominators, rename the fractions so they have a common denominator. $\frac{a}{c} + \frac{b}{c} = \frac{a + b}{c} \qquad \frac{a}{c} - \frac{b}{c} = \frac{a - b}{c}$	$\frac{3}{5} + \frac{1}{5} = \frac{3+1}{5} = \frac{4}{5}$ $\frac{2}{3} - \frac{1}{4} = \frac{8}{12} - \frac{3}{12}$ $\qquad\quad = \frac{8-3}{12}$ $\qquad\quad = \frac{5}{12}$
Multiplication of Fractions Property The product of two fractions is the product of the numerators over the product of the denominators. $\frac{a}{b} * \frac{c}{d} = \frac{a * c}{b * d}$	$\frac{5}{8} * \frac{3}{4} = \frac{5 * 3}{8 * 4}$ $\qquad\quad = \frac{15}{32}$
Division of Fractions Property The quotient of two fractions is the product of the dividend and the reciprocal of the divisor. $\frac{a}{b} \div \frac{c}{d} = \frac{a}{b} * \frac{d}{c} = \frac{a * d}{b * c}$	$9 \div \frac{2}{3} = 9 * \frac{3}{2} = \frac{27}{2}$, or $13\frac{1}{2}$ $\frac{5}{6} \div \frac{1}{4} = \frac{5}{6} * \frac{4}{1} = \frac{20}{6}$, or $3\frac{1}{3}$
Powers of a Number Property If a is any number and b is a positive whole number, then a^b is the product of a used as a factor b times. a^0 is equal to 1. $a^b = \underbrace{a * a * a * \ldots * a}_{b \text{ factors}}$	$5^2 = 5 * 5 = 25$ $\left(\frac{2}{3}\right)^4 = \frac{2}{3} * \frac{2}{3} * \frac{2}{3} * \frac{2}{3}$ $\qquad\quad = \frac{16}{81}$ $34^0 = 1$

Geometry is the mathematical study of space and objects in space.

Plane geometry concerns two-dimensional objects (figures) on a flat surface (a plane). Figures studied in plane geometry include lines, line segments, angles, polygons, and circles. In *Everyday Mathematics* you began exploring plane geometry in kindergarten. The subject is presented in depth in a high-school course that is usually offered in the ninth or tenth grade.

Solid geometry is the study of three-dimensional objects. These objects are often simplified ("idealized") versions of familiar things in the everyday world—for example, cylinders (suggested by food cans), spheres (balls, marbles, soap bubbles) and prisms (boxes). In *Everyday Mathematics* you have been studying solid geometry since kindergarten.

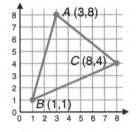

Graphs, coordinates, and coordinate grids have also been part of *Everyday Mathematics*. The branch of geometry dealing with figures on a coordinate grid is called **coordinate geometry** or **analytic geometry**. Analytic geometry combines algebra with geometry.

Transformation geometry is the study of geometric properties under motion. **Translations** (slides), **reflections** (flips), and **rotations** (turns), are familiar operations in transformation geometry.

Geometry originated in ancient Egypt and Mesopotamia as a practical tool for surveying land and constructing buildings. (The word *geometry* comes from the Greek *ge*, "the Earth," and *metron*, "to measure.") About 300 B.C., the Greek mathematician Euclid gathered the geometric knowledge of his time into a book known as the *Elements*. Euclid's *Elements* is one of the great achievements of human thought. It begins with ten unproved statements called "postulates" and "common notions." In modern wording, one of the postulates reads, "Through a given point not on a given line, there is exactly one line parallel to the given line."

There is exactly one line through point *F* parallel to $\overleftrightarrow{DE}$.

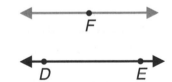

Euclid used logic to deduce several hundred "propositions" (theorems) from the postulates and common notions—for example, "In any triangle, the side opposite the greater angle is greater."

Mathematicians began to develop other forms of geometry in the seventeenth century, beginning with René Descartes' analytic geometry (1637). The problem of perspective in paintings led to **projective geometry**. In the nineteenth century, mathematicians explored the results of changing Euclid's postulate about parallel lines quoted above. In **non-Euclidean geometry**, there are either no lines parallel to the given line, or at least two lines parallel to the given line. **Topology**, a modern branch of geometry, deals with properties of geometric objects that do not change when their shapes are changed.

The Geometry Template

The **Geometry Template** was designed to serve a number of mathematical purposes. Look closely and see how many functions you can identify.

You already may have noticed that the Template has two measuring scales—one to measure with inch units and the other with centimeter units. Each inch is subdivided into sixteenth-inch intervals and each centimeter into millimeter intervals. The Template also serves nicely as a straightedge with which to draw straight lines.

The Template includes a collection of 22 geometric figures. Look at the drawing on the next page to help you identify the different shapes. The figures labeled "PB" are **pattern-block shapes**; they are half the size of real pattern blocks. Each pattern-block shape is represented on the Template—a hexagon, a trapezoid, two different rhombuses, an equilateral triangle, and a square. These will come in handy for some of the activities you do this year.

Notice that the equilateral triangle pattern block is also labeled "T1." It is one of five triangles on the Geometry Template—each one labeled with a T and a number. Triangles "T2" and "T5" are right triangles, "T3" is a scalene triangle, and "T4" is an isosceles triangle.

The remaining shapes are an assortment of 2-dimensional figures: a variety of circles and squares, a regular octagon, a regular pentagon, a kite, a rectangle, a parallelogram, and an ellipse.

The two circles near the inch-scale on the left-hand side of your template can be used as ring-binder holes to easily store your Template in your notebook.

The **half-circle** and **full-circle protractors** at the bottom of the Template are used to measure and draw angles. The **Percent Circle** at the top left of the Template is used to construct and measure circle graphs. It is divided into 1% intervals with some common fractions marked at the appropriate places.

Notice that there are tiny holes near the 0-, $\frac{1}{4}$-, $\frac{2}{4}$-, and $\frac{3}{4}$-inch marks of the inch scale and at each inch mark from 1 to 7. On the centimeter side, the holes are placed at each centimeter mark from 0 to 10. These holes can be used to draw circles of a specified radius. For example, to draw a circle with a 4-inch radius, place one pencil point in the hole at 0 inches (the center of the circle) and one in the hole at 4 inches. Hold the pencil at 0 inches steady and rotate the pencil at 4 inches (along with the Template).

Hold this pencil steady.

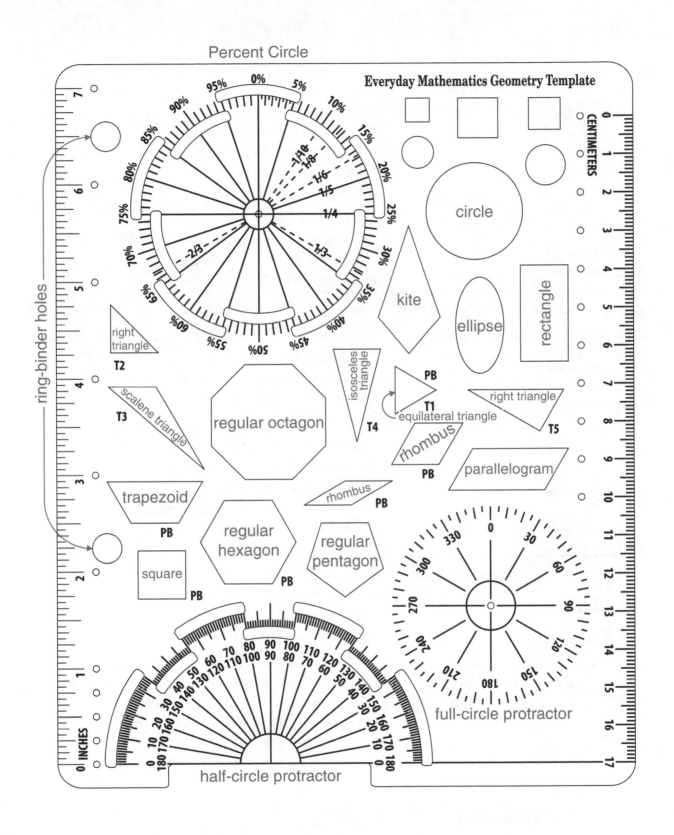

Percent Circle

Everyday Mathematics Geometry Template

Line Segments, Rays, Lines, and Angles

Figure	Name	Description	Notation
point A	**point** A	A location in space	A
endpoints E F	**line segment** EF or line segment FE	A straight path between two points, called its **endpoints**. Points E and F are the endpoints of line segment EF. A line segment is the shortest path between two points.	$\overline{EF}$ or $\overline{FE}$
N M endpoint	**ray** MN	A straight path that extends infinitely from a point, called its **endpoint**. Point M is the endpoint of ray MN.	$\overrightarrow{MN}$
P R	**line** PR or line RP	A straight path that extends infinitely in both directions.	$\overleftrightarrow{PR}$ or $\overleftrightarrow{RP}$
vertex S T P	**angle** STP or angle PTS	Two line segments or rays with a common endpoint, called the vertex of the angle. Point T is the **vertex** of angle STP.	$\angle STP$ or $\angle PTS$
D Z Q P G	**intersecting lines** DG and PQ	Lines that meet. Two intersecting lines meet at exactly one point. Lines DG and PQ meet at point Z. Intersecting rays or line segments are rays or line segments that meet.	
B Q T H	**perpendicular lines** BH and QT	Lines that intersect at right angles. Perpendicular rays or line segments are rays or line segments that meet at right angles, or are on perpendicular lines.	$\overleftrightarrow{BH} \perp \overleftrightarrow{QT}$
W V Y R	**parallel lines** VW and RY	Lines that are everywhere the same distance apart. Parallel lines never meet. Parallel rays or line segments are rays or line segments that are the same distance apart.	$\overleftrightarrow{VW} \parallel \overleftrightarrow{RY}$

Check Your Understanding

Draw and label each of the following.

1. point D 2. $\overleftrightarrow{GH}$ 3. $\angle BEN$ 4. $\overline{QR}$ 5. $\overleftrightarrow{XY} \parallel \overleftrightarrow{JK}$ 6. $\overrightarrow{NO}$

Two angles that have a common side and whose interiors do not overlap are called **adjacent angles**.

Angles *a* and *b* in Figure 1 are adjacent angles.

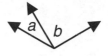

Figure 1

When two lines intersect, the angles opposite each other are called **vertical angles** or **opposite angles**. The measures of any pair of vertical angles are equal.

Example:

> The intersecting lines in Figure 2 form four angles, numbered 1, 2, 3, and 4. Angles 1 and 3 are vertical angles and have the same measure. Angles 2 and 4 are also vertical angles and have the same measure.

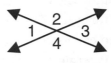

Figure 2

The sum of the measures of adjacent angles, formed by two intersecting lines, is 180°. Pairs of angles whose measures total 180° are called **supplementary angles**.

A line that crosses two lines is called a **transversal**.

The lines in Figure 3 are parallel. Any two angles formed by one of the lines and the transversal either have the same measure or they are supplementary angles.

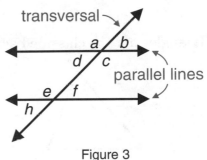

Figure 3

Examples:

> Angles *b* and *d* are vertical angles. Therefore, they have the same measure.
>
> Angles *a* and *b* are supplementary angles. Therefore, the sum of their measures is 180°.

Pairs of angles between two parallel lines that are on the same side of the transversal are supplementary angles.

Example:

> Angles *c* and *f* in Figure 3 are supplementary angles. The sum of their measures is 180°.

If two lines are parallel, the measures of the four angles at one intersection of one of the lines and the transversal have the same pattern as the measures of the four angles at the other intersection.

Check Your Understanding

1. Refer to Figure 3 above. Which of the following pairs of angles have the same measure? Which are supplementary angles?
   a. angles *e* and *g*   b. angles *d* and *e*   c. angles *b* and *g*
   d. angles *d* and *c*   e. angles *c* and *e*   f. angles *h* and *b*

2. In the parallelogram at the right, what is the measure of—
   a. ∠1?   b. ∠2?   c. ∠3?

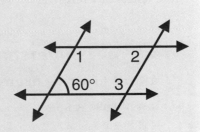

Classification of Angles and Triangles

Angles may be classified according to their size.

  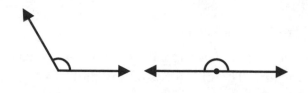

A right angle is an angle whose sides form a square corner. A right angle measures 90°.

An acute angle is an angle whose measure is between 0° and 90°.

An obtuse angle is an angle whose measure is between 90° and 180°.

A straight angle measures 180°.

A reflex angle is an angle whose measure is between 180° and 360°.

Triangles may be classified according to the size of their angles.

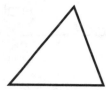 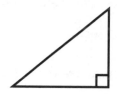 

An acute triangle is a triangle all of whose angles are acute.

A right triangle is a triangle with one right angle.

An obtuse triangle is a triangle with one obtuse angle.

Triangles may be classified according to the length of their sides.

 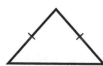 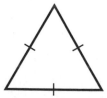

A scalene triangle is a triangle all of whose sides have different lengths.

An isosceles triangle is a triangle that has two sides of the same length.

An equilateral triangle is a triangle all of whose sides are the same length.

Check Your Understanding

Draw the following figures.

1. an obtuse angle
2. an isosceles triangle
3. a right scalene triangle

A **polygon** is a figure made up of line segments, called **sides**. A polygon can have any number of sides, as long as it has at least three. The **interior** (inside) of the polygon is not a part of the polygon. A polygon can have only one interior.

In a polygon:

- The figure is closed.
- Pairs of sides meet only at an endpoint. These endpoints are the **vertices** (or **vertexes**) of the polygon. There are exactly the same number of sides as vertices.
- No two sides may cross or form a line segment.
- No three vertices can be on the same line.

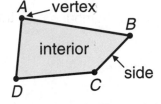

Polygon *ABCD*

A **convex** polygon is a polygon in which all sides are pushed outward.

A **nonconvex** or **concave** polygon is a polygon in which at least one side is pushed in.

A **regular polygon** is a convex polygon all of whose sides are all the same length, and whose angles are all the same size.

Polygons are named after their numbers of sides.

triangle

quadrangle or quadrilateral

pentagon

Prefixes	
tri-	3
quad-	4
penta-	5
hexa-	6
hepta-	7
octa-	8
nona-	9
deca-	10
dodeca-	12

hexagon

heptagon

octagon

nonagon

Check Your Understanding

1. Which of the polygons above are— **a.** convex? **b.** concave? **c.** regular?
2. What is the name of a polygon having— **a.** 6 sides? **b.** 4 sides? **c.** 8 sides?

Classification of Quadrilaterals

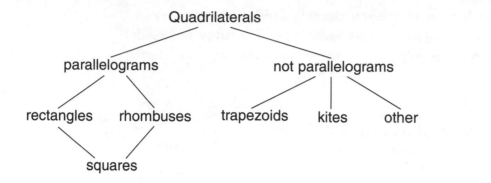

Quadrilaterals
- parallelograms
  - rectangles
  - rhombuses
    - squares
- not parallelograms
  - trapezoids
  - kites
  - other

Quadrilaterals (or **quadrangles**) are four-sided polygons. Some quadrilaterals have two pairs of parallel sides. These are called **parallelograms**.

parallelogram

Parallelograms

rectangle		**Rectangles** are parallelograms that have four right angles. The sides of a rectangle do not all have to be the same length.
rhombus		**Rhombuses** are parallelograms whose sides are all the same length. The angles of a rhombus are usually not right angles, but they may be right angles.
square		**Squares** are parallelograms that have four right angles and whose sides are all the same length. Thus, all squares are rectangles and all squares are rhombuses.

Quadrilaterals that are not Parallelograms

trapezoid		**Trapezoids** are quadrilaterals that have exactly one pair of parallel sides. No two sides of a trapezoid need to be the same length.
kite		**Kites** are quadrilaterals that have two pairs of sides of the same length (congruent). Each pair of congruent sides has a common vertex.
other		Any closed, four-sided figure.

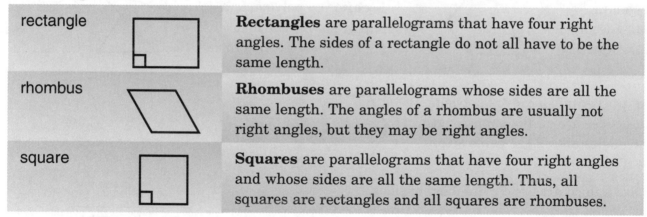

Check Your Understanding

What is the difference between—

1. a square and a rectangle?

2. a trapezoid and a parallelogram?

3. a rhombus and a kite?

A **geometric solid** is a 3-dimensional shape enclosed by surfaces. Although they are called solids, geometric solids are hollow, or empty. The enclosing surfaces can be curved or flat.

The surfaces of a geometric solid meet in curves or line segments. These curves or line segments are the **edges** of the solid.

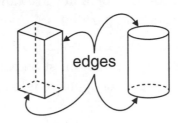
edges

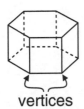

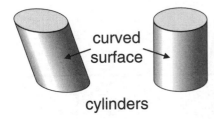
vertices

As with polygons, a "corner" of a geometric solid is called a **vertex** (plural *vertexes* or *vertices*). Edges meet at *vertices*.

A **polyhedron** is a geometric solid whose surfaces are formed by polygons. These surfaces are the **faces** of the polyhedron. **Prisms** and **pyramids** are polyhedrons.

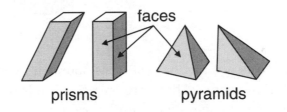
faces

prisms   pyramids

curved surface

cylinders

A **cylinder** has 3 surfaces: a flat "top" and a flat "bottom" formed by circles or ellipses and a **curved surface** that connects them. The top and bottom are the faces of the cylinder.

A **cone** has 2 surfaces: a flat surface formed by a circle or ellipse and a curved surface that comes to a point.

cones

sphere

Like a circle, a **sphere** is the set of all the points that are the same distance from its center. But these are points in space, not just in one plane.

The faces (flat surfaces) of a cylinder are called its **bases**. The bases are opposite each other and parallel.

Like cylinders, prisms have a pair of opposite, parallel bases. All edges that connect the bases of a prism must be parallel to each other. In a rectangular prism, any pair of opposite faces can be its bases.

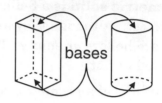

bases

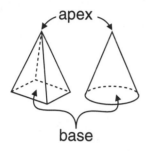

apex

base

Pyramids and cones have exactly one base. The vertex opposite the base is called the **apex** of the pyramid or cone.

Spheres have no bases at all.

sphere

Regular polyhedrons are made up of faces bounded by identical (congruent) regular polygons. There are only five kinds of regular polyhedrons. Their faces can only be equilateral triangles, squares, or regular pentagons.

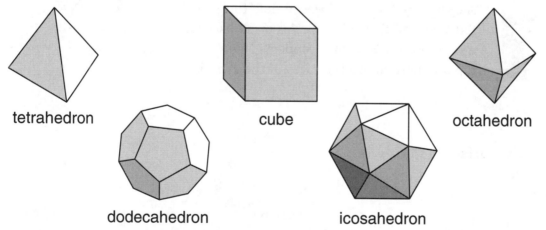

tetrahedron

cube

octahedron

dodecahedron

icosahedron

Check Your Understanding

1. Name an object that looks like—
   a. a prism.   b. a cylinder.   c. a sphere.

2. Which solids have—
   a. all flat surfaces?   b. no flat surfaces?   c. both flat and curved surfaces?

3. a. How are prisms and cylinders alike?   b. How do they differ?

4. a. How are pyramids and cones alike?   b. How do they differ?

A **polyhedron** is a geometric solid whose surfaces are formed by polygons. **Prisms** and **pyramids** are polyhedrons.

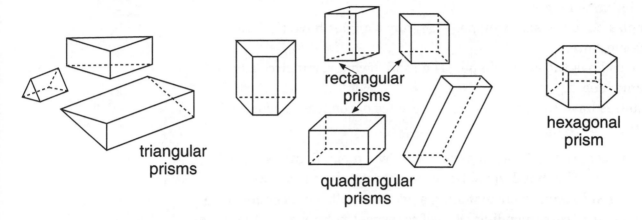

triangular prisms

rectangular prisms

quadrangular prisms

hexagonal prism

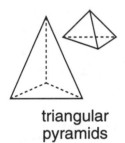

triangular pyramids

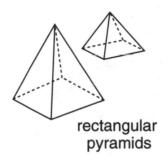

rectangular pyramids

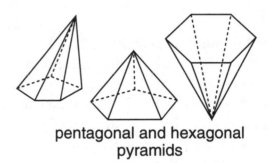

pentagonal and hexagonal pyramids

An Interesting Fact

The sum of the numbers of faces and vertices of a polyhedron is 2 more than the number of edges. For example, a rectangular prism has 6 faces, 8 vertices, and 12 edges. The sum of its faces and vertices is 6 + 8, or 14. This is 2 more than the number of edges.

This rule is called **Euler's Formula**, named after the 18th-century Swiss mathematician, Leonhard Euler. Euler's Formula is true for any polyhedron.

Check Your Understanding

1. **a.** How are prisms and pyramids alike?
    b. How do they differ?

2. An octahedron has 8 faces and 6 vertices. How many edges does it have?

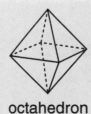

octahedron

Congruent Figures

Two figures that are the same size and have the same shape are **congruent.**

- All line segments have the same shape. Congruent line segments have the same length.
- All angles have the same shape. Congruent angles have the same degree measure.
- All circles have the same shape. The radii of congruent circles have the same length.
- All squares have the same shape. The sides of congruent squares have the same length.

Two figures are congruent if they match exactly when one figure is placed on top of the other. The matching sides of congruent polygons are called **corresponding sides** and their matching angles are called **corresponding angles.** Each pair of corresponding sides of congruent polygons are the same length and each pair of corresponding angles have the same degree measure.

Example:

Quadrilaterals *ABCD* and *RSTU* are congruent. The slash marks and arcs are used to identify pairs of corresponding sides and angles. Sides with the same number of slash marks are corresponding sides and angles with the same number of arcs are corresponding angles. The number of slashes or arcs has nothing to do with the length of the sides or the size of the angles.

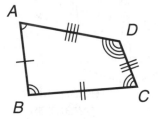 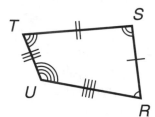

Corresponding sides	Length	Corresponding angles	Degree measure
$\overline{AB}$ and $\overline{RS}$	1.9 cm	$\angle A$ and $\angle R$	60°
$\overline{BC}$ and $\overline{ST}$	2.8 cm	$\angle B$ and $\angle S$	110°
$\overline{CD}$ and $\overline{TU}$	1.3 cm	$\angle C$ and $\angle T$	70°
$\overline{DA}$ and $\overline{UR}$	2.6 cm	$\angle D$ and $\angle U$	120°

When naming congruent polygons, the corresponding vertices of the polygons are listed in the same order for both polygons. In the example, we could say that polygon *CDAB* is congruent to polygon *TURS*, but we would not say that polygon *ABCD* is congruent to polygon *TURS*.

Check Your Understanding

Which of the following triangles is not congruent to the other three?

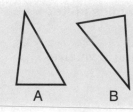 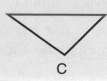

Similar figures are figures that have the same shape. Similar figures may also be the same size, but they don't have to be. If two figures are similar, one figure is an enlargement of the other. The **size-change factor** tells the amount of enlargement.

In similar polygons, the size of the angles does not change. But if one polygon is an enlargement of another polygon, each of the sides of the smaller polygon is enlarged by the same size-change factor. Each side and its enlargement form a pair of sides called **corresponding sides**.

Example 1:

Triangles *CAT* and *DOG* are similar.

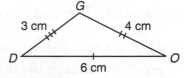

Length of Corresponding Sides	side *DO*: 6 cm	side *OG*: 4 cm	side *GD*: 3 cm
	side *CA*: 3 cm	side *AT*: 2 cm	side *TC*: 1.5 cm
Ratio of Lengths	$\frac{6}{3} = \frac{2}{1}$	$\frac{4}{2} = \frac{2}{1}$	$\frac{3}{1.5} = \frac{2}{1}$

The size-change factor is 2X. Each side in the larger triangle is twice the size of the corresponding side in the smaller triangle.

Example 2:

Quadrilaterals *ABCD* and *MNOP* are similar. What is the length of side *AB*?

Since the quadrilaterals are similar, the ratio of the lengths of the corresponding sides are equal. Find the ratio of the length of a longer side to the length of the corresponding shorter side. Choose any pair of corresponding sides.

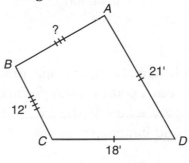

$$\frac{\text{length of } \overline{BC}}{\text{length of } \overline{NO}} = \frac{12}{4} = \frac{3}{1}$$

To find the length of side *AB*, solve the following equation.

$$\frac{3}{1} = \frac{x}{5} \quad \begin{array}{l} (\text{length of } \overline{AB}) \\ (\text{length of } \overline{MN}) \end{array}$$

$$\frac{3 * 5}{1 * 5} = \frac{15}{5}$$

The length of side *AB* is 15 feet.

Check Your Understanding

Polygons *RUDI* and *JOAN* are similar.

Find the length of—

1. side *JO*.   **2.** side *ID*.

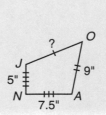
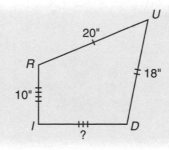

Isometry Transformations

In geometry, a **transformation** is an operation on a figure that produces another figure. Transformations are sometimes thought of as motions that take a figure from one place to another. **Reflections** (flips), **translations** (slides), and **rotations** (turns) are familiar operations in **transformation geometry**.

These three types of transformations produce a new figure, called the **image**. The image has the *same size and shape* as the original figure, called the **preimage**. The image and the preimage are congruent figures.

Reflections, translations, and rotations are called **isometry transformations**. They do not change the distances between points. The term *isometry* comes from the Greek *iso*, meaning same, and *metron*, meaning measure.

Reflection

Translation

Rotation

Reflections

The reflection image of a figure appears to be a "reverse" or "flip" of the preimage. Each point on the preimage is the same distance from the *line of reflection* as the corresponding point on the image. The preimage and image are on opposite sides of the line of reflection.

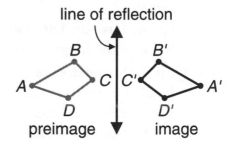

Translations

When a figure is translated, each point on the preimage slides a certain distance in the same direction to create the image. Imagine a figure on a coordinate plane.

If the same number (for example, 4) is added to the x-coordinates of all the points in the figure, and the y-coordinates are not changed, the result is a horizontal translation. *See Figure A.*

87

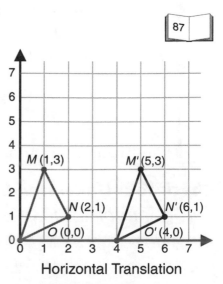

Horizontal Translation

Figure A

If the same number (for example, 4) is added to all the y-coordinates, and the x-coordinates are not changed, the result is a vertical translation. *See Figure B.*

If the same number (for example, 4) is added to all the x-coordinates, and this number or another number is added to all the y-coordinates, the result is a diagonal translation. *See Figure C.*

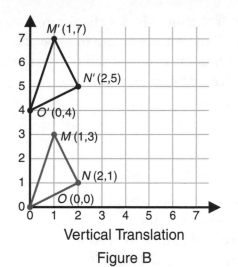

Vertical Translation

Figure B

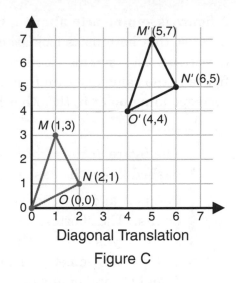

Diagonal Translation

Figure C

Rotations

When a figure is rotated, it is turned a specific number of degrees in a specific direction around a specific point. A figure can be rotated *clockwise* (the way clock hands usually move) or *counterclockwise* (the opposite of the way clock hands usually move).

A figure may be rotated around a point outside the figure or inside the figure—see page 82.

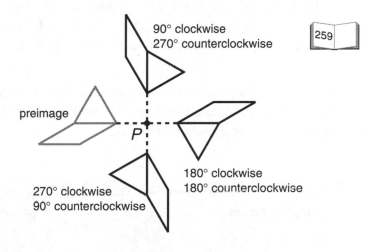

259

Check Your Understanding

1. Name the word that results when the figure is reflected over line *AB*.

2. Triangle *C'A'T'* is a slide image of triangle *CAT*. Point *C* is at (1,1), point *A* at (3,9), point *T* at (8,5), and point *C'* at (4,7). What are the coordinates of *A'* and *T'*?

3. Which figure is a 90° clockwise rotation of the given figure?

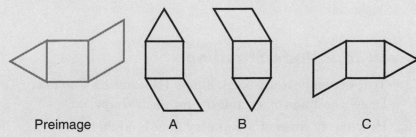

Preimage   A   B   C

Line Symmetry

A figure is **symmetric about a line** if the line divides the figure into two parts so that both parts look exactly alike, but are facing in opposite directions. In a symmetric figure, each point in one of the halves of the figure is the same distance from the **line of symmetry** as the corresponding point in the other half.

Example:

The figure at the right is symmetric about the dashed line. The dashed line is its line of symmetry.

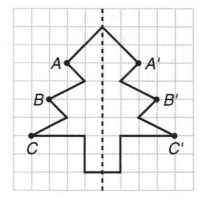

Points *A* and *A'* (read "A prime") are corresponding points. The shortest distance from *A* to the line of symmetry is equal to the shortest distance from *A'* to the line of symmetry. The same is true of *B* and *B'*, of *C* and *C'*, and of any other pairs of corresponding points. The line of symmetry is the **perpendicular bisector** of line segments connecting corresponding points such as *A* and *A'*. It bisects each line segment and it is perpendicular to each line segment.

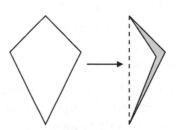

An easy way to check whether a figure has line symmetry is to fold it in half. If the two halves match exactly, then the figure is symmetric about the fold.

Some figures have more than one line of symmetry.	Some figures have no lines of symmetry.
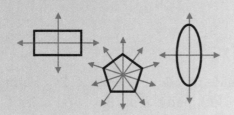	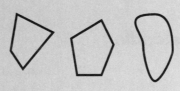

Check Your Understanding

1. Trace each pattern-block shape (PB) on the Geometry Template onto a sheet of paper. Draw the lines of symmetry for each shape.
2. How many lines of symmetry does a circle have?

A figure has **rotation symmetry** if it can be rotated around a point in such a way that the resulting figure exactly matches the original figure. The rotation must be more than 0 degrees, but less than 360 degrees. The figure isn't flipped over.

In other words, a figure has rotation symmetry if it can be rotated so that the image and preimage match exactly, without flipping the figure over.

If a figure has rotation symmetry, its **order of rotation symmetry** is the number of different ways it can be rotated to match itself exactly. "No rotation" is counted as one of the ways.

Example: Consider square *ABCD*. The points (*A, B, C, D*) are labeled to help identify the rotations. They are not part of the figure.

The square can be rotated in four different ways to match itself exactly (without flipping it over).

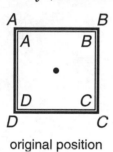 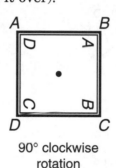 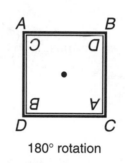 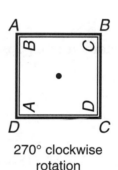

original position 　　　 90° clockwise rotation 　　　 180° rotation 　　　 270° clockwise rotation

The order of rotation symmetry for square *ABCD* is 4.

Point Symmetry

A figure has **point symmetry** if it can be rotated 180° around a point to match the original figure exactly. A figure with point symmetry has rotation symmetry of at least order 2.

Example:

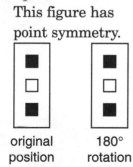

This figure has point symmetry.

original position 　 180° rotation

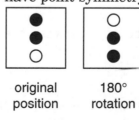

This figure does not have point symmetry.

original position 　 180° rotation

Check Your Understanding

1. Draw a square. Color or shade the interior of the square in such a way that the resulting figure still has rotation symmetry of order 4.

2. Draw a rectangle. Color or shade the interior of the rectangle in such a way that the figure has point symmetry.

Tessellations

A **tessellation** is a pattern of shapes that completely covers a surface.

256 257

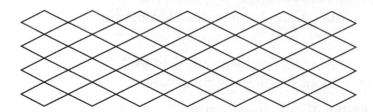

- The shapes in a tessellation do not overlap.

overlap

gap

- There are no gaps between shapes.

A **vertex point** of a tessellation is a point where vertices of the shapes meet.

- The sum of the measures of the angles around a vertex point must be exactly 360°.

vertex

120° 60°
60° 120°

$$120° + 60° + 120° + 60° = 360°$$

- If the sum is less than 360°, there will be gaps between the shapes. The pattern is not a tessellation.

- If the sum is greater than 360°, the shapes will overlap. The pattern is not a tessellation.

Regular Tessellations

A tessellation made up of one kind of regular polygon is called a **regular tessellation.**

For example, a regular tessellation can be made up of regular hexagons.

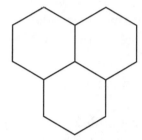

In a regular tessellation—

- All of the polygons are **congruent**. (They are the same size and shape.)
- Vertices of at least three polygons meet at each vertex point.
- There are at least three angles around each vertex point.

Regular tessellations are named by giving the number of sides of the polygons that meet at a vertex point. The numbers are separated by periods. For example, the name of the regular tessellation above is 6.6.6.

Semiregular Tessellations

A tessellation made up of two or more kinds of regular polygons is called a **semiregular tessellation**.

For example, a semiregular tessellation can be made up of equilateral triangles and squares.

vertex point

- In a semiregular tessellation, the angles around any vertex point must be congruent to the angles around any other vertex point.

Notice that at every vertex point of the tessellation at the right, there are, in the same order, the vertices of three equilateral triangles and two squares.

Semiregular tessellations, like regular tessellations, are named by giving, in order, the number of sides of the polygons at a vertex point. Begin with a polygon that has the fewest sides. Move clockwise or counterclockwise around the vertex point and write the number of sides of the polygons. If two or more polygons with the fewest sides are adjacent (next to each other), begin with these and take them as a group. For example, the name of the semiregular tessellation in the margin is 3.3.4.3.4.

The Theorem of Pythagoras

A right triangle is a triangle that has a right angle (90°).

In a right triangle, the side opposite the right angle is called the **hypotenuse.** The other two sides are called **legs**.

In the diagram at the right, a and b represent the lengths of the legs, and c represents the length of the hypotenuse.

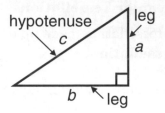

There is a surprising connection between the lengths of the three sides of any right triangle. It is probably the most useful property in all of geometry, and is known as the Pythagorean Theorem.

> **Pythagorean Theorem**
>
> If the legs of a right triangle have lengths a and b, and the hypotenuse has length c, then $a^2 + b^2 = c^2$.

6

Nobody knows when this relationship was first discovered. The Babylonians, Egyptians, and Chinese knew this relationship before the Greeks. But Pythagoras, a Greek philosopher born about 572 B.C., was the first person to prove that the relationship is true for any right triangle. It is called a **theorem** because it is a statement that has been proved.

A Chinese proof of the Pythagorean Theorem (written about A.D. 40) is shown below. Two identical squares, each with sides of length $(a + b)$, are partitioned in different ways.

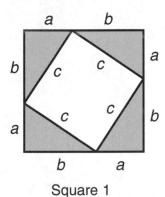

Square 1

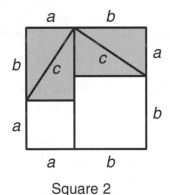

Square 2

Square 1 contains four identical right triangles and one square whose area is $c * c = c^2$.

Square 2 contains four identical right triangles and two squares whose areas are a^2 and b^2.

The four right triangles inside Square 1 and the four right triangles inside Square 2 all have the same area. Therefore, the area of the large square (c^2) inside Square 1 must be equal to the total area of the two smaller squares ($a^2 + b^2$) that are inside Square 2. That is, c^2 must equal $a^2 + b^2$.

A **rectangular coordinate grid** is used to name points in the plane. It is made up of two number lines, called **axes**, that meet at right angles at their zero points. The point where the two lines meet is called the **origin**.

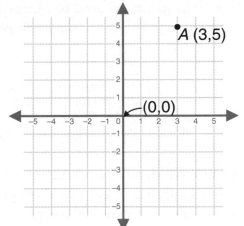

Every point on a coordinate grid can be named by an **ordered number pair**. The two numbers that make up an ordered number pair are called the **coordinates** of the point. The first coordinate is always the *horizontal* distance of the point from the origin. The second coordinate is always the *vertical* distance of the point from the origin. For example, the ordered number pair (3,5) names point *A* on the grid at the right. The numbers 3 and 5 are the coordinates of point *A*. The number pair (0,0) names the origin.

Every ordered number pair can be plotted on a coordinate grid.

Example:

Plot the ordered number pair (5,3).

Step 1: Locate 5 on the horizontal axis.

Step 2: Locate 3 on the vertical axis.

Step 3: Draw a vertical line from point 5 on the horizontal axis and a horizontal line from point 3 on the vertical axis.

The point (5,3) is located at the intersection of the two lines.

Note that the order of the numbers in a number pair is important. The number pair (5,3) does not name the same point as the number pair (3,5).

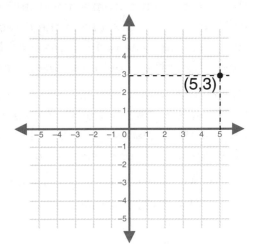

Example:

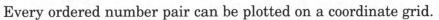

Locate (−2,3), (−4, −1), and (3½, 0).

For each number pair, locate the first coordinate on the horizontal axis and the second coordinate on the vertical axis. Draw intersecting lines from these two points.

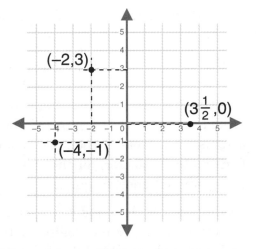

Check Your Understanding

Draw a coordinate grid on graph paper and plot the following points.

1. (2,4)　　　　**2.** (−2,−2)　　　　**3.** (0,−5)　　　　**4.** (−1,3)

Perspective Drawing

Drawings are often used to represent real or imagined objects. Which of the drawings below do you think represents a cube?

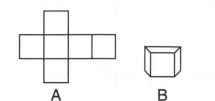 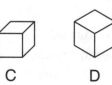

A   B   C   D   E   F

A small child, an ancient Egyptian, or a modern French painter such as Marie Laurencin (1883–1956) might pick Figure A. It shows all of the faces of the cube as squares—the way you might draw them after feeling the cube with your eyes closed. In a similar way, the ancient Egyptians showed the human figure from several different points of view at the same time. Each part was drawn from the direction that would make it most recognizable. The head, arms, and legs were drawn in profile (from the side), while the shoulders, chest, and eyes were shown from the front.

Greek and Roman artists experimented with ways of making pictures that would resemble the way we actually see an object with our eyes. Philosophers discussed how vision might be explained with geometry. They noticed several features of human sight, including the following.

- An object moving away from the viewer seems to get smaller.
- Parallel lines moving away from the viewer seem to get closer together.

After the Roman period, European artists returned to a flat style of painting. When they did try to show depth, they often drew a figure like **B** to represent a cube.

In the late Middle Ages, artists and scholars rediscovered the writings of the Greek philosophers and mathematicians, and also began their own experiments with representing three-dimensional space. Their first attempts looked something like Figures C and D. Giotto di Bondone (about 1266–1337) astonished viewers by the illusion of depth that he created in frescos (paintings done on fresh plaster) for the Arena Chapel in Padua, Italy. In addition to using slanted lines, he shaded his figures to make them look solid.

During the next hundred years, many artists, especially in Italy, experimented with these ideas. They created more and more "realistic" images. In 1425, architect and engineer Filippo Brunelleschi (1377–1466) demonstrated what is now known as geometric **perspective** (also called linear perspective or Renaissance perspective). This system uses geometry to produce an illusion of depth, as if the flat surface of a painting were a window looking onto a three-dimensional scene. The term *perspective* is derived from the Latin *per* or *pro* (through or forward) and *specere* (to look).

Brunelleschi discovered that to create a convincing illusion of three dimensions, objects should be drawn smaller the farther they are from the viewer. Parallel lines moving away from the viewer should meet at a common point, which came to be called the **vanishing point.** Figure E shows a cube drawn using this system. Later artists perfected a system using two vanishing points as shown in Figure F.

In 1435, architect Leon Battista Alberti (1404–1472) wrote a book about painting that included detailed rules of perspective. Leonardo da Vinci (1452–1519) also experimented with perspective. Dissatisfied with Alberti's rules, he worked on a system of "natural" perspective that came closer to human vision. In his system, shapes were projected onto a curved surface, like the retina of the human eye, rather than onto the flat surface of a painting. These investigations, and others that followed, led to a branch of mathematics known as **projective geometry**.

The painting at the left was made in the twelfth century. There is no illusion of depth. The ships in the distance (at the top of the painting) are the same size as the ones in the foreground (at the bottom of the painting). The castle at the center of the painting is drawn in the style of Figure B on page 88.

The painting at the right, *A View of the Grand Canal* by Canaletto (1697–1768), shows a similar subject, this time using the rules of perspective to create an illusion of three dimensions. The building and ships in the foreground are larger than those in the background. The lines in the buildings meet at a vanishing point (on the right side of the painting).

When German artist Albrecht Dürer (1471–1528) visited Italy, he was exposed to new ideas circulating among artists and scholars. He later wrote a manual on painting, which included the following woodcut. It shows an easy way to make a drawing with correct perspective. (Some of Dürer's best known works are woodcuts, a type of print that is made in the same way as designs printed with a rubber stamp.)

The artist looks through a grid made of threads in a wooden frame. He copies what he sees onto a similar grid on paper. The object directly in front of the artist helps him keep his eye in the same position.

Return to the question posed at the beginning of this essay: Which of the drawings below do you think represents a cube?

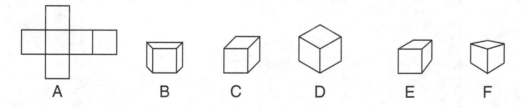

After reading this essay, your answer may be, "They all do." Depending on your personal taste or how you want to use a drawing, any one of the above may be the "best" representation of a cube.

If you are interested in learning more about perspective drawing, look in an encyclopedia under topic headings such as drafting, Greek art, human perception, Medieval art, perspective, projection, projective geometry, Renaissance art, and Roman art.

260

Topology is a branch of mathematics that has many connections with geometry. In topology, two geometric shapes are said to be equivalent if one shape can be stretched, squeezed, crumpled, twisted, or turned inside out—but not torn or broken—until it looks like the other shape. These changes are called **topological transformations**.

Topology studies the properties of geometric shapes that are not changed by topological transformations. The number of holes in an object is one of these properties.

For this reason, it is sometimes said that a topologist (a mathematician who studies topology) can't tell the difference between a coffee mug and a doughnut. They are **topologically equivalent**. A coffee mug, as well as a doughnut, will always have one hole, no matter how they are transformed.

Consider a juice glass and a doughnut. They are *not* topologically equivalent. No matter how much stretching, twisting, or squeezing you might do, a juice glass cannot be transformed into a doughnut, except by punching a hole in it. This is because a juice glass has no holes, and a doughnut has one.

In topology, geometric shapes are sorted by the number of holes they have. This property is called the **genus** (pronounced "GEE-nuss") of the shape. Objects with the same genus are topologically equivalent.

The objects below all have genus 0.

The objects below all have genus 1.

Topology (continued)

The objects below all have genus 2.

Topology is sometimes called **rubber-sheet geometry**. If you think of a figure as being drawn on a rubber sheet, or a shape as being made from rubber, it may help you to see which properties remain the same after a topological transformation.

For example, the first diagram below shows a circle drawn on a rubber sheet. When the rubber sheet is stretched, the circle is transformed into other figures, as shown in the other diagrams.

 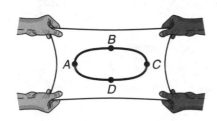 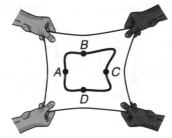

No matter how the circle is transformed, the resulting figure is still a closed curve. Points that were originally inside remain inside, and points that were outside remain outside. Points on the circle stay in the same position relative to each other—point B stays between points A and C, and so on.

Properties that do not change when a figure is distorted are called **topological properties**.

Check Your Understanding

1. Triangle ABC is drawn on a rubber sheet. The sheet is stretched to represent a topological transformation. Which of the following must be true?

   a. The distance from point A to point B remains the same.
   b. The measure of angle A remains the same.
   c. The image of side AB might not be a line segment.
   d. The image of triangle ABC is a triangle.
   e. Figure ABC remains closed.

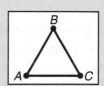

2. **Challenge** Imagine that this shape is made of clay. It may not seem possible, but the loops can be separated— without cutting or tearing them—by a series of topological transformations.

   Draw a series of diagrams to show how this might be done.

   Source: David Wells, *You Are a Mathematician*.

Many geometric figures can be drawn using a compass and straightedge only. The compass is used to draw circles and to mark off lengths. The straightedge is used to draw straight lines.

Compass-and-straightedge constructions are very helpful for studying properties of geometric figures. These properties are used in many ways in the workplace: for example, they are used by architects in making blueprints and architectural drawings, by engineers in developing structural designs, and by graphics artists in creating illustrations on a computer.

When making compass-and-straightedge constructions, you are allowed to use only three tools: a compass, a straightedge, and something to draw with, preferably a pencil with a sharp point. You may not measure the lengths of line segments with a ruler or the size of angles with a protractor.

Always draw on a stack of several sheets of paper: this will keep the point of the compass (also called the **anchor**) from slipping as the pencil is rotated; also, it will prevent damage to the desk or tabletop.

There are two methods for drawing circles with a compass. The directions below for these methods are for right-handed people.

Method 1: Press the anchor of the compass firmly on the paper. Rotate the pencil point of the compass about the anchor, keeping the paper fixed in place. If the pencil is rotated clockwise, start with the pencil near where the 5 is located on a clockface. If counterclockwise, start near the 7.

Method 2: Rotate a single sheet of paper, keeping the anchor and pencil point fixed in place. This is especially helpful when drawing smaller circles.

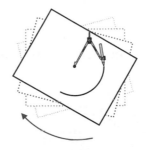

Check Your Understanding

Concentric circles are circles that have the same center.

Use a compass to draw three concentric circles.

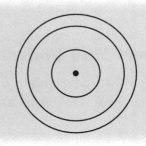

Copying a Line Segment

Step 1: Draw line segment *AB*.

Step 2: Draw a second line segment. It should be longer than $\overline{AB}$. Label one of its endpoints *C*.

Step 3: Place the anchor of the compass at *A* and the pencil point at *B*. Without changing your compass opening place the anchor of the compass on *C* and draw a small arc that crosses the line segment. Label the point where the arc crosses the line segment point *D*.

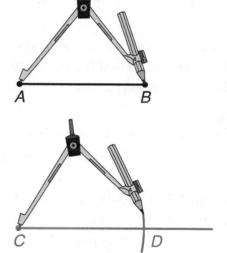

Line segment *CD* is **congruent** to line segment *AB*. The segments have the same length.

Check Your Understanding

Draw a line segment 6 centimeters long. Using a compass and straightedge only, copy the line segment. Do not measure the second line segment.

Step 1: Draw a triangle *ABC* and a line segment longer than *AB*. Copy line segment *AB* onto it. (See page 94.) Label the endpoints of the copy *D* and *E*.

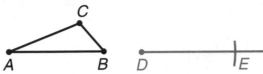

Step 2: Place the anchor of the compass at *A* and the pencil point at *C*. Without changing your compass opening, place the anchor of your compass on *D* and draw an arc.

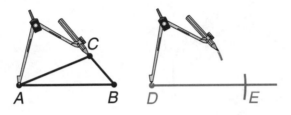

Step 3: Place the anchor of the compass at *B* and the pencil point at *C*. Without changing your compass opening, place the anchor of your compass on *E* and draw another arc. Label the points where the arcs intersect *F*.

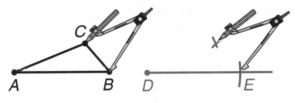

Step 4: Draw line segments *DF* and *EF*.

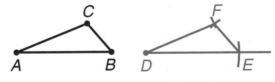

Triangles *ABC* and *DEF* are **congruent**, that is, they are the same size and shape.

Check Your Understanding

Draw a triangle. Using a compass and straightedge, copy the triangle. Cut out the copy and place it on top of the original triangle to check that the triangles are congruent.

Constructing a Parallelogram

71 94
93

Step 1:   Draw an angle *ABC*.

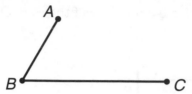

Step 2:   Place the anchor of the compass at *B* and the pencil point at *C*.
Without changing your compass opening, place the anchor of your
compass on point *A* and draw an arc.

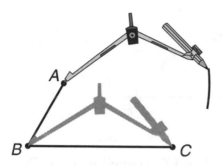

Step 3:   Place the anchor of the compass at *B* and the pencil point at *A*.
Without changing your compass opening, place the anchor of your
compass on point *C* and draw another arc that crosses the first arc.
Label the point where the two arcs cross point *D*.

Step 4:   Draw line segments *AD* and *CD*.

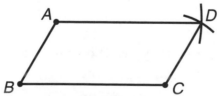

Check Your Understanding

Using a compass and straightedge, construct:

1. a parallelogram.   **2.** a rhombus.

Step 1: Draw a circle. Keep the same compass opening for Steps 2 and 3. Make a dot on the circle. Place the anchor of your compass on the dot and make a mark with the pencil point on the circle.

Step 2: Place the anchor of your compass on the mark you just made and make another mark with the pencil point on the circle.

Step 3: Do this four more times to divide the circle into 6 equal parts. The 6th mark should be on the dot you started with or very close to it.

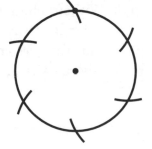

Step 4: With your straightedge, connect the 6 marks **on** the circle to form a regular hexagon.

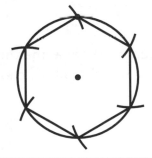

Use your compass to check that the sides of the hexagon are the same length.

Check Your Understanding

1. Draw a circle. Using a compass and straightedge, construct a regular inscribed hexagon.

2. Draw a line segment from the center of the circle to each vertex of the hexagon to form 6 triangles. Use your compass to check that the sides of each triangle are the same length.

3. What kind of triangles are these?

93

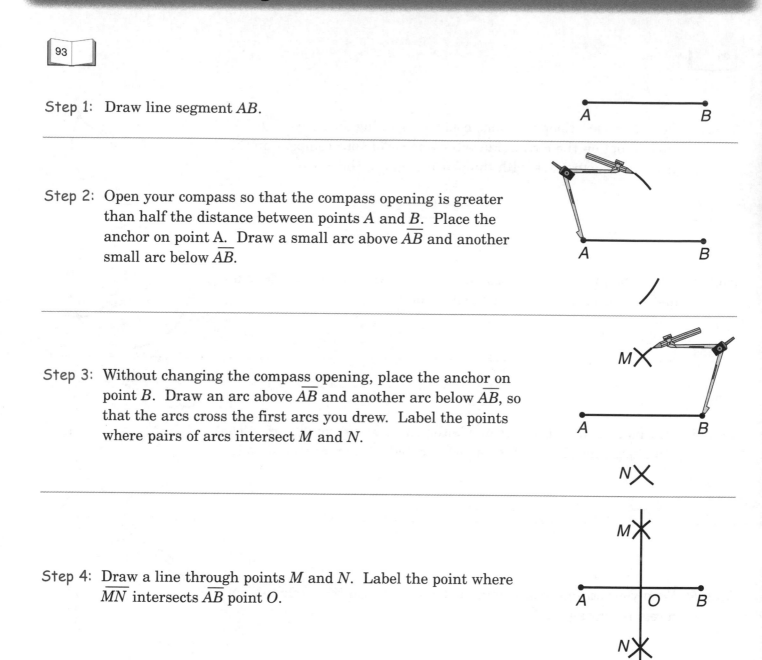

Step 1: Draw line segment AB.

Step 2: Open your compass so that the compass opening is greater than half the distance between points A and B. Place the anchor on point A. Draw a small arc above $\overline{AB}$ and another small arc below $\overline{AB}$.

Step 3: Without changing the compass opening, place the anchor on point B. Draw an arc above $\overline{AB}$ and another arc below $\overline{AB}$, so that the arcs cross the first arcs you drew. Label the points where pairs of arcs intersect M and N.

Step 4: Draw a line through points M and N. Label the point where $\overline{MN}$ intersects $\overline{AB}$ point O.

Line MN **bisects** $\overline{AB}$ at point O. The distance from A to O is the same as the distance from B to O.

Check Your Understanding

Draw a line segment. Use a compass and straightedge to bisect it. Then measure to check that the line segment has been divided into two equal parts.

93 | 98

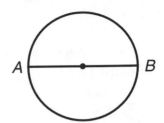

Step 1: Draw a circle with a compass.

Step 2: Draw a line segment through the center of the circle with endpoints on the circle. Label the endpoints points A and B.

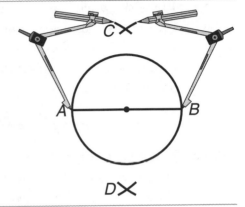

Step 3: Increase the compass opening. Place the anchor of the compass on point A. Draw an arc above the center of the circle and another arc below the center of the circle.

Step 4: Without changing the compass opening, place the anchor of the compass on point B. Draw arcs that cross each arc you drew in Step 3. Label the points where the arcs intersect points C and D.

Step 5:

Draw line CD. Label the points where $\overleftrightarrow{CD}$ intersects the circle points E and F.

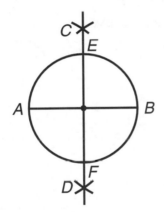

Step 6:

Draw line segments AE, EB, BF, and FA.

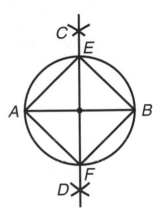

Check with your compass that all four line segments are the same length. Check with the corner of your straightedge or some other square corner that all four angles are right angles.

Check Your Understanding

Use a compass and straightedge to construct an inscribed square.

Constructing a Line Segment Perpendicular to Another Line Segment from a Point *on* the Line Segment

Step 1: Draw line segment AB. Make a dot on $\overline{AB}$ and label it point P.

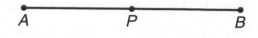

Step 2: Place the anchor of your compass on P, and draw an arc that crosses line segment AB at point C. Keeping the anchor of your compass on point P and the same compass opening, draw another arc that crosses $\overline{AB}$ at point D.

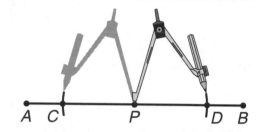

Step 3: Make sure the compass opening is greater than the length of $\overline{CP}$. Place the anchor of your compass on point C and draw an arc above $\overline{AB}$. Keeping the same compass opening, place the anchor of your compass on point D and draw another arc above $\overline{AB}$ that crosses the first arc. Label the point where the two arcs cross point Q.

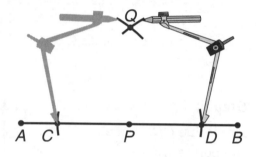

Step 4: Draw $\overline{QP}$.

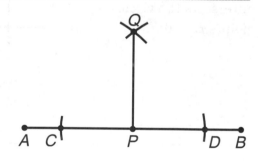

$\overline{QP}$ is **perpendicular** to $\overline{AB}$.

Check Your Understanding

Draw a line segment. Draw a point on the segment and label it point R. Using a compass and straightedge, construct a line segment perpendicular to point R.

Constructing a Line Segment Perpendicular to Another Line Segment from a Point *not on* the Line Segment

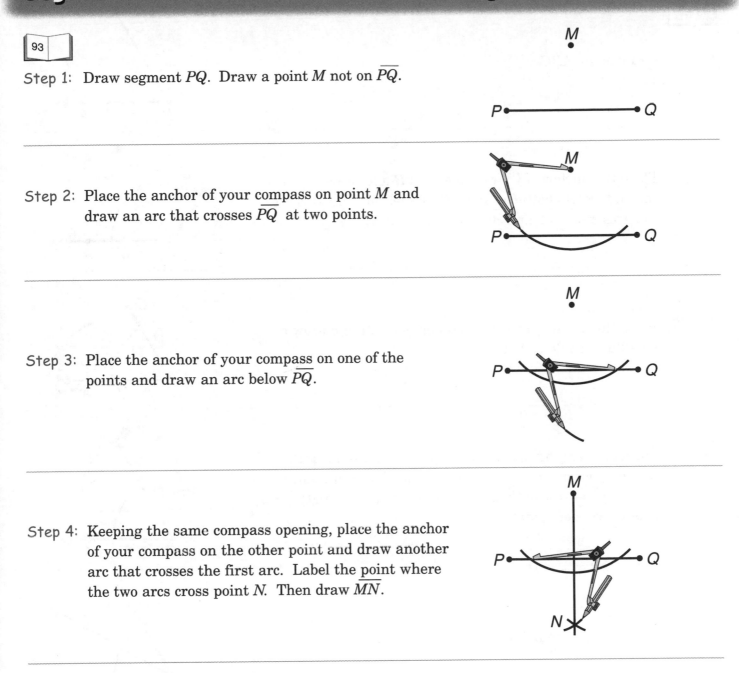

93

Step 1: Draw segment *PQ*. Draw a point *M* not on $\overline{PQ}$.

Step 2: Place the anchor of your compass on point *M* and draw an arc that crosses $\overline{PQ}$ at two points.

Step 3: Place the anchor of your compass on one of the points and draw an arc below $\overline{PQ}$.

Step 4: Keeping the same compass opening, place the anchor of your compass on the other point and draw another arc that crosses the first arc. Label the point where the two arcs cross point *N*. Then draw $\overline{MN}$.

$\overline{MN}$ is **perpendicular** to $\overline{PQ}$.

Check Your Understanding

1. Draw a line segment *HI* and a point *G* above the line segment. Using a compass and straightedge, construct a line segment from point *G* perpendicular to $\overline{HI}$.

2. Use the Geometry Template to draw a parallelogram. Then construct a line segment to show the height of the parallelogram.

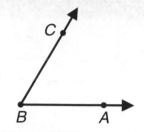

📖 93

Step 1: Draw angle *ABC*.

Step 2: Place the anchor of your compass on *B* and draw an arc that intersects both $\overrightarrow{BA}$ and $\overrightarrow{BC}$. Label the points where the arcs cross $\overrightarrow{BA}$ and $\overrightarrow{BC}$ points *M* and *N*.

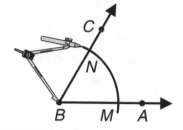

Step 3: Place the anchor of the compass on point *M* and draw a small arc inside ∠ *ABC*.

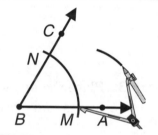

Step 4: Without changing the compass opening, place the anchor of the compass on point *N* and draw a small arc that intersects the arc you drew in Step 3. Label the point where the two small arcs meet point *P*.

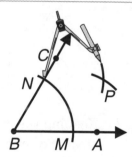

Step 5: Draw a ray from point *B* through point *P*.

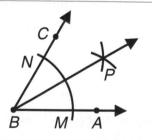

Ray BP **bisects** ∠ *ABC*. The measure of ∠ *ABP* is equal to the measure of ∠ *CBP*.

Check Your Understanding

Draw an obtuse angle. Use a compass and straightedge to bisect it.

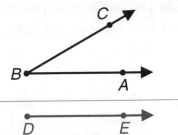

`93` `78`

Step 1: Draw an angle ABC.

Step 2: To start copying the angle, draw $\overrightarrow{DE}$.

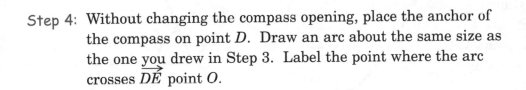

Step 3: Place the anchor of the compass on point B. Draw an arc that crosses both $\overrightarrow{BA}$ and $\overrightarrow{BC}$. Label the point where the arc crosses $\overrightarrow{BA}$ point M and the point where the arc crosses $\overrightarrow{BC}$ point N.

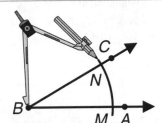

Step 4: Without changing the compass opening, place the anchor of the compass on point D. Draw an arc about the same size as the one you drew in Step 3. Label the point where the arc crosses $\overrightarrow{DE}$ point O.

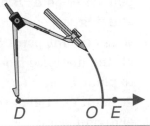

Step 5: Place the anchor of the compass on point M and the pencil point on point N.

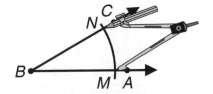

Step 6: Without changing the compass opening, place the anchor of the compass on point O. Draw a small arc where the pencil point crosses the larger arc and label it point P.

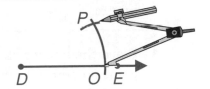

Step 7: Draw a ray from point D through point P.

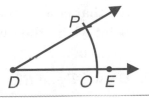

$\angle EDP$ is **congruent to** $\angle ABC$, that is, the two angles have the same degree measure.

Check Your Understanding

Draw an angle. Use a compass and straightedge to copy the angle. Then measure the two angles with a protractor to check that they are the same size.

Copying a Quadrilateral

Before you can copy a quadrilateral with compass and straightedge, you need to know how to copy a line segment and an angle. Those constructions are described on pages 94 and 103.

Step 1: Draw a quadrilateral *ABCD*. Copy ∠*BAD*. Label the new angle *PQR*. Ray *QP* should be longer than $\overline{AB}$ and ray *QR* should be longer than $\overline{AD}$.

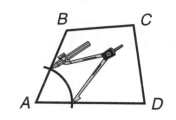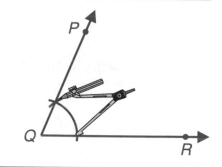

Step 2: Mark off the distance from point *A* to point *B* onto $\overrightarrow{QP}$, starting at point *Q*. Label the endpoint point *S*. Mark off the distance from point *A* to point *D* onto $\overrightarrow{QR}$, starting at point *Q*. Label the endpoint point *U*.

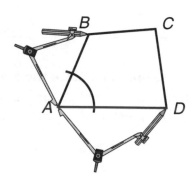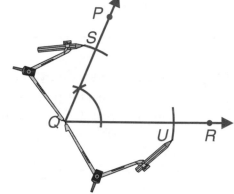

Step 3: Place the anchor of the compass on point *B* and the pencil point on point *C*. Without changing the compass opening, place the anchor of the compass on point *S* and make an arc.

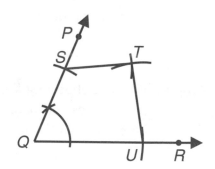

Step 4: Place the anchor of the compass on point *D* and the pencil point on point *C*. Without changing the compass opening, place the anchor of the compass on point *U* and make an arc that crosses the arc you made in Step 4. Label the point where the two arcs meet point *T*.

Step 5: Draw $\overline{ST}$ and $\overline{RT}$.

Quadrilateral *QSTU* is **congruent to** quadrilateral *ABCD*. The two quadrilaterals are the same size and shape.

Check Your Understanding

Draw a quadrilateral. Use a compass and straightedge to copy the quadrilateral.

Step 1: Draw line AB and ray AC.

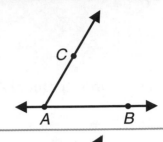

Step 2: Place the anchor of the compass on point A. Draw an arc that crosses both $\overrightarrow{AB}$ and $\overrightarrow{AC}$. Label the point where the arc crosses $\overrightarrow{AB}$ point D and the point where the arc crosses $\overrightarrow{AC}$ point E.

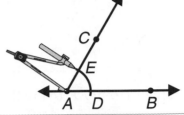

Step 3: Without changing the compass opening, place the anchor of the compass on point C. Draw an arc the same size as the one you drew in Step 2. Label the point where the arc crosses $\overrightarrow{AC}$ point F.

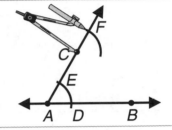

Step 4: Place the anchor of the compass on point E and the pencil point on point D.

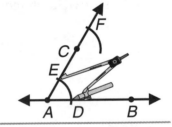

Step 5: Without changing the compass opening, place the anchor of the compass on point F. Draw a small arc where the pencil point crosses the larger arc and label it point G.

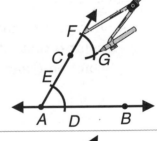

Step 6: Draw a line through points C and G.

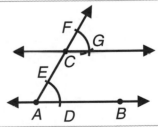

Line CG is **parallel** to line AB. Angle CAB is **congruent to** $\angle FCG$.

Check Your Understanding

Draw a line. Use a compass and straightedge to draw a line parallel to it.

Constructing a Golden Rectangle

Step 1: Draw a square *ABCD*.

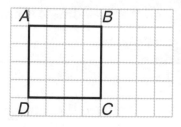

Step 2: Draw $\overline{EF}$ to divide the square in half.

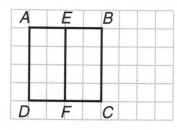

Step 3: Draw the diagonal $\overline{FB}$. Extend $\overline{DC}$.

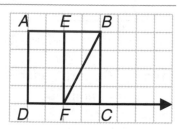

Step 4: Use your compass to draw an arc from point *F* through point *B* that intersects $\overrightarrow{DC}$ at point *G*. (Place the compass point on *F* and the pencil point on *B*. Draw the arc.)

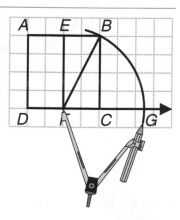

Step 5: Extend $\overline{AB}$. Draw a line segment perpendicular to $\overrightarrow{DC}$ at point *G* and that intersects the extension of $\overline{AB}$ at point *H*.

Rectangle *AHGD* is a Golden Rectangle.

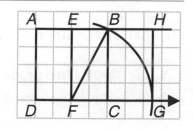

Measurement

Measurement is a process of associating numbers with physical objects and events. Measurement is very important in technical fields as well as everyday life—in science, engineering, medicine, building trades, travel, shopping, cooking, and so on.

The first step in measurement is to identify the **quantity** to be measured—for example, length, mass (weight), capacity, area, and so on. The second step is to compare that quantity with a **standard**, or agreed-upon **unit quantity** of the same kind—for example, the inch, kilogram, liter, acre, and so on.

Over past centuries, people established many different standard measures. These varied from place to place and from time to time, and these variations complicated trade and communication. The earliest standards appeared in ancient Mediterranean cultures. One widely used unit of length was the Egyptian *cubit*, which dates back to 3000 B.C. At first it was based on the length of the arm from the elbow to the extended fingertips, which would vary from person to person. Later a royal cubit of black granite was used as a standard, against which Egyptian measuring sticks were regularly compared. An early measure of mass was the Babylonian *mina*. One surviving standard weighs about 640 grams (about 1.4 pounds), another about 978 grams (about 2.15 pounds). The ounce, inch, pound, and mile come from Roman versions of earlier Greek units; current versions of these units are part of the **U.S. customary system**, used in the United States but almost nowhere else.

In modern times, there have been international agreements on basic standards (such as units of length, mass, elapsed time, and temperature), and on units obtained by combining other units (such as units of volume, pressure, and power). These standards are part of the **metric system** (see pages 108–110), used throughout the world. Standards in the U.S. customary system are based on metric standards.

Measurement nearly always involves a device such as a ruler or weighing scale. The precision of measuring devices varies widely. So does the ability of humans to read them. Hence, every measurement is an **estimate** of the "true" situation, never an **exact** figure. Some measurements are better estimates than others. Part of any practical measure exercise is to decide on how many of the digits obtained are reliable—that is, how many **significant figures** there are in the measurements.

132

Example:

A rectangle is measured to have a width of 3.4 cm and a length of 5.6 cm. Using these measurements, its area, given by the formula $A = l * w$, is calculated as 19.04 cm^2. However, the measured width, 3.4 cm, and the measured length, 5.6 cm, are not exact measurements: The actual width could be any measure between 3.35 cm and 3.45 cm and the actual length any measure between 5.55 cm and 5.65 cm. So the area is between 18.5925 cm^2 (3.35 * 5.55 = 18.5925) and 19.4925 cm^2 (3.45 * 5.65 = 19.4925). A more reliable estimate than the calculated area of 19.04 cm^2 is 19 cm^2.

The Metric System

The metric system of measurement is used throughout the world. The United States is the only large nation in which the metric system is not part of most people's daily life. We are likely to use the **U.S. customary system** instead. However, industries in the United States, such as automobile companies, make extensive use of the metric system. Scientists work almost entirely in the metric system. Metric measures are common in sports such as track and field, ice skating, and swimming. Food labels often include metric measures.

Today's metric system is sometimes called **SI**, from its French name *Le Système International d'Unités*. It was established by international agreement in 1960.

Basic Ideas Like all modern measurement systems, the metric system begins with **standards** that people agree on—basic units of length, mass, temperature, and so on. The metric system is a **decimal** system: Larger and smaller units are defined by multiplying or dividing basic units by powers of 10. This makes it easy to convert from one metric unit to another, unlike units in the U.S. customary system. (For example, there are 12 inches in 1 foot, 3 feet in 1 yard, and 1760 yards in 1 mile.)

Metric units are named by prefixes that identify the power of 10.

	Smaller Units			Basic Unit	Larger Units		
Factor	0.001	0.01	0.1	1	10	100	1000
	1 thousandth	1 hundredth	1 tenth		1 ten	1 hundred	1 thousand
Power	10^{-3}	10^{-2}	10^{-1}	10^0	10^1	10^2	10^3
Prefix	milli-	centi-	deci-		deka-	hecto-	kilo-
Symbol	m	c	d		da	h	k
Example	millimeter	centimeter	decimeter	meter	dekameter	hectometer	kilometer
Symbol	mm	cm	dm	m	dam	hm	km
Relation		1 cm = 10 mm	1 dm = 10 cm [Unit dm not often used]	1 m = 10 dm = 100 cm = 1000 mm	1 dam = 10 m [Unit dam not often used]	1 hm = 100 m [Unit hm not often used]	1 km = 1000 m

Other prefixes include nano- (n, 1 billionth), micro- (μ, 1 millionth), mega- (M, 1 million), and giga- (G, 1 billion).

Length The **meter** is the basic unit of length in the metric system. The symbol for meter is m. The **millimeter** (mm) and **centimeter** (cm) are used for shorter lengths. The **kilometer** (km) is used for longer lengths, such as distances between cities.

$$1 \text{ mm} = 0.001 \text{ m} \qquad 1 \text{ cm} = 0.01 \text{ m} \qquad 1 \text{ km} = 1000 \text{ m}$$

The meter was originally defined as one ten-millionth of the distance from the North Pole to the equator. It is now defined in terms of the distance light travels in a specified time.

1 cm 1 mm

Area Area is usually measured in square units, such as the **square centimeter**, which is the area of a square with sides 1 centimeter in length. (*Square centimeter* can be shortened to cm².) Land is measured in **hectares**; 1 hectare equals 10,000 square meters (1 ha = 10,000 m²).

1 cm²

Volume and Capacity Volume is usually measured in cubic units, such as the **cubic centimeter**, which is the volume of a cube with sides 1 centimeter in length. (*Cubic centimeter* can be shortened to cm³.) The **liter** (L) is a unit of capacity, equal to 1000 cubic centimeters, or the capacity (volume) of a cube with sides 10 cm in length. Since there are 1000 cubic centimeters in a liter, and 1 **milliliter** (1mL) is $\frac{1}{1000}$ of a liter, 1 cm³ = 1 mL.

$$1 \text{ L} = 1000 \text{ mL} = 1000 \text{ cm}^3$$

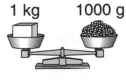
1 kg   1000 g

Mass (Weight) Volume and mass are linked in the metric system: 1 cubic centimeter (1 milliliter) of pure water (under specified conditions) has a mass of 1 **gram** (1 g). So 1 liter of pure water has a mass of 1000 grams or 1 **kilogram** (1 kg). (The kilogram rather than the gram is actually the basic unit in the metric system. The standard kilogram is a special metal block kept near Paris, France.) Note: There is a distinction between the mass of an object (the amount of substance in the object) and its weight (the force with which gravity pulls on the object). However, the terms *mass* and *weight* are often used as though they mean the same thing.

Temperature Both the Celsius and the Kelvin scales are used in the metric system. The freezing point of pure water is defined to be 0 degrees Celsius (0°C), and the boiling point to be 100 degrees Celsius (100°C), under specified conditions. Between 0 and 100, the Celsius scale is divided into 100 intervals (degrees) of equal size. Intervals on the Kelvin scale (K) are the same size as on the Celsius scale, but the starting point is at "absolute zero"; 0°K = −273.16°. A temperature change of 1 degree Celsius is equal to $\frac{9}{5}$, or 1.8 degrees Fahrenheit.

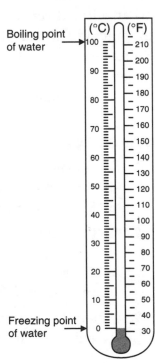
Boiling point of water
Freezing point of water

Time Metric time is the same as U.S. customary time. The basic unit is the **second**. There are 60 seconds in 1 minute, 60 minutes in 1 hour, and 24 hours in 1 day. People have tried to introduce decimal units of time—even a calendar with 10 months—but these efforts have not been successful.

Other Units Here are some other units in the metric system:

Unit	Symbol	Quantity
ampere	A	electrical current
hertz	Hz	frequency (cycles per second)
joule	J	energy
mole	mol	amount of substance
newton	N	force
ohm	Ω	electrical resistance
pascal	Pa	pressure
radian	rad	angle measure
volt	V	electric potential
watt	W	power

Note: Shortened forms of names for metric units, such as m for meter, are called symbols, not abbreviations. A unit symbol is never followed by a period unless it is at the end of a sentence.

History Development of the metric system began in France during the French Revolution over two hundred years ago. The purpose was to create a simple, easy-to-use, uniform system of weights and measures that would replace many different systems. People who were satisfied with their old measures resisted the metric system, but gradually (sometimes through force) it spread around the world. In the United States, leaders such as John Quincy Adams supported the metric system. Its use was made legal in 1866, and many people since then have urged that the United States "go metric."

Conversions It is possible to make accurate conversions between U.S. customary and metric measurements. For example, 1 inch is exactly 2.54 centimeters. However, it's usually best to think in one system or the other, without converting. It may be handy to keep a few approximations in mind, at least until the metric system is commonly used in the United States. For example, 1 centimeter is about $\frac{3}{8}$ inch; 1 meter is about 10% longer than 1 yard; 1 kilometer is about $\frac{5}{8}$ or $\frac{6}{10}$ of a mile; 1 liter is a little more than 1 quart; 1 kilogram is a little more than 2 pounds.

Check Your Understanding

1. Complete:
   a. 2 meters = ? centimeters = ? millimeters
   b. ? milliliters = 3.5 liters
   c. 5.5 km = ? m
   d. ? kg = 3200 g
   e. 12 cm^3 = ? mL

2. Tell which unit would be best to measure each of the following:
   a. mass of a truck   kilometer   kilogram   kiloliter
   b. thickness of a hair   millimeter   milligram   milliliter
   c. capacity of a bottle   meter   gram   liter

3. Name the unit each symbol stands for.
   a. mg   b. kL   c. °C   d. m^3

Length is the measure of a distance between two points. The length is the number of unit segments and fractions of unit segments needed to cover this distance, without overlaps and without gaps.

Length is reported in **linear units**, such as inches (in), feet (ft), yards (yd), millimeters (mm), centimeters (cm), and meters (m) for smaller distances, in miles (mi) and kilometers (km) for larger land distances, and in Astronomical Units (AU) and light years for vast distances in outer space. One Astronomical Unit is the average distance from the earth to the sun (about 93 million miles). One light year is the distance light travels in one year in a vacuum (about 5.8 trillion miles).

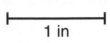

1 in

Area is the measure of a region inside a 2-dimensional figure. The area of a region is the number of unit squares and fractions of unit squares needed to cover the region, without overlaps and without gaps between the unit squares and the fractions of unit squares.

Area is reported in **square units**, such as square inches (in^2), square feet (ft^2), square yards (yd^2), square centimeters (cm^2), and square meters (m^2) for smaller regions, and acres, square miles (mi^2), hectares (ha), and square kilometers (km^2) for large land areas.

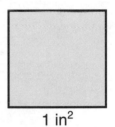

1 in^2

Volume is the measure of the amount of space inside a 3-dimensional figure. The volume of a 3-dimensional figure is the number of unit cubes and fractions of unit cubes needed to fill the figure without overlaps and without gaps.

Volume is usually reported in **cubic units**, such as cubic inches (in^3), cubic feet (ft^3), cubic yards (yd^3), cubic centimeters (cm^3), and cubic meters (m^3).

1 cm^3

The volume of a container that can be filled with a liquid, such as a milk carton or a gas tank, is often called its **capacity**. Capacity is usually reported in units such as gallons (gal), quarts (qt), pints (pt), cups (c), liters (L), and milliliters (mL).

Measuring and Drawing Angles

Angles are measured in **degrees**. When writing the measure of an angle, a small raised circle (°) is used as a symbol for the word *degree*.

Angles are measured with a tool called a **protractor**. You will find both a full-circle and half-circle protractor on your Geometry Template. Since there are 360 degrees in a circle, a 1° angle marks off $\frac{1}{360}$ of a circle.

The full-circle protractor on the Geometry Template is marked off in 5° intervals from 0° to 360°. It can be used to measure angles, but not to draw angles of a given measure.

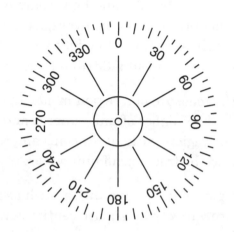

The half-circle protractor on the Geometry Template is marked off in 1° intervals from 0° to 180°. Notice that it has two scales: one is read clockwise, the other counterclockwise, both starting at 0°. The half-circle protractor can be used both to measure and to draw angles of a given measure.

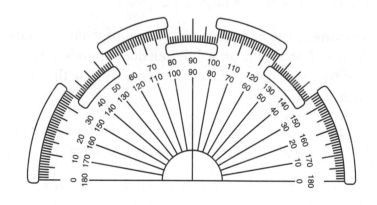

Two rays starting from the same endpoint may form either a **reflex angle** with measures between 180° and 360°, or a smaller angle with measures between 0° and 180°.

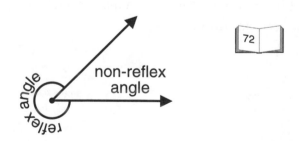

reflex angle

non-reflex angle

72

How to Measure an Angle with a Full-Circle Protractor

When measuring an angle with a full-circle protractor, it helps to think of the angle as representing a clockwise rotation of one of its sides about its endpoint, as in the minute hand of a clock: one side of the angle represents the minute hand as it appears at the beginning of a time interval and the other side as it appears some time later.

Example:

> To measure angle *IJK* with a full-circle protractor:
>
> Step 1: Place the center of the protractor over point *J*, the vertex of the angle.
>
> Step 2: Align the 0° mark on the protractor with ray *JI*.
>
> Step 3: Read the degree measure where ray *JK* crosses the edge of the protractor.

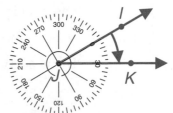

measure of
angle *IJK* = 30°

Example:

> To measure reflex angle *EFG*:
>
> Step 1: Place the center of the protractor over point *F*.
>
> Step 2: Align the 0° mark on the protractor with ray *FG*.
>
> Step 3: Read the degree measure where ray *FE* crosses the edge of the protractor.

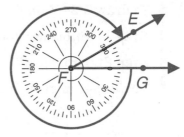

measure of
angle *EFG* = 330°

How to Measure an Angle with a Half-Circle Protractor

Example:

> To measure angle *PQR* with a half-circle protractor:
>
> Step 1: Align the baseline of the protractor with ray *QR*.
>
> Step 2: Slide the protractor so that the center of the baseline is over point *Q*, the vertex of the angle.
>
> Step 3: Read the degree measure where ray *QP* crosses the edge of the protractor. Use the counterclockwise (inner) scale.

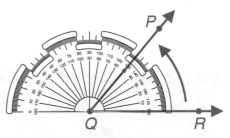

measure of
angle *PQR* = 50°

How to Draw an Angle with a Half-Circle Protractor

Example:

To draw a 40° angle:

Step 1: Draw a ray from point A.

Step 2: Align the baseline of the protractor with the ray.

Step 3: Slide the protractor so that the center of the baseline is over point A.

Step 4: Make a mark at 40° on the protractor.

Step 5: Draw a ray from point A through the mark.

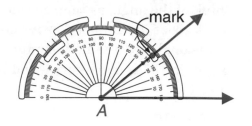

To draw a reflex angle using the half-circle protractor, subtract the measure of the reflex angle from 360°. Use this as the measure of the smaller angle.

Example:

To draw a 240° angle:

Step 1: Subtract: 360° − 240° = 120°.

Step 2: Draw a 120° angle.

The larger angle is a 240° angle.

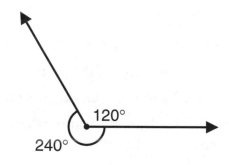

Check Your Understanding

Measure each angle to the nearest degree.

1.

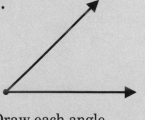

2.

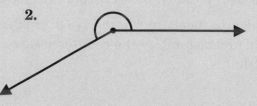

3.

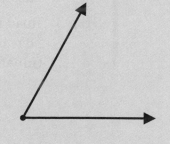

Draw each angle.

4. a 70° angle   **5.** a 275° angle   **6.** a 53° angle

The sum of the measures of the angles of any triangle is 180°. This fact can be used to find the sum of the measures of the angles of any polygon and the measure of each angle of a regular polygon.

Finding the Sum of the Measures of the Angles of a Polygon

Any polygon can be divided into triangles. Since the sum of the measures of the angles of a triangle is 180°, the sum of the measures of the angles of a polygon is equal to the number of triangles in a polygon multiplied by 180°.

Example:

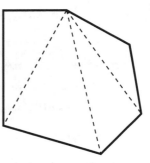

What is the sum of the measures of the angles of a hexagon?

Step 1: Draw any hexagon and divide it into triangles.

Step 2: Multiply the number of triangles by 180°.

- The hexagon can be divided into 4 triangles.

- The sum of the measures of the angles of each triangle is 180°.

Therefore, the sum of the measures of the angles = 4 * 180° = 720°.

Finding the Measure of an Angle of a Regular Polygon

Since all the angles of a regular polygon have the same measure, the measure of an angle is equal to the sum of the measures of the angles of the polygon divided by the number of angles.

Example:

What is the measure of an angle of a regular hexagon?

- The sum of the measures of the angles of any hexagon is 720°.

- A hexagon has 6 angles.

Therefore, the measure of an angle of a regular hexagon is $\frac{720}{6} = 120°$.

Check Your Understanding

1. Into how many triangles can you divide:
   a. a quadrilateral?   b. a pentagon?   c. an octagon?   d. a 12-sided polygon?

2. If you know the number of sides of a polygon, how can you calculate the number of triangles into which it can be divided, without drawing a picture?

3. What is the sum of the measures of the angles of a pentagon?

4. What is the measure of an angle of a regular octagon?

Perimeter

The distance around a polygon is called its **perimeter**.

To find the perimeter of any polygon, you can add the lengths of its sides.

73

Example:

> The perimeter of polygon *ABCDE* is
> 2 cm + 2 cm + 1.5 cm + 2 cm + 2.5 cm = 10 cm.

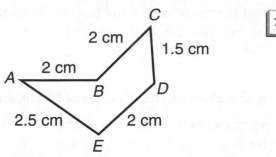

Perimeter Formulas

Rectangles	Squares	Regular Polygons
$p = 2 * (l + w)$	$p = 4 * s$	$p = n * s$
p is the perimeter, l is the length, and w is the width of the rectangle.	p is the perimeter and s is the length of one of the sides of the square.	p is the perimeter, n is the number of sides, and s is the length of a side.

Examples:

Find the perimeter of each polygon.

159 160

Rectangle

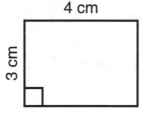

Use the formula $p = 2 * (l + w)$.
- length (l) = 4 cm; width (w) = 3 cm
- perimeter (p) = 2 * (4 cm + 3 cm)
$$= 2 * 7 \text{ cm}$$
$$= 14 \text{ cm}$$

Square

Use the formula $p = 4 * s$.
- length of side (s) = 2 ft
- perimeter (p) = 4 * 2 ft
$$= 8 \text{ ft}$$

2 ft

Regular octagon

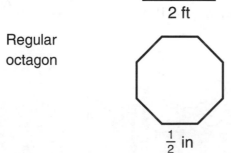

$\frac{1}{2}$ in

Use the formula $p = n * s$.
- number of sides (n) = 8; length of side (s) = $\frac{1}{2}$ in
- perimeter (p) = 8 * $\frac{1}{2}$ in
$$= 4 \text{ in}$$

Check Your Understanding

Solve. Be sure to include the unit in your answers.

1. Find the perimeter of a rectangle whose dimensions are 8 feet and 5 feet.
2. Find the perimeter of a regular hexagon whose sides are 12 yards long.

A **circle** is a set of points, each of which is the same distance from a point, called the **center of the circle**. Neither the center nor the interior is part of the circle.

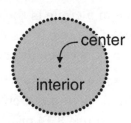
center
interior

The **radius** of a circle is any line segment that connects the center of the circle with any point on the circle. The **diameter** of a circle is any line segment that passes through the center of the circle and has both endpoints on the circle.

The terms *radius* and *diameter* may be used in two ways: to refer to a line segment or to the length of the line segment. The diameter of a circle is equal to twice its radius.

The **circumference** of a circle is the distance around the circle. It is not possible to measure the circumference of a circle exactly because measures are always estimates. If we could measure circles exactly, the ratio of the circumference (c) to the diameter (d) would be the same for every circle.

118

The ratio of the circumference of a circle to its diameter ($\frac{c}{d}$) is called **pi** and is written as the Greek letter π. It is not possible to write π exactly with digits. Its value can only be *approximated*. Since ancient times, mathematicians have worked on finding better and better approximations of π.

In recent times, computers have been used to calculate the value of π. In 1949, π was calculated to 37,000 decimal places on ENIAC, one of the first computers. Later, π was computed to 100,000 digits on an IBM 7090 computer, and in 1981 to 2 million digits on a NEC supercomputer. In the next few years, these calculations were extended to 17.5 million digits, then 34 million digits, then past 200 million digits, and in 1989 to more than 1 billion digits! No pattern has ever been found in the digits of these decimals.

$\pi = 3.14159265358979323846264338327950288419716939937511\ldots$

In your work with the number π, you can use 3.14 or $3\frac{1}{7}$ as approximate values for π, or use a calculator with a π key.

Check Your Understanding

On a calculator, calculate $5 * \pi$.

Circumference and Area of Circles

The **circumference** of a circle is the distance around the circle. The ratio of the circumference of a circle to its diameter (c/d) is the same for any circle. This ratio can be written as the Greek letter π (read "pi").

117

It is not possible to write π exactly with digits, because the decimal for π goes on forever. When solving a problem that involves the circumference or area of a circle, you can use 3.14 or $3\frac{1}{7}$ as approximate values for π, or you can enter a value of π into a calculator by pressing the π key.

Circle Formulas	
Circumference	**Area**
$c = \pi * d$	$A = \pi * r^2$
c is the circumference and d is the diameter of the circle.	A is the area and r is the radius of the circle.

111

Examples:

Find the circumference of the circle.

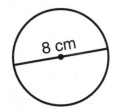

8 cm

Use the formula $c = \pi * d$.
- diameter (d) = 8 cm
- circumference (c) = $\pi * 8$ cm

Using the π key on the calculator or 3.14 as an approximate value for π:
- circumference (c) = 25.1 cm, rounded to the nearest tenth of a centimeter

159 160

Find the area of the circle.

3 in

Use the formula $A = \pi * r^2$.
- radius (r) = 3 in
- area (A) = $\pi * 3$ in $* 3$ in

Using the π key on the calculator or 3.14 as an approximate value for π:
- area (A) = 28.3 in^2, rounded to the nearest tenth of an inch

Check Your Understanding

Find the circumference and the area of each circle. Round the answer to the nearest tenth of a centimeter. Be sure to include the unit in your answers.

1.

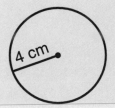

4 cm

2.

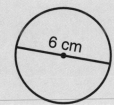

6 cm

You can think of the area of a rectangle as the total number of unit squares and fractions of unit squares needed to cover its interior, without gaps or overlaps. They can be arranged into rows, each containing the same number of squares and fractions of squares.

Example:

Find the area of the rectangle.

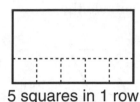

5 squares in 1 row

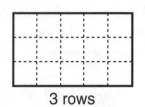

3 rows

3 rows with 5 squares in each row for a total of 15 squares

Area = 15 square units

Either pair of parallel sides in a rectangle can be chosen as its **bases**. The **height** of a rectangle is the shortest distance between its bases. The area of a rectangle is the product of the length of its base (the number of squares in one row) multiplied by its height (the number of rows).

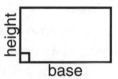

base

Area Formulas

Rectangle	**Square**
$A = b * h$	$A = s^2$
A is the area, b is the length of a base, and h is the height of the rectangle.	A is the area and s is the length of a side of the square.

Example:

Find the area of the rectangle.

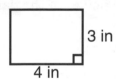
3 in
4 in

Use the formula $A = b * h$.
- length of base (b) = 4 in; height (h) = 3 in
- area (A) = 4 in * 3 in = 12 in^2

159 160

Example:

Find the area of the square.

6 ft

Use the formula $A = s^2$.
- length of a side (s) = 6 ft
- area (A) = 6 ft * 6 ft = 36 ft^2

Check Your Understanding

Find the area of the following figures. Be sure to include the unit in your answers.

1. 3 units / 2 units

2. 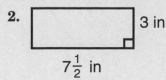 3 in / $7\frac{1}{2}$ in

3. 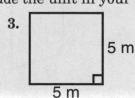 5 m / 5 m

Area of Parallelograms

In a parallelogram, either pair of opposite sides can be chosen as its **bases**. The **height** of the parallelogram is the shortest distance between the two bases.

74 111

In the parallelograms below, the height is shown by a dashed line that is **perpendicular** (at a right angle) to the base. In the third parallelogram, the base has been extended and the dashed height falls outside the parallelogram.

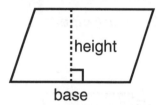
base

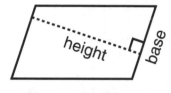

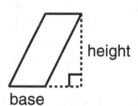
base

Any parallelogram can be cut into two pieces and the pieces rearranged to form a rectangle whose base and height are the same as the base and height of the parallelogram. The rectangle has the same area as the parallelogram. Therefore, you can find the area of the parallelogram in the same way you find the area of the rectangle—by multiplying the length of the base by the height.

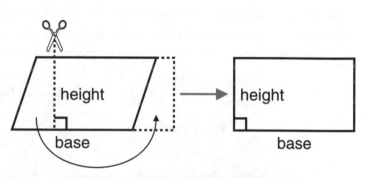

Formula for the Area of Parallelograms

$$A = b * h$$

A is the area, b is the length of the base, and h is the height of the parallelogram.

Example:

Find the area of the parallelogram.

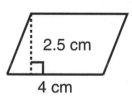
2.5 cm
4 cm

Use the formula $A = b * h$.
- length of base (b) = 4 cm
- height (h) = 2.5 cm
- area (A) = 4 cm * 2.5 cm
  = 10 cm^2

159 160

Check Your Understanding

Find the area of each parallelogram. Be sure to include the unit in your answers.

1.
11 ft
15 ft

2.

8 in
6 in

3.
3.2 cm
2.6 cm
1 cm

Any of the sides of a triangle can be chosen as its **base**. The **height** of the triangle (for that base) is the shortest distance between the base and the **vertex** opposite the base. It is always perpendicular to the base.

111

In the triangles below, the height is shown by a dashed line that is **perpendicular** (at a right angle) to the base. In the fourth triangle, the base has been extended and the dashed height falls outside the triangle.

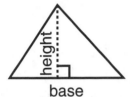 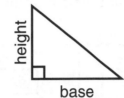 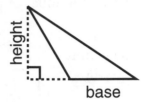

Any triangle can be combined with a second triangle of the same size and shape to form a parallelogram.

Each triangle at the right has the same base and height as the parallelogram. The area of each triangle is half the area of the parallelogram. Therefore, the area of a triangle is half the product of the base multiplied by the height.

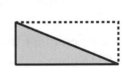

Area Formulas	
Parallelograms	**Triangles**
$A = b * h$	$A = \frac{1}{2} * (b * h)$
A is the area, b is the length of a base, and h is the height.	A is the area, b is the length of a base, and h is the height.

120

Example:

Find the area of the triangle.

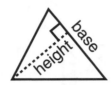

Use the formula $A = \frac{1}{2} * (b * h)$.
- length of base (b) = 7 in
- height (h) = 4 in
- area (A) = $\frac{1}{2} * (7 \text{ in} * 4 \text{ in})$
  $= \frac{1}{2} * 28 \text{ in}^2 = 14 \text{ in}^2$

159 160

Check Your Understanding

Find the area of each triangle. Be sure to include the unit in your answers.

1.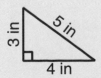

2.

3.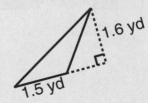

Volume of Geometric Solids

You can think of the volume of a geometric solid as the total number of unit cubes and fractions of unit cubes needed to fill the interior of the solid, without gaps or overlaps.

75 111
76

Prisms and Cylinders

In a prism or cylinder, the cubes can be arranged in layers, each containing the same number of cubes or fractions of cubes.

Example:

Find the volume of the prism.

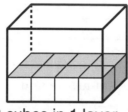
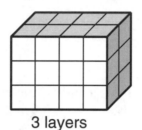

8 cubes in 1 layer   3 layers

3 layers with 8 cubes in each layer for a total of 24 cubes

Volume = 24 cubic units

The **height** of a prism or cylinder is the shortest distance between its **bases**. The volume of a prism or cylinder is the product of the area of the base (the number of cubes in one layer) by its height (the number of layers).

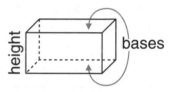

Pyramids and Cones

The height of a pyramid or cone is the shortest distance between its base and the vertex opposite its base.

If a prism and pyramid have the same base and height, then the volume of the pyramid is one-third the volume of the prism. Similarly, if a cylinder and cone have the same base and height, then the volume of the cone is one-third the volume of the cylinder.

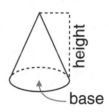

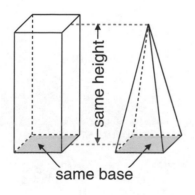

same base

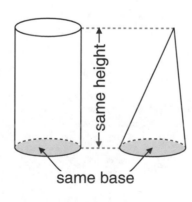

same base

Volume of Rectangular and Triangular Prisms

Volume of Prisms	**Area of Rectangles**	**Area of Triangles**
$V = B * h$	$A = b * h$	$A = \frac{1}{2} * (b * h)$
V is the volume, B is the area of the base, and h is the height of the prism.	A is the area, b is the length of the base, h is the height of the rectangle.	A is the area, b is the length of the base, h is the height of the triangle.

Example:

Find the volume of the rectangular prism.

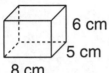

Step 1
Find the area of the base (B).
Use the formula $A = b * h$.
- length of the rectangular base
  (b) = 8 cm
- height of the rectangular base
  (h) = 5 cm
- area of base
  (B) = 8 cm * 5 cm = 40 cm^2

Step 2
Multiply the area of the base by the height of the rectangular prism.
Use the formula $V = B * h$
- area of base (B) = 40 cm^2
- height of prism (h) = 6 cm
- volume (V) =
  40 cm^2 * 6 cm = 240 cm^3

Example:

Find the volume of the triangular prism.

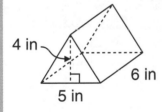

Step 1
Find the area of the base (B).
Use the formula $A = \frac{1}{2} * (b * h)$.
- length of the triangular base
  (b) = 5 in
- height of triangular base
  (h) = 4 in
- area of base
  (B) = $\frac{1}{2}$ * (5 in * 4 in) = 10 in^2

Step 2
Multiply the area of the base by the height of the triangular prism.
Use the formula $V = B * h$.
- area of base (B) = 10 in^2
- height of prism (h) = 6 in
- volume (V) =
  10 in^2 * 6 in = 60 in^3

Check Your Understanding

Find the volume of each prism. Be sure to include the unit in your answers.

1.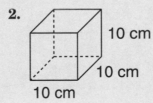

2.

3.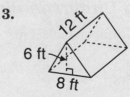

Volume of Cylinders and Cones

Volume of Cylinders	**Volume of Cones**	**Area of Circles**
$V = B * h$	$V = \frac{1}{3} * (B * h)$	$A = \pi * r^2$
V is the volume, B is the area of the base, and h is the height of the cylinder.	V is the volume, B is the area of the base, and h is the height of the cone.	A is the area and r is the radius of the base.

75 118
76

159 160

Example:

Find the volume of the cylinder.

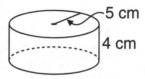
5 cm
4 cm

Step 1
Find the area of the base (B). Use the formula $A = \pi * r^2$.
- radius of base (r) = 5 cm
- area of base (B) = $\pi * 5$ cm $* 5$ cm

Using the π key on a calculator or 3.14 as an approximate value for π:
- area of base (B) = 78.5 cm^2, rounded to the nearest tenth of a square centimeter.

Step 2
Multiply the area of the base by the height of the cylinder. Use the formula $V = B * h$.
- area of base (B) = 78.5 cm^2
- height of cylinder (h) = 4 cm
- volume (V) = 78.5 cm$^2 * 4$ cm = 314.0 cm^3

Example:

Find the volume of the cone.

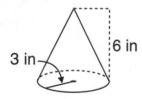
3 in
6 in

Step 1
Find the area of the base (B). Use the formula $A = \pi * r^2$.
- radius of base (r) = 3 in
- area of base (B) = $\pi * 3$ in $* 3$ in

Using the π key on a calculator, or 3.14 as an approximate value for π:
- area of base (B) = 28.3 in^2, rounded to the nearest tenth of a square inch.

Step 2
Find $\frac{1}{3}$ of the product of the area of the base multiplied by the height of the cone. Use the formula $V = \frac{1}{3} * (B * h)$.
- area of base (B) = 28.3 in^2
- height of cone (h) = 6 in
- volume (V) = $\frac{1}{3} * 28.3$ in$^2 * 6$ in = 56.6 in^3

Check Your Understanding

Find the volume of each figure. Be sure to include the unit in your answers.

1.
4 cm
Area of base = 35 cm^2

2.
10 ft
3 ft

3.
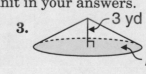
3 yd
Area of base = 113 yd^2

Volume of Rectangular and Triangular Pyramids

76 121
119

Volume of Pyramids	Area of Rectangles	Area of Triangles
$V = \frac{1}{3} * (B * h)$	$A = b * h$	$A = \frac{1}{2} * (b * h)$
V is the volume, B is the area of the base, and h is the height of the pyramid.	A is the area, b is the length of the base, h is the height of the rectangle.	A is the area, b is the length of the base, h is the height of the triangle.

Example:

159 160

Find the volume of the rectangular pyramid.

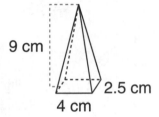

Step 1
Find the area of the base (B).
Use the formula $A = b * h$.
- length of base (b) = 4 cm
- height of base (h) = 2.5 cm
- area of base (B)
  = 4 cm * 2.5 cm = 10.0 cm^2

Step 2
Find $\frac{1}{3}$ of the product of the area of the base multiplied by the height of the rectangular pyramid. Use the formula $V = \frac{1}{3} * (B * h)$.
- area of base (B) = 10.0 cm^2
- height of pyramid (h) = 9 cm
- volume (V)
  = $\frac{1}{3}$ * 10.0 cm^2 * 9 cm = 30.0 cm^3

Example:

Find the volume of the triangular pyramid.

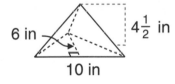

Step 1
Find the area of the base (B).
Use the formula $A = \frac{1}{2} * (b * h)$.
- length of base (b) = 10 in
- height of base (h) = 6 in
- area of base (B)
  = $\frac{1}{2}$ * (10 in * 6 in) = 30 in^2

Step 2
Find $\frac{1}{3}$ of the product of the area of the base multiplied by the height of the triangular pyramid. Use the formula $V = \frac{1}{3} * (B * h)$.
- area of base (B) = 30 in^2
- height of pyramid (h) = $4\frac{1}{2}$ in
- volume (V)
  = $\frac{1}{3}$ * 30 in^2 * $4\frac{1}{2}$ in = 45 in^3

Check Your Understanding

Find the volume of each pyramid. Be sure to include the unit in your answers.

1.
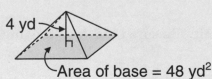
4 yd
Area of base = 48 yd^2

2.
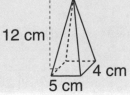
12 cm
4 cm
5 cm

3.

5 ft   6 ft
20 ft

Volume of Spheres

Suppose you drew a point *A* on a sheet of paper. Now imagine that you could draw every point that is 2 inches from point *A*. You would get a circle whose **center** is point *A* and whose **radius** is 2 inches long. The points inside the circle are not part of the circle; they form the **interior** of the circle.

Now imagine all of the points in space that are 2 inches from point *A*, in every direction. You would get a figure that looks like the surface of a ball. This figure is called a **sphere**. Point *A* is the center of the sphere. The distance from Point *A* to any point on the sphere is the **radius of the sphere**.

Just as with the circle, the points inside the sphere are not part of the sphere. A good way to think of a sphere is to think of a soap bubble. Another way is to imagine a circle with a rod passing through its center. If the circle is rotated a half-turn around the rod, the path of the circle will form a sphere.

If a sphere is cut in half, each half is a figure called a **half-sphere**. The rim of the half-sphere is a circle whose center is the center of the sphere.

Like the formulas for the circumference and area of a circle, the formula for finding the volume of a sphere involves the number π.

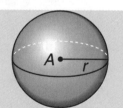

Formula for the Volume of a Sphere

$$V = \frac{4}{3} * \pi * r^3$$

V is the volume and *r* is the radius of the sphere.

Example:

> Find the volume of the sphere.
>
> Use the formula $V = \frac{4}{3} * \pi * r^3$.
>
> - radius (*r*) = 5 cm
> - volume $V = \frac{4}{3} * \pi * 5 * 5 * 5$
>
> Using the π key on the calculator, or 3.14 as an approximate value for π:
>
> - volume = 523.6 cm³, rounded to the nearest tenth of a cubic centimeter.

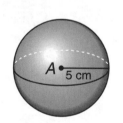

159 160

Check Your Understanding

Find the volume of each sphere to the nearest tenth of a cubic unit. Be sure to include the unit in your answers.

1. radius of sphere = 2 inches

2. diameter of sphere = 8 centimeters

A rectangular prism has 6 flat surfaces, or **faces**. The **surface area** of a rectangular prism is the sum of the areas of all 6 faces of the prism. One way to find the surface area of a rectangular prism is to think of the 6 faces as 3 pairs of opposite, parallel faces. Since opposite faces have the same area, you can find the area of one face in each pair of opposite faces, then find the sum of the 3 areas, and double the result.

The dimensions of a rectangular prism are its length (l), width (w), and height (h), as shown in the prism at the right. You can derive the formula for finding the surface area of rectangular prisms, as follows:

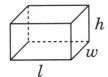

Step 1: Find the area of one face in each pair of opposite faces.
- area of base $= l * w$
- area of front face $= l * h$
- area of side face $= w * h$

Step 2: Find the sum of the areas of the 3 faces.
- sum of areas $= (l * w) + (l * h) + (w * h)$

Step 3: Multiply the sum of the 3 areas by 2.
- surface area of prism $= 2 * ((l * w) + (l * h) + (w * h))$

Surface Area of Rectangular Prisms

$$S = 2 * ((l * w) + (l * h) + (w * h))$$

S is the surface area, l the length of the base,
w the width of the base, and h the height of the prism.

Example:

Find the surface area of the rectangular prism.
Use the formula $S = 2 * ((l * w) + (l * h) + (w * h))$.
- length (l) = 4 in   width (w) = 3 in   height (h) = 2 in
- surface area (S)

$= 2 * ((4 \text{ in} * 3 \text{ in}) + (4 \text{ in} * 2 \text{ in}) + (3 \text{ in} * 2 \text{ in}))$

$= 2 * (12 \text{ in}^2 + 8 \text{ in}^2 + 6 \text{ in}^2)$

$= 2 * 26 \text{ in}^2$

$= 52 \text{ in}^2$

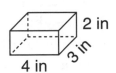

Check Your Understanding

Find the surface area of each prism. Be sure to include the unit in your answer.

1.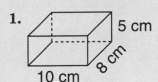
10 cm, 5 cm, 8 cm

2. 3 in, 2.5 in, 3 in

3.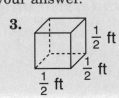
$\frac{1}{2}$ ft, $\frac{1}{2}$ ft, $\frac{1}{2}$ ft

Surface Area of Right Cylinders

A cylinder may stand "straight up" or it may "lean" to one side. A cylinder that stands straight up is called a **right cylinder**. A leaning cylinder is called a **slanted cylinder**.

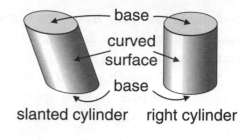

A right cylinder has two circular faces, called **bases** and a curved surface. Its bases are parallel and have the same areas.

To find the area of the curved surface of a cylinder, imagine a soup can with a label. If you cut the label perpendicular to the top and bottom of the can, peel off the label, and lay it flat on a surface, you will get a rectangle. The length of the rectangle is the same as the circumference of the base of the cylinder, and the width of the rectangle is the height of the can. Therefore, the area of the curved surface is the product of the circumference of the base and the height of the can.

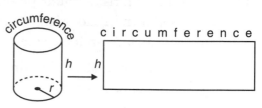

- circumference of base = $2 * \pi * r$
- area of curved surface = $(2 * \pi * r) * h$

The surface area of a cylinder is the sum of the areas of the two bases (2 times $\pi * r^2$) and of the curved surface.

Surface Area of Right Cylinders
$S = (2 * \pi * r^2) + ((2 * \pi * r) * h)$
S is the surface area, r is the radius of the base, and h is the height of the cylinder

Example:

Find the surface area of the cylinder.

Use the formula $S = (2 * \pi * r^2) + ((2 * \pi * r) * h)$.

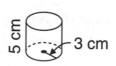

159 160

- radius of base = 3 cm
- height = 5 cm

Using the π key on the calculator, or 3.14 as an approximate value for π:

- surface area = $(2 * \pi * 3 \text{ cm} * 3 \text{ cm}) + ((2 * \pi * 3 \text{ cm}) * 5 \text{ cm})$

$= (\pi * 18 \text{ cm}^2) + (\pi * 30 \text{ cm}^2)$

$= 150.8 \text{ cm}^2$, rounded to the nearest tenth of a square centimeter

Check Your Understanding

Find the surface area of the cylinder to the nearest tenth of an inch.
Be sure to include the unit in your answer.

Problem solving can be difficult because no single method works for every problem. What you do to solve a problem depends on the problem itself. However, there are some basic strategies that may help you solve problems.

- For simple number stories, you can sometimes go directly from reading or hearing the problem to doing some arithmetic (perhaps with a calculator), and then recording answers (numbers with appropriate units).

- If the problem has more information than you need, it is a good idea to list the data and experiment with it, until you know exactly what you do need. When doing this, you may even find that you do not have all the information you need to solve the problem.

- Sometimes you may want to list all the data you have first, identify what you want to find out, and then return to the data.

- At other times, you may try to make clear what the problem is all about, and then figure out what data you need to solve the problem.

- It is often helpful to act out the problem with the help of objects, such as counting chips, by making pictures of what is going on, by filling in tables or diagrams, or with whatever else may help you. People who go straight to doing the arithmetic usually are not the better problem solvers.

Whatever else you do, always go back to the problem to check whether your answer makes sense. If you need to, "go back to the drawing board." Check your arithmetic, look at the data again, even review the problem to see whether the question you are trying to answer is the right question.

Use the following diagram to remind you of these basic strategies. The double arrows tell you that you can start anywhere and go back and forth between steps.

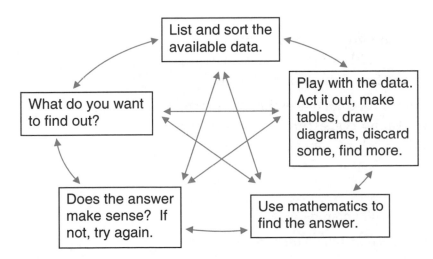

Making Estimates

In many situations it is not necessary to find an exact answer; a "ballpark" answer, called an **estimate**, will do. For example, if you go to the store with $10 and you want to buy several cans of tennis balls that cost $2.89 a can, you don't need to calculate the exact cost to decide how many cans you can buy with the $10. Since $2.89 is almost $3, 3 cans will cost a little under $9, and 4 cans will cost under $12, but more than $10. Therefore, you can buy at most 3 cans with $10.

In some cases, it is impossible to find an exact answer; for example, it is impossible to get an exact population count for a city. Even if it were possible, the count would change in the next moment.

Thus, when solving a problem, you must decide whether it is possible to find an exact answer, and, even if it is possible, whether an exact answer is needed, or whether an estimate will do.

If you choose to estimate an answer, you must decide how accurate your estimate should be. Keep in mind that an estimate is not a guess. A guess is just an opinion that you might state without having much background information.

One kind of very rough estimate is called a **magnitude estimate**. When making a magnitude estimate, ask yourself: "Is the answer in the tens? In the hundreds? In the thousands?" and so on. These are good questions to ask yourself to check answers displayed on a calculator or to judge whether information you read or hear makes sense.

A more accurate estimate can be made by **rounding** the numbers in the problem.

> *Example:*
>
> Mr. Huber has started a new job at a salary of $1957 a month. He expects to get a raise after 6 months. About how much can he expect to earn in the first 6 months?
>
> To estimate the answer, you can round $1957 to $2000 and multiply the rounded number by 6. Since 6 * $2000 = $12,000, he can expect to earn a little under $12,000 in the first 6 months on the job.

When a range of possible values is more useful than one estimated value, it is best to make an **interval estimate**. An interval estimate consists of two numbers. One number is less than and the other number is greater than the exact value.

> *Examples:*
>
> Most cars weigh between 2000 and 4000 pounds.
>
> The number of students who eat lunch at school on a given day is greater than 125 but less than 175.

In many situations exact numbers are not needed. For example, the planet Jupiter revolves around the Sun every 4332.6 Earth days and Neptune every 10,759.2 Earth days. If you want to compare the length of a year on these two planets, it would be easier to first round the numbers to the nearest thousand: A year on Jupiter is about 4000 Earth days and a year on Neptune is about 11,000 Earth days. Using the rounded numbers, you can easily see that a year on Neptune is about $2\frac{1}{2}$ times as long as a year on Jupiter.

It is also useful to round numbers when estimating results of operations such as addition and multiplication.

Here is a way to round a number to a given place:	Example 1: Round 4538 to the nearest hundred.	Example 2: Round 26,781 to the nearest thousand.	Example 3: Round 5295 to the nearest ten.	Example 4: Round 3.573 to the nearest tenth.
Step 1: Find the digit in the place you are rounding to.	4<u>5</u>38	2<u>6</u>,781	52<u>9</u>5	3.<u>5</u>73
Step 2: Rewrite the number, replacing all digits to the right of this digit with zeros. This is the lower number.	4500	26,000	5290	3.500
Step 3: Add 1 to the digit in the place you are rounding to. If the sum is 10, write 0 and add 1 to the digit to its left. This is the higher number.	4600	27,000	5300	3.600
Step 4: Is the number I am rounding closer to the lower number or to the higher number?	lower number	higher number	halfway	higher number
Step 5: Round to the closer of the two numbers. If it is halfway between the higher and the lower number, round to the higher number.	4500	27,000	5300	3.600 = 3.6

Check Your Understanding

Round 35,481.746 to the nearest:

1. hundred
2. ten thousand
3. thousand
4. hundredth

Estimates and Significant Figures

Measurements are estimates. The accuracy of a measurement is limited by the accuracy of whatever measuring tool (ruler, scale, and so on) is used to obtain the measurement, and by the skill of the humans who interpret the tool.

The only exact measurement relationships are those that are defined. For example, 1 inch is exactly 2.54 centimeters, by international agreement.

The measurements in the table at the right are not only estimates, they are averages of other measurements, and they are rounded.

Notice that the numbers in the table have been rounded to two **significant figures.**

> *Example:*
>
> ▌ 7900 miles   7 and 9 are significant figures.

A significant figure is a digit in a measurement that is reliable. We can be sure that it accurately represents the quantity being measured. Zero is usually not a significant figure, unless it is between two nonzero significant figures, or is the result of rounding.

Planet	Average Diameter (Miles)
Mercury	3000
Venus	7500
Earth	7900
Mars	4200
Jupiter	89000
Saturn	75000
Uranus	31000
Neptune	30000
Pluto	1600

> *Example:*
>
> ▌ The line segment in the diagram is between 35 and 36 millimeters long. You would report its length as 35 mm, or perhaps 35.2 mm. That would be two or three significant figures. That's as many significant digits as you can get from this particular measuring tool (the ruler).

As you work with measurements, try not to report results that seem to be more accurate (have more significant figures) than the original data.

> *Example:*
>
> ▌ Earth travels about 600,000,000 miles per year in its orbit. What is its average speed of revolution in miles per hour?
>
> Hours in 1 year: 365.25 days * 24 hours/day = 8766 hours
>
> 600,000,000 miles ÷ 8766 hours = 68,446.2696 miles/hour
>
> But 600,000,000 has only one significant figure.
>
> So the answer should be reported as "about 70,000 miles per hour."

Interpreting the Remainder in Division Problems

When solving a number story that involves division of whole numbers, you need to decide what to do about the remainder. There are three possibilities. Depending on what makes most sense for the problem, you may:

1. Round up the quotient to the next whole number.
2. Ignore the remainder. The quotient is the answer.
3. Report the remainder as a fraction or decimal. The remainder is part of the answer.

Example:

The 5th and 6th grade classes at Emmett School are going on a field trip. 105 students and teachers will go on buses. Each bus can seat up to 28 people. How many buses are needed? 105/28 → 3 R21

The remainder represents the number of people left over after 3 buses are completely filled. Since an extra bus is needed for the left-over people, round the quotient to the next whole number. Four buses will be needed to transport all 105 people.

Example:

The hens on Mr. Yaglom's farm laid 306 eggs yesterday. He packed the eggs into cartons, 12 to a carton. How many egg cartons did he fill? 310/12 → 25 R10

The remainder represents the number of eggs that are left over. Since there are not enough left-over eggs to fill a carton, the remainder is ignored. Mr. Yaglom was able to fill 25 cartons with eggs.

Example:

Sonya is building a bookcase. She cuts a 10-foot board into 4 same-sized pieces to use as shelves. What is the length of each shelf? 10/4 → 2 R2

The remainder represents $\frac{2}{4}$, or $\frac{1}{2}$ foot. Therefore, each piece is $2\frac{1}{2}$ feet long.

0 1 2 3 4 5 6 7 8 9 10 ft

Check Your Understanding

Solve the problems. Decide what to do with the remainder so that your answer makes sense.

1. Four people went out for breakfast. The total bill came to $14. They shared the cost equally. How much did each person pay?

2. Jorge is buying shirts that cost $8 apiece. He has $27 to spend. How many shirts can he buy?

3. A troop of 28 scouts is setting up tents for the night. Each tent can sleep 3 scouts. How many tents do they need?

Finding Part of a Collection

The egg carton at the right has 12 slots. 8 of the slots contain an egg. We say that $\frac{2}{3}$ of the slots are filled, because 8 is $\frac{2}{3}$ of 12.

Statements such as "8 is $\frac{2}{3}$ of 12" contain three pieces of information: a part, the whole, and a fraction that expresses the relationship between the part and the whole.

The following examples show how to find the part of the whole.

8 is $\frac{2}{3}$ of 12.

part   fraction   whole

Example:

> Jack earned $9 baby-sitting. He bought a can of tennis balls that cost $\frac{1}{3}$ of his earnings. How much did he spend?
>
> *Solution:* To find $\frac{1}{3}$ of $9, you can divide 9 by 3. 9/3 = 3, so the can of tennis balls costs $3.

Example:

> Jacqueline has 45 baseball cards in her collection. $\frac{3}{5}$ of the cards are of players who play for teams in the National League. How many cards are of National League players?
>
> Step 1
> Find $\frac{1}{5}$ of 45 by dividing 45 by 5.
> 45/5 = 9
>
> Step 2
> $\frac{3}{5}$ of 45 is 3 times as much as $\frac{1}{5}$ of 45, so multiply the 9 by 3.
> 27 = 3 * 9, so $\frac{3}{5}$ of 45 is 27.

Example:

> Find $\frac{3}{4}$ of 39 on a calculator.

184 185

> One way:
> Multiply the numerator, 3, by 39 and divide the result by the denominator, 4:
>   3 [×] 39 [÷] 4 [=]
> The display shows 29.25.
>
> Another way:
> If you can enter a fraction on your calculator, key in:
>   3 [/] 4 [×] 39 [=]
> Then press [Ab/c] to get a mixed number answer.
> Display: 29u1/4
> Or press [F⇄D] to get a decimal answer.
> Display: 29.25

Check Your Understanding

Solve.

1. $\frac{1}{4}$ of 20   2. $\frac{3}{4}$ of 20   3. $\frac{4}{5}$ of 35   4. $\frac{3}{8}$ of 32   5. $\frac{5}{6}$ of 42

To find a percent of a number, rename the percent as a fraction or decimal and multiply it by the whole amount (the amount equivalent to 100%).

36 134
52

Example:

> Judy earned $20 shoveling snow. She spent 80% of her earnings and saved the rest. How much did she spend?
>
> *Method 1:* Rename 80% as a fraction and multiply.
>
> Since $80\% = \frac{80}{100} = \frac{4}{5}$, 80% of $20 = $\frac{4}{5}$ of $20.
>
> **── 100% ──**
> amount earned
>
> $\frac{4}{5}$ of $20 = $\frac{4}{5} * \$20 = \frac{4 * \$20}{5} = \frac{\$80}{5} = \$16$
>
> *Method 2:* Rename 80% as a decimal and multiply.
>
> Since 80% = 0.8, 80% of $20 = 0.8 of $20.
> 0.8 of $20 = 0.8 ∗ $20 = $16

When the numbers are "easy," it is usually better to rename the percent as a fraction. The multiplication can be done mentally or with pencil and paper.

When the numbers are more difficult, rename the percent as a decimal and use the calculator.

Example:

> According to a recent survey by the American Federation of Teachers, the duration of an average school year in the U.S. public schools is 73% of a year. About how many weeks is school in session?
>
> In this problem, it is easier to rename the percent as a decimal and multiply with a calculator. Since 73% = 0.73, key in [.] 73 [×] 52 [=]. The display shows 37.96.
>
> **── 100% ──**
> number of
> weeks in 1 year
>
> Thus, U.S. public schools are in session for about 38 weeks of a year.

If you use the [%] key on the calculator, key in 73 [%] [×] 52 [=].
Note that the [%] key renames the percent as a decimal.

186

Check Your Understanding

Solve. Use a calculator for Problems 3 and 4.

1. 25% of 60 = ?   **2.** 60% of 25 = ?   **3.** ? = 42% of 36   **4.** 5.3% of 50 = ?

Using Unit Fractions to Find the Whole

A **unit fraction** is any fraction with 1 in its numerator. For example, $\frac{1}{2}$, $\frac{1}{10}$, and $\frac{1}{25}$ are unit fractions. If you know the part of a whole, represented by a unit fraction, you can find the whole by multiplying the part of the whole by the denominator of the unit fraction.

Example:

> Mark owns 2 white shirts. This is $\frac{1}{4}$ of the total number of shirts he owns. How many shirts does he own?
>
> If 2 shirts are $\frac{1}{4}$ of the total number of shirts, then the total number of shirts, or $\frac{4}{4}$, is 4 times that number.
>
> Since $4 * 2 = 8$, Mark owns a total of 8 shirts.

```
┌──Whole──┐
│  shirts │
│Mark owns│
└─────────┘
```

Unit fractions are used to solve problems in which the part is given as a fraction of the whole and you need to find the whole.

Example:

> Sara lives 8 blocks from the library. This is $\frac{2}{3}$ of the distance from her home to school. How many blocks is it from Sara's home to school?

```
┌───Whole───┐
│ distance  │
│ to school │
└───────────┘
```

Step 1
Find $\frac{1}{3}$ of the distance to school. 8 blocks is $\frac{2}{3}$ of the distance to school.

Therefore, to find $\frac{1}{3}$ of the distance, divide 8 blocks by 2.

$$8/2 = 4$$

Step 2
Find the distance to school. 4 blocks is $\frac{1}{3}$ of the distance to school.

Therefore, to find the total distance to school (or $\frac{3}{3}$ of the distance), multiply 4 blocks by 3.

$$4 * 3 = 12$$

If you can enter a fraction on your calculator, divide the number of blocks by the fraction.

Key in: 8 [÷] 2 [/] 3 [=]

Then, press [Ab/c] or [F⇄D]. The display shows 12.

```
184 185
```

Check Your Understanding

1. If 9 counters are $\frac{1}{5}$ of a set, how many counters are in the set?

2. If 9 counters are $\frac{3}{4}$ of a set, how many counters are in the set?

A **unit fraction** is any fraction with 1 in its numerator. Unit fractions are used in solving problems in which the part of the whole is given as a fraction and you need to find the whole.

Example:

Ms. Partee spends $1000 a month. This amount is $\frac{4}{5}$ of her monthly earnings. How much does she earn per month?

Whole
monthly earnings

Step 1
Find $\frac{1}{5}$ of her monthly earnings.

$1000 is $\frac{4}{5}$ of her monthly earnings. Therefore, to find $\frac{1}{5}$ of her earnings, divide $1000 by 4.

$$\$1000/4 = \$250$$

Step 2
Find her monthly earnings.

$250 is $\frac{1}{5}$ of her monthly earnings. Therefore, to find her total earnings (or $\frac{5}{5}$ of her earnings), multiply $250 by 5.

$$\$250 * 5 = \$1250$$

Unit percent is another name for 1%. Unit percents are used in solving problems in which the part of the whole is given as a percent and you need to find the whole.

Example:

Ms. Partee spends $1000 a month. This amount is 80% of her monthly earnings. How much does she earn per month?

100%
monthly earnings

Step 1
Find 1% of her monthly earnings.

$1000 is 80% of her monthly earnings. Therefore, to find 1% of her earnings, divide $1000 by 80.

$$\$1000/80 = \$12.50$$

Step 2
Find her monthly earnings.

$12.50 is 1% of her monthly earnings. Therefore, to find her total earnings (or 100% of her earnings), multiply $12.50 by 100.

$$\$12.50 * 100 = \$1250$$

Note that the only difference between the two examples is that in the first example, the part is given as a **fraction** and in the second example as a **percent** of her earnings.

186

Check Your Understanding

All bicycles at Art's Cycles Shop are on sale at 75% of the regular price. If the sale price of a bicycle is $150, how much did the bicycle cost before it was put on sale?

Rates and Rate Tables

A **rate** tells how many of one thing there are for a certain number of another thing. Rates often contain the word **per** meaning "for each," "for every," "in," or a similar phrase. Each rate has a **rate unit** that is made up of two different units.

Examples:

Alan rode his bicycle a distance of 12 miles in one hour. He traveled at a rate of 12 *miles per hour*. This rate describes the distance Alan traveled and the time it took him to cover the distance. "Miles per hour" is the rate unit.

Other examples of rates:

50 *words per minute*	(average typing speed)
21.8 *students per class*	(average class size)
$14\frac{1}{2}$ *cents per ounce*	(average cost)
17 *points per game*	(average number of points)
5.4 *French francs for each U.S. dollar*	(exchange rate)
−2500 *dollars a month*	(business loss)

Some rate units have special abbreviations. For example, *miles per hour* can be written as *mph* and *miles per gallon* as *mpg*.

Rate information can be used to make a **rate table**.

Example:

Make a rate table for the statement, "A computer printer prints 4 *pages per minute*."

pages	4	8	12	16	20	24	28
minutes	1	2	3	4	5	6	7

The table shows that if a printer prints 4 pages per minute, it will print 8 pages in 2 minutes, 12 pages in 3 minutes, and so on.

Rate units are often written with a slash (/) or a horizontal fraction bar. The slash and fraction bar are read as "per" or "for each."

		Slash	Fraction bar
per-hour rate:	65 miles per hour	65 miles/hour	$65\frac{miles}{hour}$
per-candy rate:	$\frac{1}{2}$ cent per candy	$\frac{1}{2}$ cent/candy	$\frac{1}{2}\frac{cent}{candy}$

Check Your Understanding

Write each rate in two ways: with a slash and with a fraction bar. Make a rate table for each rate.
1. Joan baby-sits for 5 dollars per hour.
2. Water weighs about 8 pounds per gallon.

Rates such as "2 dollars per gallon," "12 miles per hour," and "4 words per minute" are called **per-unit rates** because these rates tell how many of a thing there are for **one** of another thing. We say that "2 dollars per gallon" is a **per-gallon rate**, "12 miles per hour" is a **per-hour rate**, and "4 words per minute" is a **per-minute rate**.

Every rate can be expressed as a per-unit rate in two different ways.

Example 1:

The A & M Supermarket sells milk for $2 per gallon.

dollars	2	4	6	8	20	1	$\frac{1}{2}$
gallons	1	2	3	4	10	$\frac{1}{2}$	$\frac{1}{4}$

The two different ways to show the information in the table as a per-unit rate are as follows.

per-gallon rate: 2 dollars per gallon   2 dollars/gallon $2\frac{\text{dollars}}{\text{gallon}}$

per-dollar rate: $\frac{1}{2}$ gallon per dollar $\frac{1}{2}$ gallon/dollar $\frac{1}{2}\frac{\text{gallon}}{\text{dollar}}$

If milk costs $2 per gallon, then $1 will buy $\frac{1}{2}$ gallon.

Example 2:

1 yard = 3 feet

feet	3	6	9	12	18	1	$\frac{1}{3}$
yards	1	2	3	4	6	$\frac{1}{3}$	$\frac{1}{9}$

Two ways to express this conversion fact as a per-unit rate are as follows.

per-yard rate: 3 feet per yard   3 feet/yard $3\frac{\text{feet}}{\text{yard}}$

per-foot rate: $\frac{1}{3}$ yard per foot $\frac{1}{3}$ yard/foot $\frac{1}{3}\frac{\text{yard}}{\text{foot}}$

Since 3 feet = 1 yard, 1 foot = $\frac{1}{3}$ yard.

Check Your Understanding

Express the information in each rate table as a per-unit rate in two ways.

1. June ran at a rate of 5 miles per hour.

miles	5	10	15	1
hours	1	2	3	$\frac{1}{5}$

2. 1 gallon = 4 quarts

quarts	4	8	12	1
gallons	1	2	3	$\frac{1}{4}$

Solving Rate Problems

Each rate in a rate table is **equivalent** to each of the other rates in the table.

In most problems that involve rates, a rate is given and you need to find an equivalent rate.

Problems in which you need to find an equivalent rate when a unit rate is given can be solved by multiplication.

Example:

> Bill's new car can travel 35 miles on 1 gallon of gasoline. At this rate, how far can the car travel on 7 gallons?
>
> If the car can travel 35 miles on 1 gallon, it can travel 7 times as far on 7 gallons.
>
> $7 * 35 = 245$, so the car can travel 245 miles on 7 gallons of gas.

In other problems, a rate that is not a unit rate is given and you need to find the equivalent unit rate. Such problems can be solved by division.

Example:

> Keisha received an allowance of $20 in 4 weeks. At this rate, how much did she get per week?
>
> If she receives $20 in 4 weeks, she receives $\frac{1}{4}$ as much in 1 week.
>
> $\frac{20}{4} = 5$, so Keisha receives $5 per week.

There are problems in which a rate that is not a unit rate is given and you need to find an equivalent rate that is not a unit rate. To solve such problems, first use division to find the equivalent unit rate; then use multiplication to find a rate equivalent to the unit rate.

Example:

> A gray whale's heart beats 24 times in 3 minutes. At this rate, how many times does it beat in 2 minutes?
>
> If the whale's heart beats 24 times in 3 minutes, it beats $\frac{1}{3}$ of 24 times in 1 minute ($\frac{24}{3} = 8$) and twice as many times in 2 minutes ($2 * 8 = 16$). The whale's heart beats 16 times in 2 minutes.

Check Your Understanding

1. There are 3 feet in 1 yard. How many feet are there in 5 yards?
2. Bob saved $300 last year. How much did he save per month?
3. A carton of 12 eggs costs 72 cents. At this rate, how much do 8 eggs cost?

In her monthly report, the manager of a grocery store wrote: "We sold three times as many quarts of ice cream as quarts of frozen yogurt." This statement is an example of a comparison of two like quantities called a **ratio**. We say that the ratio of quarts of ice cream to quarts of frozen yogurt sold is 3 to 1. This means that for every 3 quarts of ice cream the store sold, it sold one quart of frozen yogurt.

All of the following are statements of ratios.

- It is estimated that by the year 2020, there will be *5 times as many* people at least 100 years old as there were in 1990.
- Elementary school students make up about *14 percent of* the U.S. population.
- On an average evening, about $\frac{1}{3}$ *of* the U.S. population watches TV.
- The chances of winning a prize in a lottery can be less than *1 in 1 million*.
- A common scale for doll houses is *1 inch to 12 inches*.

Some ratios compare quantities that involve a whole and its parts.

> *Example:*
>
> In a class of 20 students, there are 12 girls and 8 boys.
>
> You can think of the 20 students as the **whole** and the 12 girls and 8 boys as **parts of the whole**.
>
> A **part-to-whole** ratio compares a part of the whole to the whole. The statements "8 out of 20 students are boys," and "12 out of 20 students are girls," each express a part-to-whole ratio.
>
> A **part-to-part** ratio compares a part of the whole to another part of the whole. The statement "There are 8 boys for every 12 girls," expresses a part-to-part ratio.

Ratios can be expressed in a number of ways. For the above example, the ratio of girls to the total number of students can be expressed—

- In words:

  Twelve out of 20 students are girls.
  Twelve in 20 students are girls.
  There are 12 girls for every 20 students.
  The ratio of girls to all students is 12 to 20.

- With a fraction: $\frac{12}{20}$ or $\frac{3}{5}$ of the students are girls.
- With a percent: 60% of the students are girls.
- With a colon between the two numbers being compared: The ratio of girls to all students is 12:20 ("twelve to twenty").

Part-to-part ratios are usually not expressed by a percent.

Ratios that can be named by equivalent fractions are called **equivalent ratios**. The ratios 12 to 20, 6 to 10, and 3 to 5 are equivalent ratios, because $\frac{12}{20} = \frac{6}{10} = \frac{3}{5}$. If 12 out of 20 students are girls, it can also be said that 6 out of 10 students are girls, and 3 out of 5 students are girls. Similarly, the ratios 12 to 8, 6 to 4, and 3 to 2 are equivalent ratios, because $\frac{12}{8} = \frac{6}{4} = \frac{3}{2}$. If there are 12 girls for every 8 boys, it can also be said that there are 6 girls for every 4 boys, or 3 girls for every 2 boys. Ratios made up of smaller numbers, such as the ratio 3 to 2, are useful because they are usually easier to understand.

The ratio of girls to boys is 3 to 2.

Every ratio can be converted to a ratio of some number to 1. These are called **unit ratios**. One way to convert any ratio to a unit ratio is to divide the first number in the ratio by the second number. For example, to convert the ratio of 3 girls to 2 boys to a unit ratio, divide 3 by 2. The answer is 1.5. This means that the ratio of girls to boys is 1.5 to 1, that is, there are 1.5 girls for every boy. Another way to state this is to say that there are 1.5 times as many girls as boys. Unit ratios are useful when comparing several ratios.

Some ratios compare two quantities that are not part of the same whole.

Example:

A book appears in both a hardcover version and a paperback version. The hardcover version costs $25 and the paperback version costs $10.

The ratio of the cost of the hardcover version to the cost of the paperback version is 25 to 10, or, in simpler form, 5 to 2. To find the unit ratio, divide: 5/2 = 2.5. Thus, the hardcover version costs 2.5 times as much as the paperback version.

Check Your Understanding

Last month, Mark received an allowance of $20. He spent $12 and saved the rest.

1. What is the ratio of the money he spent to his total allowance?
2. What is the ratio of the money he saved to the money he spent?
3. The money he spent is how many times the money he saved?
4. What percent of his allowance did he save?

You are familiar with many situations that produce a **size change**. A magnifying glass, a microscope, and an overhead projector all produce size changes that enlarge the original image. Most copying machines can be used to create a variety of size changes—both enlargements and reductions of the original document.

Similar figures are figures that have the same shape, but not necessarily the same size. In the examples of size changes above, the enlargement or reduction will be **similar** to the original, that is, they will have the same shape.

The **size-change factor** is a number that tells the amount of enlargement or reduction. For example, if you use a copy machine to make a 2X change in size, then every length in the copy will be enlarged to twice the size of the original. We say that the size-change factor is 2. If you make a 0.5X change in size, then every length in the copy will be reduced to half the size of the original. In this reduction, the size-change factor is 0.5.

You can think of the size-change factor as a ratio. For a 2X size change, the ratio of a length in the copy to the corresponding length in the original is 2 to 1. For a 0.5X size change, the ratio of a length in the copy to a corresponding length in the original is 0.5 to 1.

Devices that Magnify and Reduce

A photographer uses an enlarger to make prints from negatives. If the size of the negative is 2" by 3" and the size of the print is 6" by 9", then the size-change factor is 3. Binoculars that are 8X, or "8 power," magnify all the lengths you see with the naked eye to 8 times their actual size.

Scale Models

A carefully designed model that is an exact replica of an actual object is called a **scale model**. You are probably familiar with scale models of cars, trains, and airplanes. The size-change factor in scale models is usually called the **scale factor**.

Doll houses often have a scale factor of $\frac{1}{12}$. We can write this as " $\frac{1}{12}$ of actual size," "scale 1:12," or " $\frac{1}{12}$ scale." All the dimensions of an E-scale model railroad are $\frac{1}{96}$ of the actual size. We can write this as "scale 1:96," or "scale: $\frac{1}{8}$ inch represents 1 foot," or "scale: 0.125 inch represents 1 foot." *Note:* The scale is 1:96 since $\frac{1}{8}$ inch:1 foot is the same as $\frac{1}{8}$ inch:12 inches which is the same as 1 inch:96 inches.

Maps and Scale Drawings

The size-change factor for maps and scale drawings is usually called the **scale**. Maps are similar to the actual land they represent, but with all the actual distances greatly reduced. If a map scale is 1:25,000, then every length on the map is $\frac{1}{25,000}$ of the actual length and any real distance is 25,000 times the distance shown on the map.

If an architect's scale drawing shows "scale $\frac{1}{4}$ inch:1 foot" or "scale $\frac{1}{4}$ inch represents 1 foot," then the drawing is $\frac{1}{48}$ of the actual size.

You may see scales written with an equal sign. For example, $\frac{1}{4}$ inch = 1 foot. Since the two measures are obviously *not equal*, the equal sign is being used as a symbol for the word "represents."

The Golden Ratio

Which of the following rectangles do you like best?

It has been shown that Rectangle D, called the **Golden Rectangle**, is chosen more often than any other rectangle. In a Golden Rectangle, the ratio of the length of the longer side to the length of the shorter side is about 1.618 to 1. This ratio is known as the **Golden Ratio**.

The popularity of the Golden Ratio dates back to the ancient Greeks who used it in many of their works of art and architecture. For example, the front of the Parthenon in Athens fits almost exactly into a Golden Rectangle, as do many parts of the temples in the ancient Greek city of Paestum (Poseidonia).

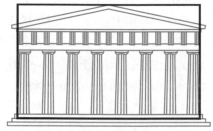

The Greek symbol for the Golden Ratio was the letter ϕ (pronounced phi), perhaps chosen for the name of the Athenian sculptor Phidias (about 490–430 B.C.).

Many artists throughout the ages have found that by using the Golden Ratio, they could create a feeling of order in their works. For example, in the picture of St. Jerome, painted about the year 1483 by Leonardo da Vinci, the figure of St. Jerome fits perfectly into a Golden Rectangle. It is believed that this was not an accident, but that da Vinci used the Golden Ratio because of his great interest in mathematics.

A **mobile** is a piece of sculpture constructed of rods and other objects that are suspended in midair by wires, twine, or thread. The rods and objects are connected so that the sculpture is balanced when it is suspended.

The point at which the rod is suspended is called the fulcrum. The **fulcrum** may be the center point of the rod or some other point on the rod. The objects may be hung at the ends of the rods or at some points between the ends of the rod and the fulcrum.

The mobile at the right, titled *Sea Scapes*, was made by Alexander Calder (1898–1976) in 1947. It is made of painted wood, sheet metal, string, and wire; it is 60 inches wide.

Suppose the fulcrum is the center point of a rod, and you hang two objects from some points on the rod, one on each side of the fulcrum.

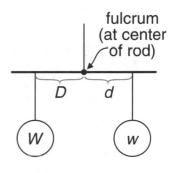

Let W = the weight of one object

D = the distance of this object from the fulcrum

w = the weight of the second object

d = the distance of this object from the fulcrum

The mobile will balance if $W * D = w * d$.

Example:

In the mobile at the right, what is the missing distance?

Replace the variables in the formula $W * D = w * d$ with the values shown in the diagram. Then solve the equation.

$W = 6 \qquad D = 7 \qquad w = 10 \qquad d = x$

Solution: $\quad W * D = w * d$

$\qquad 6 * 7 = 10 * x$

$\qquad\quad 42 = 10 * x$

$\qquad\quad 4.2 = x$

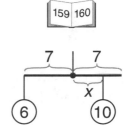

Therefore, the distance x to the fulcrum is 4.2 units.

Check Your Understanding

Decide whether the mobiles in Problems 1 and 2 are in balance. Find the weight of the object on the left of the fulcrum in Problem 3.

1.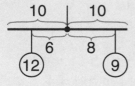

2.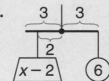

3.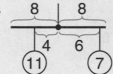

Suppose the fulcrum is **not** the center point of the rod, and you hang two objects from some points on the rod, one on each side of the fulcrum.

Let R = the weight of the rod

 L = the distance from the center of the rod to the fulcrum

 W = the weight of the object that is farthest from the fulcrum

 D = the distance of this object from the fulcrum

 w = the weight of the object that is closest to the fulcrum

 d = the distance of this object from the fulcrum

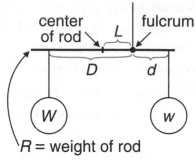

The mobile will balance if $(W * D) + (R * L) = w * d$.

Example:

In the mobile at the right, what is the missing weight?

Replace the variables in the formula $(W * D) + (R * L) = w * d$ with the values shown in the diagram. Then solve the equation.

 $W = 7$ $D = 10$ $R = 10$ $L = 2$ $w = 5x$ $d = 6$

Solution:

$$(W * D) + (R * L) = w * d$$
$$(7 * 10) + (10 * 2) = 5x * 6$$
$$70 + 20 = 30x$$
$$90 = 30x$$
$$3 = x$$

Since $x = 3$, $5x = 5 * 3 = 15$. Therefore, the weight of the object suspended on the right of the fulcrum is 15 units.

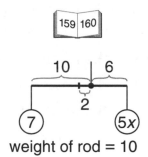

weight of rod = 10

Check Your Understanding

Decide whether the mobiles in Problems 1 and 2 are in balance. Find the weight of the object on the left of the fulcrum in Problem 3.

1.

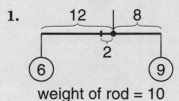

weight of rod = 10

2.

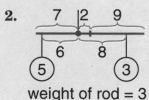

weight of rod = 3

3.

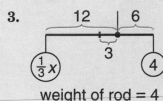

weight of rod = 4

When you trace a path around a penny, the figure you get is a circle. A compass is a device for drawing circles, as are some of the shapes on your Geometry Template.

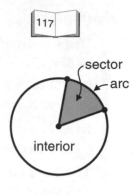

An **arc** is a piece of a circle. If you mark two points on a circle, these points and the part of the circle between them form an arc.

The region inside a circle is called the **interior** of the circle.

A **sector** is a wedge-shaped "piece" of a circle and its interior. A sector consists of two radii, the arc determined by their endpoints, and the part of the interior of the circle bounded by the radii and the arc.

A **circle graph** is sometimes called a **pie graph** because it looks like a pie that has been cut into several pieces. Each "piece" is a sector of the circle. The circle graph at the right shows the distribution of students in grades 1 to 5 at Elm Place School.

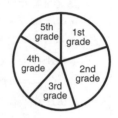

You can use the Percent Circle on your Geometry Template to find what percent of the circle graph each sector represents. Here are two methods for using the Percent Circle.

Method 1: Direct Measure
Place the center of the Percent Circle over the center of the circle graph. Rotate the template so that the 0% mark is aligned with one side (line segment) of the sector you are measuring. Read the percent at the mark on the Percent Circle located over the other side of the sector. This tells what percent the sector represents. For the circle graph of students, the sector for 1st grade represents 20%.

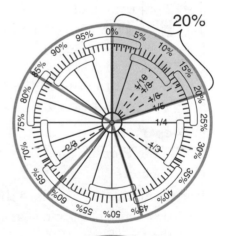

Method 2: Difference Comparison
Place the center of the Percent Circle over the center of the circle graph. Note the percent reading for one side of the sector you are measuring. (If you wish, rotate the template so that the reading is an easy number, such as 20%.) Find the percent reading for the other side of the sector (for example, 45%). Find the difference between these readings. For the circle graph of students, the sector for 2nd grade represents 45% – 20%, or 25%.

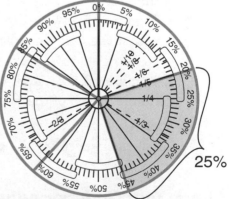

Check Your Understanding

What percents are represented by the other three sectors in the above circle graph?

Example:

Draw a circle graph to show the following information. The students in Ms. Ahmad's class were asked to name their favorite color. Eight students chose blue, 6 students chose green, 4 students chose yellow, 5 chose red, and 2 had no favorite color.

Step 1

Find what percent of the total each part represents.

The total number of students who voted is $8 + 6 + 4 + 5 + 2 = 25$.

- 8 out of 25 chose blue.
  $\frac{8}{25} = \frac{32}{100} = 32\%$, so 32% chose blue.
- 6 out of 25 chose green.
  $\frac{6}{25} = \frac{24}{100} = 24\%$, so 24% chose green.
- 4 out of 25 chose yellow.
  $\frac{4}{25} = \frac{16}{100} = 16\%$, so 16% chose yellow.
- 5 out of 25 chose red.
  $\frac{5}{25} = \frac{20}{100} = 20\%$, so 20% chose red.
- 2 out of 25 had no preference.
  $\frac{2}{25} = \frac{8}{100} = 8\%$, so 8% had no preference.

Step 2

Check that the sum of the percents is 100%.

$32\% + 24\% + 16\% + 20\% + 8\% = 100\%$

Step 3

Use the Percent Circle on the Geometry Template to mark off the sectors.

- To mark off 32%, place the center of the Percent Circle over the center of the circle graph. Make a mark at 0% and 32% on the circle.
- To mark off 24%, make a mark at 56% (32% + 24% = 56%), without moving the Percent Circle.
- To mark off 16%, make a mark at 72% (56% + 16% = 72%).
- To mark off 20%, make a mark at 92% (72% + 20% = 92%).
- Connect each of the marks with the center of the circle.

Step 4

Label each **sector** of the circle.

44

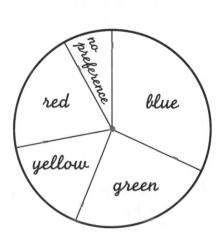

147

Check Your Understanding

Make a circle graph to display the following information.

The Hot Shots basketball team scored 30 points in one game. Sally scored 15 points. Drew and Bonita each scored 6 points. Damon scored 3 points.

Example:

Draw a circle graph to show the following information: In the month of June, there were 19 sunny days, 6 partly cloudy days, and 5 cloudy days.

112 113 114

Step 1

Find out what fraction or percent of the total each part represents. June has 30 days.

47

- 5 out of 30 were cloudy days.
  $\frac{5}{30} = \frac{1}{6}$, so $\frac{1}{6}$ of the days were cloudy.
- 6 out of 30 were partly cloudy days.
  $\frac{6}{30} = \frac{1}{5}$, so $\frac{1}{5}$ of the days were partly cloudy.
- 19 out of 30 were sunny days.
  $\frac{19}{30}$ = 19/30 = 0.633 = 63.3%, so 63.3% of the days were sunny.

Step 2

Calculate the degree measure of the sector for each piece of data.

134 135

- The number of cloudy days in June was $\frac{1}{6}$ of the total number of days. Therefore, the degree measure of the sector for cloudy days is $\frac{1}{6}$ of 360°. $\frac{1}{6}$ of 360° = 60°.

- The number of partly cloudy days in June was $\frac{1}{5}$ of the total number of days. Therefore, the degree measure of the sector for cloudy days is $\frac{1}{5}$ of 360°. $\frac{1}{5}$ of 360° = 72°.

- The number of sunny days in June was 63.3% of the total number of days. Therefore, the degree measure of the sector for sunny days is 63.3% of 360°. 0.633 * 360° = 228°, rounded to the nearest degree.

Step 3

Check that the sum of the degree measures of the sectors is 360°.

60° + 72° + 228° = 360°

Step 4

Measure each sector with a protractor. Draw and label the sector.

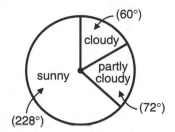

Check Your Understanding

Use your protractor to make a circle graph to display the following information. What is the degree measure of each sector, rounded to the nearest degree?

Favorite Subjects of 6th Grade Class						
Subject	Reading	Social Studies	Math	Music	Science	Art
Number of Students	6	2	4	1	2	1

What's My Rule? Problems

Imagine a machine that works like this: When a number is dropped into the machine (*the input, or "in" number*), the machine changes the number according to a rule, and a new number comes out the other end (*the output, or "out" number*). "In" and "out" numbers can be displayed in table form.

Example:

This machine adds 5 to any "in" number.

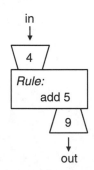

What's My Rule? table

in	out
4	9
7	12
53	58
-6	-1
.	.
.	.
.	.

If 4 is dropped in, 9 comes out. → 4 | 9

If 7 is dropped in, 12 comes out. → 7 | 12

If 53 is dropped in, 58 comes out. → 53 | 58

If –6 is dropped in, –1 comes out. → –6 | –1

A What's My Rule? problem may contain three kinds of information: "in" numbers, "out" numbers, and a rule. Some of this information is missing. To solve the problem, you need to find the missing information.

In the following examples, the solutions (the missing information) appear in parentheses.

Examples:

The rule and the "in" numbers are given. Find the "out" numbers.

Rule: subtract 7 from "in"

in	out	
9	(2)	[9 – 7 = 2]
27	(20)	[27 – 7 = 20]
0	(–7)	[0 – 7 = –7]
–5	(–12)	[–5 – 7 = –12]

The rule and the "out" numbers are given. Find the "in" numbers.

Rule: multiply "in" by 2

in	out	
(4)	8	[4 * 2 = 8]
(24)	48	[24 * 2 = 48]
($\frac{1}{2}$)	1	[$\frac{1}{2}$ * 2 = 1]
(0)	0	[0 * 2 = 0]

The "in" and "out" numbers are given. Find the rule.

Rule: (raise "in" to the second power)

in	out	
2	4	[$2^2 = 4$]
5	25	[$5^2 = 25$]
1	1	[$1^2 = 1$]
10	100	[$10^2 = 100$]

Check Your Understanding

Solve the What's My Rule? problems.

1. *Rule:* divide "in" by 3

in	out
9	?
36	?
1	?
1.5	?

2. *Rule:* subtract 4 from "in"

in	out
?	7
?	24
?	–4
?	0

3. *Rule:* ?

in	out
4	120
10	300
0	0
200	6000

Cartographers (mapmakers) represent large areas of land and water on small pieces of paper. Places that are actually thousands of miles apart are only inches apart on a map. When you use a map, you can estimate actual distances by using a **map scale**.

Different maps use different scales. For one map, 1 inch may represent 10 miles. For another map, 1 inch may represent 100 miles.

On the map scale below, the length of the bar represents 2000 actual miles. Half the length of the bar represents 1000 actual miles.

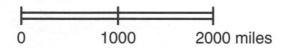

0   1000   2000 miles

Measuring Distances on a Map

There are several ways to measure distances on a map. Here are two:

First Method: Use a compass.

Step 1
Open the compass. Adjust it so that the distance between the anchor point and the pencil point is the same as a distance on the map scale.

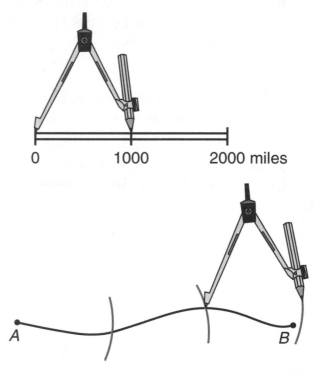

0   1000   2000 miles

Step 2
Imagine a path connecting the starting point and endpoint of the distance you want to measure. Put the anchor point of the compass at the starting point. Use the pencil point to make an arc on the path. Move the anchor point to the arc and make another arc. Continue until you reach or pass the endpoint. Be careful not to change the opening of the compass.

Step 3
Keep track of how many times you swing the compass. Each swing represents the distance indicated by the map scale. To estimate total distance, multiply the number of swings by the distance each represents.

Step 4
If the path is not along a straight line, the result will underestimate the distance. Distance along a straight line between two points is less than along a curved path between the same points.

Second Method: Use a piece of paper.

Step 1

Note the starting point and endpoint of the distance you want to measure.

Step 2

Lay the edge of a piece of paper along the path from the starting point to the endpoint.

A. If the path is straight: Mark the starting point and endpoint on the paper.

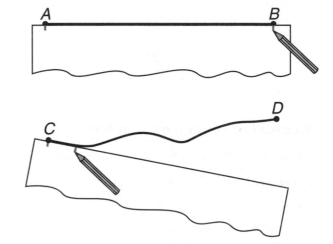

B. If the path is curved: Mark the starting point on the paper. Then mark the end of the longest straight or nearly straight distance from the starting point. Next, pivot the paper to follow the path, marking distances as you go. Make a heavy mark when you reach the endpoint.

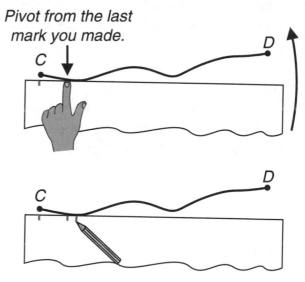

Step 3

Compare the distance from the starting point to the endpoint, as marked on your paper, with the map scale.

Pivot from the last mark you made.

Another way: Mark off the map scale repeatedly along the edge of a piece of paper. Use the paper like a ruler to read the distance directly.

Check Your Understanding

Use the map scale to estimate the distance along the path from point *X* to point *Y*.

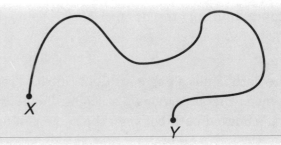

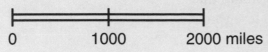

| 0 | 1000 | 2000 miles |

A **Venn diagram** is a picture that uses circles to show relationships between sets.

Example:

At Lincoln Middle School, every student is required to take music. Seventy-five students play an instrument and take a band or orchestra class. The remaining 300 students take a general music class. Students who take a band or orchestra class do not take the general music class.

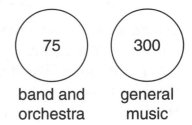

band and orchestra   general music

The Venn diagram for this situation consists of two circles that do not overlap. Students who take band or orchestra classes do not take general music classes, and students who take general music classes do not take band or orchestra classes. The Venn diagram shows that there are 375 students in Lincoln Middle School.

Example:

Ms. Barrie teaches both math and science. There are 26 students in her math class and 24 students in her science class. Five of the students are in both her math and science classes.

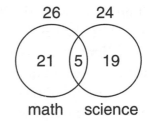

math   science

The Venn diagram for this situation consists of two overlapping circles. The overlapping part of the diagram represents the students who are in both her math and science classes.

The Venn diagram shows that there are 45 students in Ms. Barrie's classes: 21 students take math only, 19 students take science only, and 5 students take both math and science.

Example:

Students' favorite TV shows:

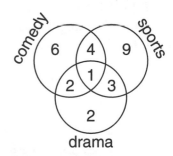

drama

sports only: 9   sports and comedy: 4 + 1 = 5
comedy only: 6   comedy and drama: 2 + 1 = 3
drama only: 2   sports and drama: 3 + 1 = 4
                                        sports, comedy, and drama: 1

Check Your Understanding

The Venn diagram at the right shows the results of a survey in which students were asked whether they write with their left hand or right hand.

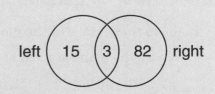

left   right

1. How many students were surveyed?

2. How many students can write with their left hand? With their right hand?

3. How many students can write with either hand?

The Global Grid System

The Earth is almost a perfect **sphere**; all points on the Earth's surface are about the same distance from the Earth's center. The Earth rotates about an **axis** (imaginary line) connecting the **North Pole** and the **South Pole**.

The Earth is divided into **hemispheres** (half-spheres) in two directions. The **equator** is an imaginary circle around the Earth that partitions the Earth into the **Northern Hemisphere** (the hemisphere north of the equator) and the **Southern Hemisphere** (the hemisphere south of the equator).

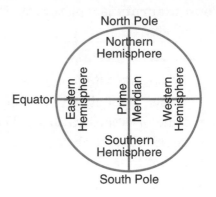

The **prime meridian** is an imaginary semicircle connecting the North Pole to the South Pole and passing through Greenwich, England. It partitions the Earth into the **Western Hemisphere** (the hemisphere west of the prime meridian) and the **Eastern Hemisphere** (the hemisphere east of the prime meridian).

The prime meridian and equator are the axes of an imaginary grid system that circles the Earth. Lines in the grid that connect the poles—like the prime meridian—are called **lines of longitude**. Lines of longitude are semicircles. Lines in the grid that are parallel to the equator are called **lines of latitude**. Lines of latitude are full circles around the globe and are sometimes called **parallels**—since they are parallel to the equator and to each other.

Any point on the globe can be located with this grid system. Lines of longitude are measured in degrees, from 0° to 180° east (E) or west (W) of the prime meridian. Lines of latitude are also measured in degrees, from 0° to 90° north (N) or south (S) of the equator.

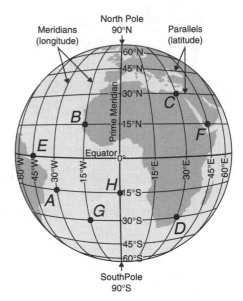

Point A is located at 15°S, 30°W.

Check Your Understanding

Refer to the picture of the globe above to answer the questions.

1. Name the point at each of the following locations.

    a. 30°N, 30°E   **b.** 45°E, 15°N   **c.** 15°S on the prime meridian

2. Give the longitude and latitude of the following points.

    a. *G*   **b.** *B*   **c.** *E*   **d.** *D*

The invention of algebra can be traced back to ancient Egypt and Babylon. Algebra got its name from the Islamic world, where it was known as the "science of restoration and balancing." (The word *algebra* comes from the Arabic word *al-jabru*, which means *restoration*.)

In early times, algebra involved solving equations with "unknowns," that is, finding the value of a missing number in an equation. These unknowns were expressed with words. Then, in the late 1500's, François Viète introduced the use of letter variables to display unknown quantities. This invention made the solving of equations much more efficient and led to a rapid explosion of discoveries, which has continued into modern times.

Most people think of algebra as a subject you first begin to study in high school, involving, for the most part, the manipulation of expressions and solutions of equations. You started to do this kind of work as early as first grade, when you were asked to find the missing number in simple equations such as $5 + \_\_ = 9$. As you advanced in your study of mathematics, the equations you were asked to solve became more complex, but the basic problem remained the same: to find the missing number in the equation.

Algebra is also used in several other ways.

In the study of the properties of number systems. For example, the commutative property of addition states that for all rational numbers a and b, $a + b = b + a$. You were introduced to this property in first grade as the "turn-around" shortcut, to help you memorize the addition facts. The procedures for solving equations are based on many of these properties. For example, the distributive property, $a * (b + c) = (a * b) + (a * c)$ is used to simplify algebraic expressions by renaming expressions in parentheses and by collecting like terms.

To express general relations or functions. These may appear as What's My Rule? tables in which the relationship between the "in" numbers and the "out" numbers is given by a rule, such as "double the 'in' number and add 1," or, using variables, as $y = 2x + 1$. Such relationships may also be graphed on a coordinate grid (see margin).

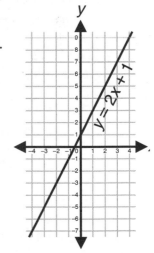

In formulas. Formulas appear frequently in everyday life, in science, in business, and in many other occupations as a compact way of expressing both simple and complex relationships. For example, the formula $d = r * t$ expresses the relationship between a distance, the rate at which one covers the distance, and the time it takes to cover the distance.

In spreadsheet computer programs. Such programs make it possible to evaluate formulas quickly and efficiently. They are very useful for making predictions based on trends.

In naming calculator key functions and to specify calculator procedures. This is especially important for the operation of graphing calculators.

In writing computer programs. Computer programs are made up of a series of "commands" that contain variables, much like the variables in equations.

Algebraic Expressions

Consider the following statement: "Marcia read 4 more books last year than Gina." You can't tell how many books Marcia read because that number depends on the number of books Gina read.

- If Gina read 8 books, then Marcia read 12 books.
- If Gina read 15 books, then Marcia read 19 books, and so on.

There are many possibilities.

One way to represent the number of books Marcia read is to write an **algebraic expression**, in which a **variable** is used to represent the number of books Gina read. For example,

> If G represents the number of books Gina read, then $G + 4$ represents the number of books Marcia read.

Examples: Represent each statement with an algebraic expression.

Statement	Algebraic Expression
Marshall is 5 years older than his sister, Carol.	If Carol is C years old, then Marshall is $C + 5$ years old.
Mrs. Roth weighs 30 pounds less than Mr. Roth.	If Mr. Roth weighs R pounds, then Mrs. Roth weighs $R - 30$ pounds.
Mrs. Martinez bought a box of crayons for each of her grandchildren, with 8 crayons in each box.	If Mrs. Martinez has G grandchildren, then she bought a total of $8 * G$ crayons.
The Cougars won $\frac{2}{3}$ as many games as the Eagles.	If the Eagles won E games, then the Cougars won $\frac{2}{3}$ of E, or $\frac{2}{3} * E$ games.
Claude earned $6 an hour and was paid an additional $3.50 for his lunch.	If Claude worked H hours, he got paid $(6 * H) + 3.50$ dollars.

Check Your Understanding

Write an algebraic expression for each situation, using the suggested variable.

1. Alan is I inches tall. If Audrey is 2 inches shorter than Alan, what is Audrey's height?

2. It takes Herman H minutes to do his homework. If it takes Sue twice as long, how long does it take Sue to complete her homework?

3. Dawn went on R rides at the amusement park. If the amusement park charges a $2 admission fee and $0.50 per ride, how much did Dawn spend at the amusement park?

Number sentences are similar to English sentences, except that they use **math symbols** instead of words.

Math Symbols

Digits	Operation Symbols		Relation Symbols		Grouping Symbols
0, 1, 2,	+	plus	=	is equal to	( ) parentheses
3, 4, 5,	−	minus	≠	is not equal to	[ ] brackets
6, 7, 8,	× or *	times	<	is less than	
9	−, /,	divided by	>	is greater than	
	or ÷		≤	is less than or equal to	
			≥	is greater than or equal to	

A number sentence *must* contain numbers and a **relation symbol**. It may or may not contain one or more **operation symbols** and **grouping symbols**.

Number sentences that contain the relation symbol "=" are called **equations**. Number sentences that contain the relation symbol "≠," "<," ">," "≤," or "≥," are called **inequalities**.

Examples of number sentences:

$$3 + 3 = 8 \qquad\qquad -27 * 4 > 42 \qquad\qquad 27 \neq 72$$

$$\tfrac{4}{5} - \tfrac{2}{3} \leq \tfrac{1}{2} \qquad\qquad (24 + 3)/9 = 3 \qquad\qquad 19 < 19$$

$$100 = 9^2 + 9 \qquad\qquad 16 \times 4 \geq 80 \div 3$$

When a number sentence is made up of such symbols, it is always possible to tell whether the sentence is **true** or **false**. For example:

- $3 + 3 = 8$ is false because $3 + 3 = 6$, not 8.

- $-27 * 4 > 42$ is false because $-27 * 4 = -108$, and -108 is not greater than 42.

- $27 \neq 72$ is true because 27 is not equal to 72.

- $\tfrac{4}{5} - \tfrac{2}{3} \leq \tfrac{1}{2}$ is true because $\tfrac{4}{5} - \tfrac{2}{3} = \tfrac{2}{15}$, and $\tfrac{2}{15}$ is less than $\tfrac{1}{2}$.

- $(24 + 3)/9 = 3$ is true because $24 + 3 = 27$, and $27/9$ is equal to 3.

- $19 < 19$ is false because 19 is not less than itself.

Check Your Understanding

Tell whether the sentence is true or false.

1. $28 - 16 = 12$
2. $3 * 8 < 30$
3. $0 = \tfrac{4}{4}$
4. $27 + 3 \leq 5 * 6$
5. $60 = 9 + (6 * 2^2)$
6. $96 \neq 96$

Parentheses in number sentences are used to tell which operation to do first. For example, in the number sentence $8 * (12 - 6) = 48$, you first subtract 6 from 12 and then multiply 8 by the result: $12 - 6 = 6$ and $8 * 6 = 48$. Therefore, the sentence is true.

There are number sentences in which one or more of the numbers are missing. Such sentences are called **open sentences**.

We write symbols, such as Δ, or ?, or a letter, such as n, in place of a missing number. When a symbol is used in place of a missing number, the symbol is called a **variable**. For example, $5 + x = 12$ is an open sentence in which the variable x stands for some number. If we replace the letter x with numbers, we get number sentences that are either true or false.

- If we replace x with 3, we get the number sentence $5 + 3 = 12$. This sentence is false.

- If we replace x with 7, we get the number sentence $5 + 7 = 12$. This sentence is true.

If the number used in place of the variable makes the number sentence true, we call this number a **solution** of the open sentence. For example, the number 7 is a solution of the open sentence $5 + x = 12$, because the number sentence $5 + 7 = 12$ is true.

Simple equations usually have just one solution. Most inequalities have many solutions. For example, 9, 3.5, $2\frac{1}{2}$, and -8 are all solutions of the inequality $x < 10$. In fact, $x < 10$ has infinitely many solutions—it may be any number less than 10.

Variables are also used:

To describe a rule in a What's My Rule? table.

Example:

in	out
(n)	$(2 * n)$
1	2
2	4
3	6

and so on

In formulas.

Example:

$A = \pi * r^2$, where A is the area of a circle and r is its radius.

To state properties of number systems.

Example:

$a + b = b + a$, for any numbers a and b.

Check Your Understanding

Find the solution of each equation.

1. $8 + c = 20$
2. $32.5 - y = 8.4$
3. $35 = 5 * z$
4. $x/3 = 6$
5. $(2 * f) + 7 = 28$
6. $5 = 5 - (9 * w)$

A **formula** is a general way of expressing a relationship between measured quantities. The quantities are represented by variables.

Example:

▌ Formula for the area of a parallelogram: $A = b * h$

In the example above, the variable A stands for the area, b for the length of the base, and h for the height of the parallelogram.

A formula is usually written with an equal sign (=), a **variable** on one side of the equal sign, and an **algebraic expression** on the other side. Some formulas include numbers; others do not.

Variables in Formulas

Letter variables in formulas are chosen carefully. Often a letter is the first letter of the quantity that it represents.

Examples:

▌ Area of parallelogram = length of base * height $A = b * h$

▌ circumference of circle = pi * diameter of circle $c = \pi * d$

▌ Michelle earns twice as much as Guy. $M = 2 * G$

A letter variable can have different meanings depending on whether it is a capital or lowercase (small) letter.

Example:

▌ The area of the shaded region in the figure at the right can be found by using the formula $A = S^2 - s^2$. Note that the variable S (capital S) stands for the length of the side of the larger square. The variable s (lowercase s) stands for the length of the side of the smaller square.

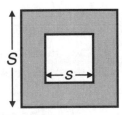

Evaluating a Formula

To **evaluate** a formula means to find the value of one variable in the formula when the values of the other variables in the formula are given.

Example:

▌ Evaluate the formula for the area of the
shaded region in the figure above when
$S = 4$ cm and $s = 2$ cm.

$$A = S^2 - s^2$$
$$A = (4 \text{ cm})^2 - (2 \text{ cm})^2$$
$$A = 16 \text{ cm}^2 - 4 \text{ cm}^2$$
$$A = 12 \text{ cm}^2$$

Units in Formulas

It is important that the **units** (hours, inches, meters, and so on) in a
formula are consistent. An area formula will not give a correct result if one
measurement is in millimeters and another is in centimeters.

> *Example:*
>
> To calculate the area of the rectangle below, you would need to
> change millimeters to centimeters or centimeters to millimeters.
>
> $A = b * h$
>
> $A = 7 \text{ mm} * 50 \text{ mm} = 350 \text{ mm}^2$
>
> $A = 0.7 \text{ cm} * 5 \text{ cm} = 3.5 \text{ cm}^2$

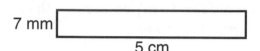

7 mm

5 cm

The formula $d = r * t$ gives the distance traveled in time t at a rate of travel
(speed) r. If the value of r is in miles per hour, the value of t should be in
hours. If the value of r is in meters per second, t should be in seconds.

> *Example:*
>
> $d = r * t$
>
> If $r = 50$ miles per hour and $t = 2$ hours, then
>
> $d = 50$ miles per hour $* 2$ hours $= 100$ miles.

Sometimes the unit for one variable automatically becomes the unit for
another variable.

> *Example:*
>
> $c = \pi * d$
>
> If the diameter of a circle is 3.0 *feet*, the circumference is about 9.4 *feet*.
>
> If the diameter of a circle is 8.0 *centimeters,* the circumference is about
> 25.1 *centimeters*.

Check Your Understanding

1. Find the area of rectangle *ABCD*.

2. If $S = 6$ meters and $s = 2$ meters, what is the area of the
   shaded region in the diagram on page 159?

3. If a car is traveling 80 feet per second, how far will it travel
   in 1 minute?

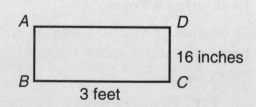

A   D

16 inches

B   3 feet   C

4. Express each of the following relationships with a formula.

   a. The volume of a cone (V) is equal to $\frac{1}{3}$ of the area of the base (B)
      times the height of the cone (h).

   b. The interest (i) earned on $1000 deposited in a savings account is
      equal to $1000 times the rate of interest (r) times the length of
      time the money is left in the account (t).

When you bake a cake, you are careful to crack the eggs *before* adding them to your batter. When playing baseball, you make sure to run to first base *after* you have hit the ball. In mathematics, there are rules that tell the order in which operations should be done. Operations should be carried out in the following order:

1. Do the operations within **P**arentheses or other grouping symbols before doing anything else.

2. Next, calculate all **E**xponential expressions.

3. Then do the **M**ultiplications and **D**ivisions in order, from left to right. Neither operation has priority over the other.

4. Finally, do the **A**dditions and **S**ubtractions in order, from left to right. Neither operation has priority over the other.

To help you remember the order of operations, you can memorize the sentence "**P**lease **E**xcuse **M**y **D**ear **A**unt **S**ally." The first letter of each word should remind you of an operation.

Please **E**xcuse **M**y **D**ear **A**unt **S**ally

Parentheses **E**xponents **M**ultiplication **D**ivision **A**ddition **S**ubtraction

Example 1:

Evaluate 15/3 + 4.	$15/3 + 4 = ?$
Divide first, then add.	$5 + 4 = 9$
Answer:	$15/3 + 4 = 9$

Example 2:

Evaluate $5 * 4 - 6 * 3 + 2$.	$5 * 4 - 6 * 3 + 2 = ?$
Multiply first.	$20 - 18 + 2 =$
Then subtract and add.	$2 + 2 = 4$
Answer:	$5 * 4 - 6 * 3 + 2 = 4$

Example 3:

Evaluate $5^2 + (3 * 4 - 2)/5$.	$5^2 + (3 * 4 - 2)/5 = ?$
Parentheses first.	$5^2 + (12 - 2)/5 =$
	$5^2 + 10 /5 =$
Exponents next.	$25 + 10 /5 =$
Divide, then add.	$25 + 2 = 27$
Answer:	$5^2 + (3 * 4 - 2)/5 = 27$

Check Your Understanding

Evaluate each expression.

1. $33 - 18/3 + 9$

2. $14 + (7 * 2^2)/4$

3. $20 * 4/2 - 30$

4. $10(18/9 + 4)/12 + 1$

Pan-Balance Problems and Equations

If several objects are placed in the pans of a pan balance and if the pans are in balance, then you can find the weight of one kind of object in terms of the other kind of object.

Example:

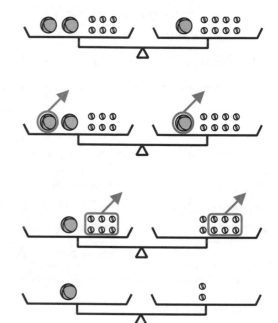

The pan balance at the right has 2 balls and 6 marbles in one pan and 1 ball and 8 marbles in the other pan. How many marbles weigh as much as 1 ball?

Step 1: If 1 ball is removed from each pan, the pan balance will remain balanced. One ball and 6 marbles will be left in the pan on the left and 8 marbles will be left in the pan on the right.

Step 2: If 6 marbles are removed from each pan, the pan balance will remain balanced. One ball will be left in the pan on the left and 2 marbles will be left in the pan on the right.

Thus, 1 ball weighs as much as 2 marbles.

When solving a pan-balance problem in this way, the pans must remain in balance after each step. If you do the same thing to the objects in both pans, then the pans will remain in balance. For example, you might remove the same number of the same kinds of objects from both pans, or you might remove half of the objects from both pans. If the pans were in balance before you removed the objects, they will remain in balance after you remove them.

You can think of pan-balance problems as models for equations. The pan-balance problem in the example above can be expressed by the equation $2B + 6M = B + 8M$.

Check Your Understanding

Write an equation for each pan-balance problem.

1.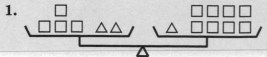

2.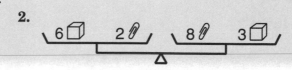

An inequality is a number sentence that contains one of the relation symbols "≠," "<," ">," "≥," or "≤". An inequality that contains one or more variables is an **open sentence**. Any number, which, when it is substituted for the variable, changes the inequality into a true number sentence, is a **solution** of the inequality.

157 158

Example 1:

> The inequality $x + 3 > 10$ is an open sentence.
>
> 100 is a solution of $x + 3 > 10$ because $100 + 3 > 10$ is a true sentence.
>
> 2 is not a solution of $x + 3 > 10$ because $2 + 3 > 10$ is not a true sentence.

Most inequalities have an infinite number of solutions. Therefore, it is usually impossible to list all the solutions. Instead we may *describe* the set of solutions, called the **solution set**, or we may show the solutions on a graph.

Example 2:

> Describe and graph the solution set of $x + 3 > 10$.
>
> Any number that is less than 7 is clearly *not* a solution of $x + 3 > 10$. For example, 6 is not a solution of $x + 3 > 10$, because $6 + 3$ is not greater than 10. The number 7 is not a solution because $7 + 3$ is equal to 10, not greater than 10. However, 7.1 is a solution of $x + 3 > 10$ because $7.1 + 3 > 10$. So is 7.09, 7.01, even 7.000000001. In fact, we can describe the solution set of $x + 3 > 10$ as the set of all numbers greater than 7. The graph of the solution set of $x + 3 > 10$ looks like this:
>
>
>
> The shaded part of the graph tells you that any number greater than 7 is a solution (for example, 7.1, 8, 10.25).
>
> Notice the unshaded circle at 7. This tells you that 7 is not part of the solution set.

Example 3:

> Graph the solution set of $y - 3 ≤ 1$.
>
> Any number less than or equal to 4 is a solution (for example, 4, 2.1, –6).
>
>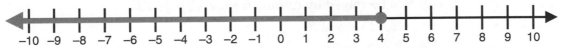
>
> Notice the shaded circle at 4. This tells you that 4 is one of the solutions.

Check Your Understanding

Describe the solution set of the inequalities in Problems 1 and 2. Graph the solution sets in Problems 3 and 4.

1. $b - 5 < 3$ **2.** $7 + f > 7$ **3.** $x ≤ 10$ **4.** $-2 + y ≥ 0$

Distributive Property

The **distributive property** is a number property that combines multiplication with addition, or multiplication with subtraction. The distributive property can be demonstrated by finding the area of a rectangle.

To show the distributive property of multiplication over addition, find the area of Rectangle A in two ways.

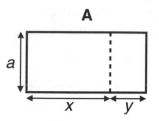

A

1. Multiply the length of the whole rectangle by its width. The length is $x + y$. Therefore the area of the rectangle is $a * (x + y)$.

2. Find the area of each smaller rectangle and add the results. The area of one rectangle is $a * x$. The area of the other rectangle is $a * y$. The sum of the areas is $(a * x) + (a * y)$.

Since both ways give the area of Rectangle A, $a * (x + y) = (a * x) + (a * y)$.

To show the distributive property of multiplication over subtraction find the area of the shaded part of Rectangle B in two ways.

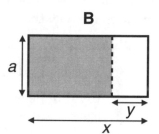

B

1. Multiply the length of the shaded rectangle by its width. The length of the shaded rectangle is $x - y$. So the area is $a * (x - y)$.

2. Subtract the area of the unshaded rectangle from the area of Rectangle B. The area of the unshaded rectangle is $a * y$. The area of Rectangle B is $a * x$. So the area of the shaded rectangle is $(a * x) - (a * y)$.

Since both ways give the area of the unshaded rectangle,

$$a * (x - y) = (a * x) - (a * y).$$

The distributive property can be stated in four different ways.

Multiplication over Addition	**Multiplication over Subtraction**
For any numbers a, x, and y:	For any numbers a, x, and y:
$a * (x + y) = (a * x) + (a * y)$	$a * (x - y) = (a * x) - (a * y)$
$(x + y) * a = (x * a) + (y * a)$	$(x - y) * a = (x * a) - (y * a)$

Example:

> Beth bought 6 greeting cards at $2.25 each and 6 stamps at $0.32 each. What was the total cost?
>
> This problem can be solved by finding $(6 * \$2.25) + (6 * \$0.32)$. By the distributive property, it can also be solved by finding $6 * (\$2.25 + \$0.32)$.
>
> $(6 * \$2.25) + (6 * \$0.32) = 6 * (\$2.25 + \$0.32)$
>
> $\$13.50 + \$1.92 = 6 * \$2.57$, or $\$15.42$
>
> The total cost was $15.42 .

Check Your Understanding

1. Use the distributive property to solve the problems.

   a. $8 * (105 + 30)$ **b.** $(32 - 12) * 6$ **c.** $11 * (90 - 6)$

2. Use a calculator to verify that $1.23 * (456 + 789) = (1.23 * 456) + (1.23 * 789)$.

When an equation has variables and constants on both sides of the equal sign, you can solve the equation by changing it into an equivalent equation with all variables on one side of the equal sign and all constants on the other side.

Example 1: Solve $3y + 10 = 7y - 6$.

Original equation:		$3y + 10 = 7y - 6$	**Explanation**
1. Subtract $3y$	S $3y$	$10 = 4y - 6$	$3y - 3y = 0y$, or 0; $7y - 3y = 4y$
2. Add 6	A 6	$16 = 4y$	$10 + 6 = 16$; $-6 + 6 = 0$
3. Divide by 4	D 4	$4 = y$	$16/4 = 4$; $4y/4 = 1y$, or y

Check: Substitute the solution, 4, for y in the original equation:

$$3 * 4 + 10 = 7 * 4 - 6$$
$$12 + 10 = 28 - 6$$
$$22 = 22$$

If an equation contains terms that are in parentheses or if there is more than one variable or constant term on either side of the equal sign, you must **simplify** the equation before you can solve it. To simplify an equation, do the following:

1. If an equation has parentheses, use the distributive property or other properties to write an equivalent equation without parentheses.
2. If an equation has two or more like terms, or more than one constant, on one side of the equal sign, combine the like terms and the constants.

Example 2: Solve $5(b + 3) - 3b + 5 = 4(b - 1)$.

Original equation:		$5(b + 3) - 3b + 5 = 4(b - 1)$	**Explanation**
Step 1: Simplify the equation.			
1. Use the distributive property to remove the parentheses.		$5b + 15 - 3b + 5 = 4b - 4$	$[5(b + 3) = 5b + 15;$ $4(b - 1) = 4b - 4]$
2. Combine like terms.		$2b + 20 = 4b - 4$	$[5b - 3b = 2b; 15 + 5 = 20]$

Step 2: Solve the simplified equation.		$2b + 20 = 4b - 4$	**Explanation**
1. Subtract $2b$	S $2b$	$20 = 2b - 4$	$[2b - 2b = 0; 4b - 2b = 2b]$
2. Add 4	A 4	$24 = 2b$	$[20 + 4 = 24; -4 + 4 = 0]$
3. Divide by 2	D 2	$12 = b$	$[24/2 = 12; 2b/2 = b]$

Check Your Understanding

1. Check that 12 is the solution of the equation in Example 2.

Solve.

2.a. $5x - 7 = 1 + 3x$ **b.** $5(s + 12) = 10(3 - s)$

Surveys and Sampling

Much of the information used to make decisions today comes from **surveys**. Manufacturers survey consumers to find out what products to make or what to change in an existing product. Television stations survey viewers to learn what programs are popular. Politicians, newspapers, and magazines survey people to obtain opinions on issues and candidates.

Methods for Collecting Data

Surveys are used to gather **data** (information). Data can be collected through:

- face-to-face interviews
- telephone interviews
- self-administered questionnaires that are returned by mail
- group discussions (often called focus groups)

Some surveys do not gather information about human beings, so that data are collected in other ways than through interviews and questionnaires. For example:

- Traffic and highway engineers sometimes make videotapes of vehicles and drivers along a street or highway. They use the videotape data to analyze vehicle speeds, traffic volume, and driving patterns.
- A bird survey is conducted during the first two weeks in June in the Chicago vicinity. Bird watchers list the different bird species they see, and the number of each species. The lists are combined to create a final data set.

Sampling

A **sample** is a relatively small part of a group chosen to represent the larger group being studied. The larger group is called the **population**. It is usually impossible to collect data from every member of the population; therefore, a representative sample of the population is surveyed.

Large samples give more precise estimates of the population characteristics than small samples. For example, if you want to estimate the percentage of adults who intend to vote for Candidate X, a sample of 100 persons will provide a more precise estimate than a sample of 10.

It is usually important that the sample be a **random sample**. A random sample is a sample taken from a population in a way that gives all members of the population the same chance of being selected. In the above example, a sample of 100 of Candidate X's best friends will not be a random sample, because people who do not know Candidate X have no chance of being selected. A sample of Candidate X's best friends will not furnish trustworthy estimates of the entire population's voting intentions, because such a sample will not be representative of the entire population.

Throughout your study of mathematics, you have had many opportunities for collecting **data**. Once the data have been collected, it helps to organize them to make them easier to understand. **Line plots** and **tally charts** are two methods of organizing data.

Example:

Mr. Jackson's class made the following scores on a 20-word spelling test. Make a line plot and a tally chart to show the following data:

20 15 18 17 20 12 15 17 19 18 20 16 16
17 14 15 19 18 18 15 10 20 19 18 15 18

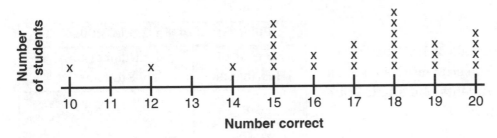

Scores on a 20-Word Spelling Test

Line Plot

In the line plot, there are 5 X's above 15. In the tally chart, there are 5 tallies to the right of 15. These are two ways to show that 5 students spelled 15 words correctly.

When the data are organized in a line plot or tally chart, it is easy to see how many students had each score on the test (for example, 4 students had a perfect score), which scores came up most often (18 correct), which came up least often (10, 12, and 14 correct), and which scores did not occur at all (0–9, 11, and 13 correct).

Scores on a 20-Word Spelling Test

Number correct	Number of Students
10	/
11	
12	/
13	
14	/
15	////
16	//
17	///
18	//// /
19	///
20	////

Tally Chart

Check Your Understanding

Here are the numbers of hits made by 12 players in a baseball game.

0 2 4 1 0 2 1 3 2 1 0 2

Organize the data in: **1.** A tally chart.   **2.** A line plot.

Organizing Data (continued)

Simple tally charts and line plots can be unwieldy when the data are spread over a wide range of numbers. In such cases, we can make tally charts in which the results are grouped. Or we may use another method for organizing data, called a **stem-and-leaf plot**.

Example:

> For a science project, the students in the 6th grade took each other's pulses (the number of heartbeats per minute). These were the results:
>
> 75 86 108 94 75 88 86 99 78 86 90 94 112 70 94
> 78 75 90 102 65 94 92 72 90 86 102 78 88 75 72
> 82 70 94 85 88 105 86 78

Tally Chart of Grouped Data

The data have been sorted in intervals of 10. The chart shows that the great majority of the students had a pulse rate between 70 and 100; more students had a pulse rate in the 70's than in any other interval.

Pulse Rates of 6th Grade Students	
Number of Heartbeats	Number of Students
60–69	/
70–79	//// //// //
80–89	//// ////
90–99	//// ////
100–109	////
110–119	/

Stem-and-Leaf Plot

In a stem-and-leaf plot, the digit or digits in the first column (the **stem**) are combined with a single digit in the second column (the **leaf**) to form a numeral. Therefore, each row has as many entries as there are digits in the second column. For example, the row with 9 in the first column has ten entries: 94, 99, 90, 94, 94, 90, 94, 92, 90, and 94.

Pulse Rates of 6th Grade Students	
Stems (100's and 10's)	Leaves (1's)
6	5
7	5 5 8 0 8 5 2 8 5 2 0 8
8	6 8 6 6 6 8 2 5 8 6
9	4 9 0 4 4 0 4 2 0 4
10	8 2 2 5
11	2

Check Your Understanding

In each of the first 12 games of the 1996 NBA Playoffs, Michael Jordan scored the following number of points: 35 29 26 44 28 46 27 35 21 35 17 45. Show these data in:

1. A tally chart of grouped data.   **2.** A stem-and-leaf plot.

The **landmarks** for a set of data are features used to interpret the data.

- The **minimum** is the smallest value.
- The **maximum** is the largest value.
- The **range** is the difference between the maximum and minimum.
- The **mode** is the value (or values) that occurs most often.
- The **median** is the middle value.

Example:

Here is a record of one week's absences at Medgar Evers School.

Monday	Tuesday	Wednesday	Thursday	Friday
27	19	12	16	16

Minimum (lowest) number: 12   Maximum (highest) number: 27

Range of numbers: 27 − 12 = 15   Mode (most frequent number): 16

To find the median (middle value), list the numbers in sequential order. Then find the middle number.

12 16 |16| 19 27

median

Example:

The **line plot** shows students' scores on a 20-word spelling test.

Scores on a 20-Word Spelling Test

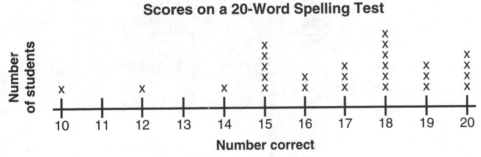

Minimum: 10   Maximum: 20   Range: 20 − 10 = 10   Mode: 18

10 12 14 15 15 15 15 15 16 16 17 17 |17 18| 18 18 18 18 18 19 19 19 20 20 20 20

middle scores

Since there are two middle scores, 17 and 18, the median is 17.5—the number halfway between 17 and 18.

Check Your Understanding

Twelve players played in a baseball game. They made the following number of hits:

0 2 4 1 0 2 1 3 2 1 0 2

Find the minimum, maximum, range, mode, and median for this set of data.

The Mean (Average)

The mean of a set of numbers is often called the *average*. To find the **mean**: First, add the numbers; then divide the sum by the number of addends.

Example:

> On the 4 days of their vacation, Jay's family drove 200, 100, 140, and 260 miles. What is the mean number of miles they drove per day?
>
> Step 1: Add the numbers: $200 + 100 + 140 + 260 = 700$.
>
> Step 2: Divide by the number of addends: $700/4 = 175$.
>
> The mean is 175 miles, so they drove an average of 175 miles per day.
>
> If you are using a calculator, key in: 200 [+] 100 [+] 140 [+] 260 [+] [÷] 4 [=].

When calculating the mean of a large set of numbers, it often helps to first organize the data in a tally chart or line plot. Then use the parentheses keys on the calculator to help you find the sum of the numbers.

Example:

The students in Mrs. Dillard's class measured each other's heights, in inches, and recorded these measurements:

51	58	49	56	61	49	52	58
60	52	55	56	58	54	55	63
56	53	52	50	58	54	56	52
60	56	55	50				

Then they organized the measurements in a tally chart (the first two columns on the right). On their calculators, they multiplied each height by the number of students of that height, and kept a running total (the last two columns on the right). Finally, they divided the final total by the number of students.

The mean, rounded to the nearest inch, is 55 inches.

Height (inches)	Number of Students	Key in:	Calculator Display
49	//	[(] 2 [×] 49 [)] [+]	98
50	//	[(] 2 [×] 50 [)] [+]	198
51	/	51 [+]	249
52	////	[(] 4 [×] 52 [)] [+]	457
53	/	53 [+]	510
54	//	[(] 2 [×] 54 [)] [+]	618
55	///	[(] 3 [×] 55 [)] [+]	783
56	~~////~~	[(] 5 [×] 56 [)] [+]	1063
57			
58	////	[(] 4 [×] 58 [)] [+]	1295
59			
60	//	[(] 2 [×] 60 [)] [+]	1415
61	/	61 [+]	1476
62			
63	/	63 [+]	1539
Total	28	[÷] 28 [=]	54.96428571

Check Your Understanding

According to the National Weather Service, the following were the highest temperatures recorded in the U.S. during the first half of January, 1996.

Date	1	2	3	4	5	6	7	8	9	10	11	12	13	14	15
Temperature (°F)	85	86	83	85	80	80	90	84	89	85	90	87	83	87	87

Use your calculator to find the mean temperature.

Bar graphs are often used to display numerical information in a way that makes it easy to show comparison.

A bar graph should have a title that describes the displayed information. Each bar should have a label. The scale should have a unit. Also, whenever possible, it should give the source of the information.

Bar graphs can be constructed so that the bars are either horizontal or vertical.

Example:

This is an example of a **vertical bar graph**. The purpose of the graph is to compare the amounts of several kinds of foods that are wasted in the average U.S. household. It is easy to see that the amount of bakery goods wasted was about 3 times as great as the amount of fast food, that only slightly more fast food was wasted than red meat, and that the amount of wasted fruit was a little over half of the amount of wasted vegetables.

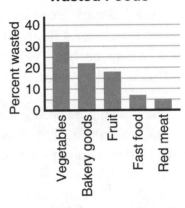

Wasted Foods

Source: The Garbage Product

Example:

This is an example of a **horizontal bar graph**. The purpose of the graph is to compare the fat content of several kinds of food.

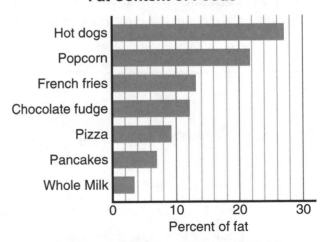

Fat Content of Foods

Source: The New York Public Library Desk Reference

Check Your Understanding

The table at the right shows the amount of money spent by schools on technology, such as computers, computer software, and supplies, during three school years. Make a bar graph to show this information.

Spending on School Technology	
School Year	Expenditure (in billions of $)
1991–92	2.1
1993–94	2.8
1995–96	4.0

Source: Quality Education Data

Step Graphs

Step graphs are used to describe situations in which changes in values are not gradual but occur in "jumps."

Example:

> The step graph at the right shows the cost of renting a bicycle from B & H Rentals.
>
> According to the graph, it costs $10 to rent a bike for 1 hour or less and $2.50 for each additional half-hour or fraction thereof. For example, it costs $10, whether you rent a bike for $\frac{1}{2}$ hour, 45 minutes, or 1 hour. It costs $12.50, whether you rent a bike for $1\frac{1}{2}$ hours or just 1 hour and 1 minute.

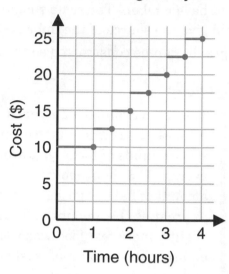

Cost of Renting a Bicycle

Note the dot at the end of the segment for the first hour. It indicates that the cost is $10 for 1 hour. There is no dot at the beginning of the segment for the second hour. This indicates that $12.50 is not the cost for 1 hour. The other dots in the graph are interpreted in the same way.

Telephone and parking-lot rates are other examples of situations that can be shown by step graphs. Such rates do not change gradually over time but change at the end of intervals of time, such as minutes or hours.

Check Your Understanding

The following step graph shows the cost of taking a cab for various distances.

1. What is the cost of taking a cab a distance of:

   a. $\frac{1}{2}$ mile?   **b.** 1.2 miles?   **c.** 2 miles?
   d. 5 miles?   **e.** 3.5 miles?

2. What is the cost of taking a cab for a distance of 1 mile or less? For each additional mile or fraction of a mile?

Cost of Taking a Cab

Line graphs are often used to display information that shows trends.

A line graph should always have a title that describes the displayed information. Also, whenever possible, it should give the source of the information.

Line graphs have a horizontal and a vertical scale, or axis (plural: **axes**). These should be labeled to show what is being measured and what the units of measure are.

When looking at a line graph, try to determine the purpose of the graph and what conclusions you can draw from the graph.

Example:

This is an example of a **broken-line graph**. The horizontal axis is labeled in 10-year intervals. The labels on the vertical axis show the median number of years of school completed. The purpose of the graph is to show the change in the level of education of a segment of the U.S. population. By studying the graph, you can see very quickly that the median number of years of school completed has been increasing with time but that this trend slowed down considerably between 1980 and 1990.

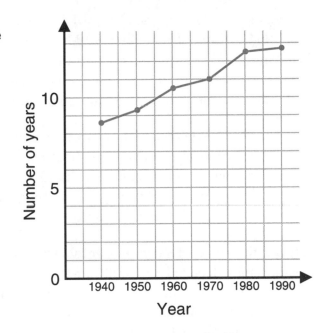

Median Number of Years of School Completed by People, Age 25 or Over, in the United States

Source: 1995 Digest of Education

Check Your Understanding

The following table shows the average precipitation for Seattle, Washington. Make a line graph to show this information.

Average Precipitation for Seattle, Washington						
Months	Jan/Feb	Mar/Apr	May/Jun	Jul/Aug	Sep/Oct	Nov/Dec
Precipitation (in)	5.1	3.0	1.5	1.0	2.7	5.6

Source: The New York Public Library Desk Reference

History and Uses of Spreadsheets

Everyday Rentals-Debit Statement for May 1964

Company	Type	Invoice #	Invoice Amount	Amount Paid	Balance Due
Electric	Utility	2704-3364	342.12	100.00	242.12
Gas	Utility	44506-309	129.43	50.00	79.43
Phone	Utility	989-2209	78.56	78.56	0.00
Water	Utility	554-2-1018	13.12		13.12
NW Bank	Mortgage	May 1964	1264.00	1264.00	0.00
Waste Rem.	Garbage	387-219	23.00		23.00
NW Lumber	Supplies	E-318	239.47	50.00	189.47
Totals			2089.70	1542.56	547.14

Above is a copy of a financial record for Everyday Rentals Corporation for May 1964. Often a financial record had more columns of figures than would fit on one sheet of paper, so accountants taped several sheets together. They folded the sheets for storage and spread them out to read or make entries. Such sheets came to be called **spreadsheets.**

Note that the "Balance Due" **column** and the "Totals" **row** are calculated from other numbers in the spreadsheet. Before they had computers, accountants wrote spreadsheets by hand. If an accountant changed a number in one row or column, several other numbers would have to be erased, recalculated, and re-entered.

For example, when Everyday Rentals Corporation pays the $23.00 owed to Waste Removal, the accountant must enter that amount in the "Amount Paid" column. That means the total of the "Amount Paid" column must be changed as well. That's not all—making a payment changes the amount in the "Balance Due" column and the total of the "Balance Due" column. One entry requires three other changes to **update** (revise) the spreadsheet.

When personal computers were developed, spreadsheet programs were among the first applications. Spreadsheet programs save time by making changes automatically. Suppose the record at the top of this page was on a computer spreadsheet. When the accountant enters the payment of $23.00, the computer automatically recalculates all of the numbers that are affected by that payment.

In mathematics and science, computer spreadsheets are used to store large amounts of data and to perform complicated calculations. People use spreadsheets at home to keep track of budgets, payments, and taxes.

Spreadsheets and Computers

A **spreadsheet program** enables you to use a computer to evaluate formulas quickly and efficiently. On a computer screen, a spreadsheet looks like a table. Each **cell** in the table has an **address**, made up of a letter and a number. The letter identifies the column and the number identifies the row in which the cell is found. For example, cell B3 is in column B and row 3.

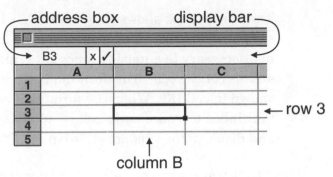

To enter information in a cell, you can use a computer mouse to click on the cell; the address of the cell will appear in the **address box**. Then you type the information you want to enter in the cell; the information will appear in the **display bar**.

There are three kinds of information that may be entered in a spreadsheet.

- **Labels** (may consist of words, numbers, or both) These are used to display information about the spreadsheet, such as the title of the spreadsheet or headings for columns and rows. Numbers in labels are never used in calculations. When a label is entered from the keyboard, it is stored in its address and it is shown in its cell on the screen.

- **Numbers** (that are not included in labels) These are used in calculations. When a number is entered from the keyboard, it is stored in its address and it appears in its cell on the screen.

- **Formulas** These tell the computer what calculations to make on the numbers in other cells. When a formula is entered from the keyboard, it is stored in its address but it is *not* shown in its cell on the screen. Instead, a number is shown in the cell. This number is the result of applying the formula to numbers in other cells.

Example:

Study the spreadsheet at the right.

All the entries in row 1 and in column A are labels. The entries in cells B3 through B6 and cells C3 through C6 are numbers that are not labels. They have been entered from the keyboard and are used in calculations. Cells D3 through D10 also display numbers, but they have not been entered from the keyboard. Instead, a formula was entered in each of these cells, and the formulas were used by the computer program to calculate the numbers that appear in column D. The numbers in column D are the results of calculations.

	Supplies ($$)		
D3 x ✓ =B3*C3			
	A	B	C	D
1	item name	unit price	quantity	totals
2				
3	pencils	0.29	6	1.74
4	graph paper	1.19	2	2.38
5	ruler	0.50	1	0.50
6	book	5.95	1	5.95
7				
8	Subtotal			10.57
9	tax 7%			.74
10	Total			$11.31

The address box shows that cell D3 has been selected; the display bar shows "= B3 * C3." This stands for the formula D3 = B3 * C3. It is not necessary to enter D3, since D3 is already identified as the address of the cell. This formula is stored in the computer; it is not shown in cell D3. When the formula is entered, the program multiplies the number in cell B3 (0.29) by the number in cell C3 (6) and displays the product (1.74) in cell D3.

Suppose that you clicked on cell C3 and changed the 6 to an 8. The entry in cell D3 would change automatically to 2.32 (= 8 * 0.29). At the same time, the entries in cells D8, D9, and D10 would also change. The entry in cell D8 is the result of a calculation involving the entry in cell D3; the entry in cell D8 is used to calculate the entry in cell D9; and the entry in cell D9 is used to calculate the entry in cell D10.

Check Your Understanding

The following spreadsheet gives budget information for a class picnic.

	A	B	C	D
		Class Picnic ($$)		
1		budget for class picnic		
2				
3	quantity	food items	unit price	cost
4	6	packages of hamburgers	2.79	16.74
5	5	packages of hamburger buns	1.29	6.45
6	3	bags of potato chips	3.12	9.36
7	3	quarts of macaroni salad	4.50	13.50
8	4	bottles of soft drinks	1.69	6.76
9			subtotal	52.81
10			8% tax	4.23
11			total	57.04

Use the spreadsheet to answer the following questions.

1. What kind of information is shown in column B?

2. What information is shown in cell C7?

3. Which cell shows the title of the spreadsheet?

4. What information is shown in cell A5?

5. Which occupied cells do not hold labels or formulas?

6. Which column holds formulas?

A **probability** is a number from 0 to 1 that indicates the likelihood that something will happen. The closer a probability is to 1, the more likely is it that an event will happen.

- A probability of 0 means that it is impossible for an event to happen. For example, the probability that you will live to the age of 150 is 0.
- A probability of 1 means that an event is certain to occur. For example, the probability that the sun will rise tomorrow is 1.
- A probability of $\frac{1}{2}$ means that in the long run, an event can be expected to occur about 1 in 2 times (half of the time, 50% of the time). The probability that a tossed coin will land heads is $\frac{1}{2}$; we often say that the coin has a "50-50 chance" of landing heads.

Probabilities can be expressed with fractions, percents, or decimals.

Example:

The weather bureau predicts that there is an 80% chance of snow today, and a 2 in 3 chance of snow tomorrow. On which day is it more likely to snow?

A 2 in 3 chance means that the probability is $\frac{2}{3}$ (or 0.6 or $66\frac{2}{3}$%). A probability of 80% can be written as 0.8, $\frac{80}{100}$, or $\frac{4}{5}$. Since 0.8 is greater than 0.6, it is more likely to snow today than tomorrow.

Calculating a Probability

Four common ways for determining probabilities are illustrated below.

Make a Guess	**Conduct an Experiment**

John guesses that he has a 90% chance (a 9 in 10 chance) of returning home by 9 o'clock.	Kathleen throws 100 tacks: 60 land point up and 40 land point down. The chance of a tack landing point up is $\frac{60}{100}$, or 60%.
Use a Data Table	**Assume Equally Likely Outcomes**
Hits 48 Walks 11 Outs 41 ——— Total 100 Art got 48 hits in his last 100 times at bat. He estimates the probability that he will get a hit the next time at bat is $\frac{48}{100}$, or 48%.	A die has 6 faces. Each face has the same chance of coming up. The probability of rolling a 4 is $\frac{1}{6}$. The probability of rolling a 4 or a 5 is double this—$\frac{2}{6}$, or $\frac{1}{3}$.

Tree Diagrams

The diagram at the right represents a maze. Without retracing their steps, people walk through the maze, taking paths at random without any pattern or preference. Some people end up in Room A. Some end up in Room B.

Diagram 1 represents this maze. It looks like an upside-down tree.

Tree diagrams can help in analyzing probability situations. Tree diagrams are especially useful when some events follow, or are affected by, other events. In a tree diagram, the branches represent different paths, possibilities, or cases.

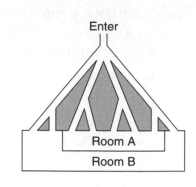

Tree diagrams can help answer questions such as the following about the maze:

- If 40 people walk through the maze, how many can be expected to end up in Room A? In Room B?

- What is the probability of ending up in Room A? In Room B?

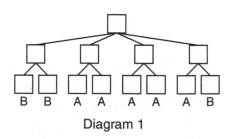

Diagram 1

Here is one way to use a tree diagram to analyze a maze.

1. In the top box of the tree diagram, record the number of people who reach the first intersection where the path divides. Suppose there are 40 people.

2. The path divides. Since there is an equal chance of selecting any one of the next paths, an equal number of people will select each path. Write this number in each box in the second row of boxes. In the example, the number is one-fourth of 40, or 10. See Diagram 2.

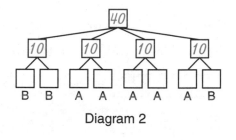

Diagram 2

3. Each path divides at the next intersection. Again, an equal number of people will select each of the next paths. Write the appropriate number in the next set of boxes. In the example, each path divides into two paths. One-half of the people will follow one path, and one-half will follow the other. One-half of 10 is 5. See Diagram 3.

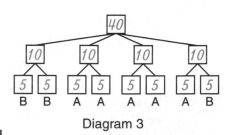

Diagram 3

Continue in this way until all the exits have been reached. Then add to find how many people reach each room. In the example, five boxes are labeled A, representing exits into Room A. Add the numbers in these boxes to find out how many of the 40 people end up in Room A (25). Three boxes are labeled B, representing exits into Room B. Add the numbers in these boxes to find out how many people end up in Room B (15).

A somewhat different kind of tree diagram can help in finding probabilities.

The tree diagram at the right represents the maze on the preceding page. The branching paths are shown, but there are no boxes.

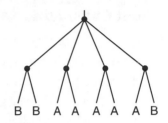

Here is one way to use this kind of tree diagram to calculate probabilities.

1. At the first place where the path divides, there is an equal chance of selecting any one of the paths. Write this probability next to each path.

   In the example, there are four paths, so the probability of taking any one path is $\frac{1}{4}$.

2. Each of those paths divides at the next intersection. Again, an equal number of people will select each of the next paths. Write the appropriate probability next to each path.

   In the example, each path divides into two paths, so the probability of taking any one path is $\frac{1}{2}$. See Diagram 4.

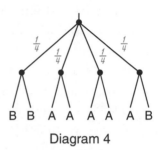

Diagram 4

3. Continue to write probabilities on the diagram until all the exits have been reached. To find the probability of reaching a particular exit, multiply the probabilities of taking the paths leading to it.

   In the example, for any exit, the probability of taking the first path to it is $\frac{1}{4}$. The probability of the next path is $\frac{1}{2}$. The probability of reaching a particular exit is $\frac{1}{2}$ of $\frac{1}{4}$ which is $\frac{1}{8}$. See Diagram 5.

4. Add to find the probability of entering each room.

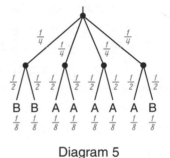

Diagram 5

In the example, there are five exits to Room A, each with a probability of $\frac{1}{8}$. So the probability of entering Room A is $\frac{1}{8} + \frac{1}{8} + \frac{1}{8} + \frac{1}{8} + \frac{1}{8}$, or $\frac{5}{8}$. There are three exits to Room B, each with a probability of $\frac{1}{8}$. So the probability of entering Room B is $\frac{1}{8} + \frac{1}{8} + \frac{1}{8}$, or $\frac{3}{8}$. Note that the sum of all the final probabilities is 1 $\left(\frac{5}{8} + \frac{3}{8}\right)$.

Check Your Understanding

The map shows the roads from the town of Alpha. Suppose you start in Alpha and drive south. When the road divides, you choose the next road at random.

What is the probability of getting to Cisco? To Ceeville? To Center? To Cedar? Draw a tree diagram to help you.

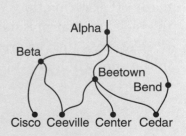

About Calculators

Throughout your study of mathematics you have used a variety of tools such as counters, rulers, tape measures, pattern blocks, compasses, protractors, the Percent Circle, and the shapes on the Geometry Template. Since kindergarten and first grade you have also used another tool, the calculator. In those earlier grades you used it to help you learn to count; now you use it for calculations with whole numbers, fractions, decimals, and percents.

A calculator can help you perform calculations quickly and accurately, but you must know when and how to use it. You must decide when it is best to solve a problem by estimating, by calculating mentally, by using paper and pencil, or by using a calculator. Even when you do choose to use a calculator, estimation should be part of your work. Remember to ask yourself if the number in the display is a possible answer. An estimate will tell you "about how much" the answer should be as a check against keying in a wrong number or operation.

All calculators cannot perform the same tasks (functions). Some calculators, called 4-function calculators, do little more than add, subtract, multiply, and divide whole numbers and decimals. Some calculators also perform operations with fractions. Still more sophisticated calculators, called scientific calculators, display numbers in scientific notation and also have special keys to do calculations you will not be asked to do until you take mathematics courses in high school.

Even calculators that can perform the same functions do not necessarily do them in the same way. Rather than try to describe how various calculators work, we have chosen one fairly typical scientific calculator to which we refer throughout this book. If your calculator works differently, you can refer to the directions that come with your calculator, or ask your teacher for help. Some calculators also come with a small card that you could use for a quick reference.

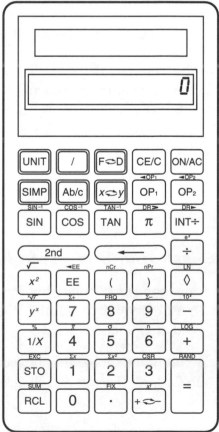

Shown here is a typical calculator that has the keys that will be referred to in this section.

A reminder: Just as carpenters, dentists, engineers, or people in many other occupations must take care of their tools if they expect the tools to perform reliably, you must take care of your calculator. Carelessness such as dropping it or, if it is solar-powered, leaving it in the sun, will leave it less reliable or even break it.

Keying In

There are different types of keys on scientific calculators. You are familiar with the number keys and the basic operation keys that enable you to do simple arithmetic. You may also have worked with some of the function keys such as those that enable you to enter fractions and mixed numbers, change fractions to decimals, store numbers in memory, and so on.

Some calculators can perform more tasks (functions) than the number of keys available. On such calculators many keys have two functions. The second function may be displayed above a key. To activate the second function of a key you must first press a key that might be labeled [2nd] (or [SHIFT] or [INV]). Read the directions that come with your calculator.

← Second function

Pressing a key on a calculator is called **keying in** or **entering**. When a key is pressed, the action is sensed and the calculator "remembers" the instructions that the key is programmed to do. It remembers until the instruction is carried out. Most calculators also have a stored **memory** where a value is kept for later use while other functions are performed.

189

A set of instructions for performing a calculation is called a **key sequence**. In this book, all keys, except keys for numbers, are shown with brackets such as [+], [=], and so on.

Correcting and Clearing   ([ON/AC], [CE/C], and [←])

Press [ON/AC] to turn on the calculator. This key clears any numbers and operations that have been entered. The display will show 0. This key also clears the storage memory and any constants.

188

When the [CE/C] key is pressed once, the last number entered is cleared.

Examples:

Key in 689. Press [CE/C] once. The display will show 0.

Key in 56 [+] 69. Press [CE/C] once. Then key in 24 [=]. The display will show 80.

The calculator "remembers" 56 and the operation add but "forgets" 69.

When [CE/C] is pressed twice, all numbers and operations that have been entered are cleared.

Example:

Key in 56 [+] 69 and press [CE/C] twice. The display will show 0. Then key in 24 [=]. The display will show 24.

The calculator "forgets" both numbers and the operation of addition.

Many calculators also have a backspace key [←] that allows you to clear only the last digit of a large number you are entering. With this key you do not need to reenter all the digits.

Example:

Key in 12345. Press [←]. The display will show 1234.

Displays and Error Indicators

Many calculators can display either 8 or 10 digits and the – sign to show negative numbers. Enter the digits 1, 2, 3, and so on until the display is full. A calculator with a 10-digit display will show 1234567890.

How many digits will your calculator display to the right of the decimal point? One way to find out is to key in 0 [.] and then 1, 2, 3, and so on until the display is full. A calculator with a 10-digit display will show 0.123456789.

Displays and Rounded Decimals: Calculators round decimals with too many places for a display in different ways. To find out what your calculator does, key in 2 [÷] 3 [=]. (Even though *Everyday Mathematics* often uses a slash, (/), to show division, the division key on calculators is labeled [÷].)

The actual quotient is 0.666666666 . . ., with the digit 6 repeating. No display can show all the digits. Some calculators are programmed to round, others **truncate,** that is, the digits that do not fit in the display are dropped. If the last digit your calculator displays is a 7, your calculator rounds to the nearest last place it can show. If the last digit displayed is a 6, your calculator truncates the quotient when the display is full.

Even when a calculator truncates or rounds numbers, it remembers the digits that are not displayed. Key in: 2 [÷] 3 [=] [×] 3. The display will show 2.

Error Indicators: Calculators that only perform the basic operations with whole numbers and fractions usually display an error message when the result of a calculation is too large for the display.

When the result of a calculation is too large for the display on a scientific calculator, the display will show the result in scientific notation.

> *Example:*
>
> | Key in: 8888888888 [×] 12 [=]
> | Display: 1.06667 11
> | This represents $1.06667 * 10^{11}$ written in scientific notation.

Some calculators display a variety of error messages to identify when you press keys that tell the calculator to do something it cannot do. For example: a display may show Error OFL (for overflow) to indicate the calculator's capacity has been exceeded; or Error Ari to indicate a calculation such as division by zero was attempted.

Display Messages: The display may also show other symbols which act as messages or reminders of what operation or function is being performed. For example: SIMP, N/D→ n/d may indicate that the fraction in the display can be simplified.

Add, Subtract, Multiply, and Divide ([+], [–], [×], [÷], [.], [=])

The basic arithmetic operations are familiar to you from earlier grades.

Key	Function	Example	Key in	Display
[+]	Adds the number in the display to the next number entered.	$47 + 68$ $4.7 + 6.8$ $\frac{3}{8} + \frac{1}{4}$	4 7 [+] 6 8 [=] 4 [.] 7 [+] 6 [.] 8 [=] 3 [/] 8 [+] 1 [/] 4 [=]	115 11.5 5/8
[–]	Subtracts the next number entered from the number in the display.	$123 - 59$ $12.3 - 5.9$ $\frac{7}{8} - \frac{1}{3}$	1 2 3 [–] 5 9 [=] 1 2 [.] 3 [–] 5 [.] 9 [=] 7 [/] 8 [–] 1 [/] 3 [=]	64 6.4 13/24
[×]	Multiplies the number in the display by the next number entered.	$35 * 74$ $3.5 * 7.4$ $\frac{4}{5} * \frac{3}{8}$	3 5 [×] 7 4 [=] 3 [.] 5 [×] 7 [.] 4 [=] 4 [/] 5 [×] 3 [/] 8 [=]	2590 25.9 12/40
[÷]	Divides the number in the display by the next number entered.	$249 \div 16$ $24.9 \div 1.6$ $\frac{5}{6} \div \frac{1}{2}$	2 4 9 [÷] 1 6 [=] 2 4 [.] 9 [÷] 1 [.] 6 [=] 5 [/] 6 [÷] 1 [/] 2 [=]	15.5625 15.5625 10/6
[.]	Decimal point	84.7	8 4 [.] 7	84.7
[=]	Completes an arithmetic operation.			

Remainders in Division with Whole Numbers [INT÷]

The result of a division with whole numbers is often not a whole number. Calculators usually display such a result as a decimal (see example above). Many calculators also have another division key [INT÷] that displays the quotient as a whole number part with a remainder.

Example: Find $39 \div 5$.
  Key in: 39 [INT÷] 5 [=]   Display: $\underset{Q}{7} \underset{R}{4}$

Positive and Negative Numbers [+⟳–]

When a number is keyed in, calculators "remember" it as a positive number. To key in a negative number, the change-of-sign key [+⟳–] must be pressed. This key changes the sign of the number in the display. It will change a positive number to a negative number and a negative number to a positive number.

Example: Enter -27.5 on your calculator.
  Key in: 27 [.] 5 [+⟳–]   Display: –27.5

Notice that the [+⟳–] key is pressed *after* the digits of a negative number have been keyed in. This is important when performing operations with negative numbers.

Example: Find $28.5 + (-16.9)$.
  Key in: 28 [.] 5 [+] 16 [.] 9 [+⟳–] [=]   Display: 11.6

Using Calculators

Entering and Simplifying Fractions and Mixed Numbers
[/], [UNIT], [Ab/c], [SIMP], [x⇄y]

Although many calculators perform the same, or similar functions, they do not necessarily use the same keys or the same key sequences. If your calculator does not have the same keys or use the same key sequences as those below, read the directions that come with your calculator.

To enter a fraction, use the [/] key.

> *Example:* Enter $\frac{3}{4}$ in your calculator.
> Key in: 3 [/] 4   Display: 3/4

> *Note:* Many calculators will only allow a certain number of digits in the denominator and will not allow zero as the denominator.

To enter a mixed number, use the [UNIT] key.

> *Example:* Enter $4\frac{2}{3}$ in your calculator.
> Key in: 4 [UNIT] 2 [/] 3   Display: 4u2/3

> The digits to the left of the symbol "u" show the whole-number part of the mixed number. The digits to the right show the fraction part.

To rename a fraction greater than one as a mixed number or a whole number, use the [Ab/c] key.

> *Examples:* Rename $\frac{15}{4}$.
> Key in: 15 [/] 4 [Ab/c]   Display: 3u3/4
>
> Rename $\frac{98}{14}$.
> Key in: 98 [/] 14 [Ab/c]   Display: 7

Sometimes the result of a computation is a mixed number with a fraction part greater than one. The [Ab/c] key may also be used when a mixed number is already in the display.

> *Example:* A display shows 7u5/4 as the result of $5\frac{3}{4} + 2\frac{2}{4}$.
> With 7u5/4 in the display, press [Ab/c].   Display: 8u1/4

The [SIMP] key on a calculator reduces a fraction to simpler terms. If you want the calculator to choose the factor by which the fraction will be simplified, enter the fraction (the fraction may already be in the display as a result of a calculation) and press [SIMP] [=].

It may take several steps for the calculator to display a fraction in simplest terms.

> *Example:* Display $\frac{50}{100}$ in simplest terms.
> Key in: 50 [/] 100 [SIMP] [=]   Display: 25/50
> [SIMP] [=]   5/10
> [SIMP] [=]   1/2

Each time the [SIMP] key was pressed, the calculator divided the numerator and denominator by a common factor. A calculator does not automatically use the greatest common factor. So in the example above, the calculator divided by 2 the first time [SIMP] was pressed and by 5 the next two times.

If you want to know the factor by which the calculator simplified the fraction, press [x⇄y] after the fraction has been simplified. Press [x⇄y] again to return to the fraction.

Example: Key in: 50 [/] 100 [SIMP] [=]   Display: 25/50
  [x⇄y]   2
  [x⇄y]   25/50

Note: Some calculators may also indicate that the fraction is not yet in simplest terms by including a symbol such as N/D → n/d in the display.

You can show the calculator how to simplify the fraction in one step by using the greatest common factor.

31

Example: Key in: 60 [/] 100 [SIMP] 20 [=]   Display: 3/5
  greatest common factor ⌐

Fraction/Decimal/Percent Conversions [F⇄D]

Calculators can be used to convert between fractions, decimals, and percents. Conversions to decimals and percents can be done on calculators that have no special keys. Conversions to fractions and mixed numbers can only be done on calculators that have special keys that allow you to enter fractions and mixed numbers. The [F⇄D] key changes a fraction to its decimal equivalent or a decimal to a fraction. Notice that fractions are not automatically given in simplest form.

46 | 47

Conversion	Example	Without special keys	With special keys	Display
Fraction to decimal	$\frac{3}{5}$	3 [÷] 5 [=]	3 [/] 5 [F⇄D]	0.6
Decimal to fraction	0.32	——	[.] 32 [F⇄D]	32/100
Decimal to percent	0.58	[.] 58 [×] 100 [=]	——	58
Percent to decimal	65%	65 [÷] 100 [=]	——	0.65
Fraction to percent	$\frac{5}{8}$	5 [÷] 8 [×] 100 [=]	5 [/] 8 [F⇄D] [×] 100 [=]	62.5
			or 5 [/] 8 [×] 100 [=] [Ab/c]	62u4/8
Percent to fraction	68%	——	68 [÷] 100 [=] [F⇄D]	68/100

The [x⇄y] key can be used to exchange the display with the previous display.

Example: Key in: 5 [/] 6 [F⇄D]   Display: 0.833333333
  Press: [x⇄y]   Display: 5/6

Using the Percent Key [%]

Convert a percent to a decimal: The percent key on a calculator divides the number in the display by 100 and displays the result as a decimal. Any percent containing a whole number, decimal, or fraction can be expressed as a decimal by entering the number and pressing the [%] key.

Examples	Key in	Display
15%	15 [%]	0.15
62.5%	62 [.] 5 [%]	0.625
0.75%	[.] 75 [%]	0.0075
$\frac{3}{8}$%	3 [/] 8 [%]	0.00375
$\frac{1}{2}$%	1 [/] 2 [%]	0.005

The percent key cannot be used to do the opposite conversion of changing a whole number, decimal, or fraction to a percent.

43

135

Find a percent of a number: Instead of converting a percent to a fraction or decimal, the percent key can be used to find a percent of a number.

> *Example:* Find 25% of 37.
>
> Key in: 25 [%] [×] 37 [=]   Display: 9.25

Add (subtract) a percent of a number to (from) the original number: The percent key makes it easier to add a percent of a number back onto the number (as in finding the total cost after adding on sales tax) or subtract a percent of a number from the number (as in finding the sale price after subtracting a discount).

> *Example:* Find the total cost of a CD priced at $16.88 in a state that charges 6.5% sales tax.
>
> Key in: 16 [.] 88 [+] 6 [.] 5 [%] [=]   Display: 17.9772
> A customer would pay $17.98 for the CD.

> *Example:* A sweater that regularly sells for $48.50 is now on sale for 20% off. What is the sale price?
>
> Key in: 48 [.] 5 [–] 20 [%] [=]   Display: 38.8
> The sweater costs $38.80.

In each key sequence notice that the display just before you press the [=] key shows the amount being added to (tax) or subtracted from (discount) the original amount.

Parentheses and Order of Operations [(], [)]

Most scientific calculators have keys for entering parentheses. The [(] key opens the expression and the [)] key closes the expression. To find the value of a numerical expression containing parentheses, just enter the parentheses where they appear in the expression.

> *Example:*   7.3 − (2.2 + 1.9) = ?
> ▌   Key in: 7 [.] 3 [−] [(] 2 [.] 2 [+] 1 [.] 9 [)] [=]   Display: 3.2

Sometimes expressions are given without all of the multiplication signs. Remember to press the multiplication key.

> *Example:*   96 − 2(19 + 27) = ?
> ▌   Key in: 96 [−] 2 [×] [(] 19 [+] 27 [)] [=]   Display: 4

Check whether your calculator follows all the rules for order of operations. Evaluate the expression 75 + 6 × 9 on your calculator.

161

Key in: 75 [+] 6 [×] 9 [=]

If you have a scientific calculator, the display will show 129. The calculator used the order of operations and multiplied first, then added. A calculator that is not a scientific calculator will probably do the operations as they are keyed in and display 729.

Formulas That Use Pi [π]

The formulas for the perimeter, area, and volume of geometric figures and solids that are circular involve the use of the special ratio pi (π). Many calculators have a special key that allows you to enter the number pi. When you press the key labeled [π], the display will show 3.141592654 (the 10-digit value for pi).

117

When the pi key is used in calculations, you will often need to round the result to an appropriate number of decimal places.

> *Examples:*
>
> ▌ Find the area of a circle with a 4-ft radius.
> Key in: [π] [×] 4 [x^2] [=]   Display: 50.26548246
>
> ▌ Find the circumference of a circle with a 15-ft diameter.
> Key in: [π] [×] 15 [=]   Display: 47.1238898

$$A = \pi * r^2$$

 190

$$C = \pi * d$$

Using Calculators

Repeating an Operation: Constants

Most calculators have a function that allows you to perform an operation with the same number over and over. It is called the **constant function** since an operation is "constantly" being carried out with the same (constant) number.

For example, in the game *Getting to One*, a player's guesses are repeatedly divided by a secret number. In earlier grades, you may have used this function on a calculator to practice counting by a certain number.

There are three steps in using the constant function. The steps are not used in the same order on all calculators. The steps are:

① Define the function (operation and number);
② Enter numbers on which the function is exercised;
③ Press a key to carry out the function on the number.

Many calculators have a special key to enter a constant value. (Some calculators even allow you to enter a second constant.) Below are two examples. Each example shows how the constant function is used on three different calculators. One calculator uses the [=] to activate the constant function, another uses a [K] key, and the third uses [OP₁].

Example: Count by 7, starting at 15.	***Example:*** Add 27 to the numbers 39, 48, 64, and 96.

Key in: 1 5 [+] 7 [=]   Display: 22
  ② ① ③
	Key in: 3 9 [+] 2 7 [=] Display: 66
	  ② ① ③

[=] 29	4 8 [=] 75
[=] 36	6 4 [=] 91
[=] 43	9 6 [=] 123

As long as the [ON/AC] is not pressed, the calculator "remembers" the constant.

Key in: 7 [+] [K] 1 5 [=] Display: 22
  ①   ② ③
	Key in: 2 7 [+] [K] 3 9 [=] Display: 66
	  ① ② ③

[=] 29	4 8 [=] 75
[=] 36	6 4 [=] 91
[=] 43	9 6 [=] 123

Key in: [+] 7 [OP₁] 1 5 [OP₁] Display: 22
  ①   ② ③
	Key in: [+] 2 7 [OP₁] 3 9 [OP₁] Display: 66
	  ① ② ③

[OP₁] 29	4 8 [OP₁] 75
[OP₁] 36	6 4 [OP₁] 91
[OP₁] 43	9 6 [OP₁] 123

To remove the constants, press [ON/AC]. Some calculators will have another key such as [←OP₁].

Using Memory [STO], [SUM], [RCL], [EXC]

The "memory" of a calculator is a place where a number can be stored while the calculator is working with other numbers and operations. The memory is very helpful as it eliminates the need to record and reenter the partial answers that lead to the final answer to a problem.

Here is a brief description of the keys used when working with the memory.

[STO]   stores the number in the display in the memory, *replacing* any number already in the memory.

[SUM]   adds the number in the display to the number in the memory.

[RCL]   recalls the number in memory and shows it in the display.

[EXC]   exchanges the number in memory with the number in the display.

[ON/AC] clears the memory as well as the display. (Pressing [STO] while zero is in the display also clears memory.)

Most calculators will display an M or similar symbol when there is a number other than zero in the memory.

Example:

Andrew went shopping for new clothes. He bought 3 shirts for $9.89 each, 2 pairs of pants for $18.49 each, a pair of shoes for $27.98, and six pairs of socks for $2.59 each. What is the total cost of these items?

Key in:	Display:
[ON/AC]	0
3 [×] 9 [.] 89 [=]	29.67
[STO]	29.67
2 [×] 18 [.] 49 [=]	36.98
[SUM] [RCL]	66.65
[+] 27 [.] 98 [=]	94.63
[STO]	94.63
6 [×] 2 [.] 59 [=]	15.54
[SUM]	15.54
[RCL]	110.17

Instead of pressing [RCL] as the last key, [EXC] could be pressed to exchange the display of 15.54 with the sum in the memory, 110.17.

Numbers can also be subtracted from memory by using the [+⟳–] key. For example, to subtract 35 from memory key in 3 5 [+⟳–] [SUM].

Using Calculators

Squares, Square Roots, and Powers $[x^2]$, $[\sqrt{}\,]$, $[y^x]$

Many calculators have a $[x^2]$ key for squaring a number (multiplying a number by itself). The $[x^2]$ key squares the number in the display. Notice that the $[=]$ key does not need to be pressed when using this key.

> *Example:* Find the area of a square with each side measuring 6 yd.
> Key in: 6 $[x^2]$ Display: 36

$$A = s^2$$

The square root key, $[\sqrt{}\,]$, allows you to "unsquare" a number. In other words, it undoes the result of squaring a number. 16 is the square of 4, so we say 4 is the square root of 16. $4^2 = 16$, so $\sqrt{16} = 4$.

Every positive number has two square roots. They are opposites of each other. The square roots of 16 are +4 and –4 because $4 * 4 = 16$ and $-4 * (-4) = 16$.

Square roots of whole numbers are either whole numbers or decimals that go on infinitely, with no repeating pattern in the digits. The $[\sqrt{}\,]$ key gives the positive square root of the number in the display or estimates its positive square root.

> *Example:* Find the square root of 576.
> Key in: 5 7 6 $[\sqrt{}\,]$ Display: 24

> *Example:* Find the square root of 2.
> Key in: 2 $[\sqrt{}\,]$ Display: 1.414213562

To check if 1.414213562 is a good estimate for $\sqrt{2}$, multiply this decimal by itself.

> Key in: 1 [.] 414213562 $[x^2]$ Display: 1.999999999

On many scientific calculators, if you check the square root of 2 while it is still in the display, the result will be displayed as 2.

> Key in: 2 $[\sqrt{}\,]$ $[x^2]$ Display: 2

The $[y^x]$ enables you to find the power of any number. It is much simpler to use than repeated multiplication.

> *Example:* You fold a piece of paper in half, then in half again, until you have folded it in half eight times. How many sections will the paper be divided into when you unfold the paper?
>
> Each time you fold, the number of sections doubles. So, to find the number of sections, compute $2 * 2 * 2 * 2 * 2 * 2 * 2 * 2$, which is the same as 2^8.
>
> Key in: 2 $[y^x]$ 8 $[=]$ Display: 256
>
> Remember to enter the base number first and the exponent after the $[y^x]$ key.

$$V = B * h$$
$$= s * s * s$$
$$= s^3$$

> *Example:* Find the volume of a cube that measures 32 cm on each side.
> Key in: 32 $[y^x]$ 3 $[=]$ Display: 32768

Finding Reciprocals [1/x]

Two numbers whose product is 1 are called reciprocals of each other. For example, 2 and $\frac{1}{2}$ are reciprocals of each other because $2 * \frac{1}{2} = 1$. All numbers except 0 have reciprocals, no matter how they are written.

For any number x, except 0, x and $\frac{1}{x}$ are reciprocals of each other.

$$x * \frac{1}{x} = 1$$

Finding the reciprocal of a number is the same as finding 1 divided by that number.

The [1/x] key calculates the reciprocal of the number in the display. When using the [1/x] key, the reciprocal is displayed as a decimal, even on calculators with special fraction keys. Calculators that can display fractions will display a reciprocal as a fraction only when the number is entered as a fraction.

Example:

Find the reciprocal of 8.

Key in: 8 [1/x]   Display: 0.125

Key in: 8 [/] 1 [1/x]   Display: 1/8

Example:

Find the reciprocal of $\frac{3}{4}$.

Key in: 3 [/] 4 [1/x]   Display: 4/3

Example:

Find the reciprocal of 12.5.

Key in: 12 [.] 5 [1/x]   Display: 0.08

To display this reciprocal as a fraction, continue the key sequence by keying in:

[F⇄D]   Display: 8/100

[SIMP] [=]   4/50

[SIMP] [=]   2/25

Using Calculators

Using Scientific Notation [EE]

Scientific calculators get their name from their use of scientific notation to display large and small numbers. Numbers with more digits than will fit in the display are automatically shown in scientific notation. Scientific notation is a system in which a number is written as the product of a number and a power of 10. The number must be 1 or greater, but less than 10. In scientific notation, 900,000 is written as $9 * 10^5$.

7

Although some calculators can display raised exponents, most do not show the base (10) and use a space or other notation to name the exponent. They also leave off the multiplication sign. Some ways scientific calculators may display 4,000,000 are shown at the right. In each case the calculator is displaying the number $4 * 10^6$.

4	06
4.	06
4	E06
4	E+06
4	EE06

To enter numbers too large or too small for the display, first convert the numbers to scientific notation.

> *Examples:* Enter 596 billion in your calculator in scientific notation.
> 596,000,000,000 is written as $5.96 * 10^{11}$
> Key in: 5 [.] 96 [EE] 11   Display: 5.96   11
>
> Enter 0.0000000000869 in your calculator in scientific notation.
> 0.0000000000869 is written as $8.69 * 10^{-11}$
> Key in: 8 [.] 69 [EE] 11 [+⇆−]   Display: 8.69   −11

For numbers with 10 digits or less, the calculator will convert to scientific notation.

> *Examples:* 400,000   Key in: 400000 [=] [EE]   Display: 4   05
> 1234567890   Key in: 1234567890 [=] [EE]   Display: 1.234567   09

Notice that the number of decimal places available in scientific notation display is limited.

Numbers displayed in scientific notation can be converted back to standard notation by pressing the [← EE]. This key will only work if the standard notation fits in the display.

> *Examples:* Display: 4.32   06   Press: [← EE]   Display: 4320000
> Display: 4.32   12   Press: [← EE]   Display: 4.32   12

Sometimes the results of calculations are too large for the display. Most scientific calculators will display the results in scientific notation.

> *Example:* Find 6500 * 4,000,000.
> Key in: 6500 [×] 4000000 [=]   Display: 2.6   10
> 6500 * 4,000,000 = 26,000,000,000

50 51

Calculations can be done with numbers written in scientific notation.

> *Example:* Find $4.8 * 10^7 + 1.4 * 10^6$.
> Key in: 4 [.] 8 [EE] 7 [+] 1 [.] 4 [EE] 6 [=]   Display: 4.94   07

Standard Notation
48000000
+ 1400000
‾‾‾‾‾‾‾‾‾
49400000

Generating Random Numbers   [RAND]

A random number is a number that has the same chance of appearing as any other number. No pattern is followed; the next number to appear is completely unpredictable. Random numbers are important in mathematics, in scientific research, and in daily life.

For example, when testing a new medicine, researchers usually give some subjects the medicine and some subjects a neutral substance. Random numbers are used to ensure that there is no bias in the selection of the subjects who will receive the medicine.

States that conduct lotteries must guarantee that the winning numbers are generated "at random" and do not follow a pattern.

To generate random numbers with a calculator, the smallest possible number and the largest possible numbers are used in the key sequence.

Example: Use your calculator to "roll a die."
Key in: 1 [RAND] 6 [=]

The calculator will randomly select 1, 2, 3, 4, 5, or 6. Each of the six numbers has the same chance of appearing in the display. The number that appears is completely unpredictable.

Example: Use your calculator to select a random day in the month of September.
Key in: 1 [RAND] 30 [=]

The calculator will randomly select 1, 2, 3, ..., 28, 29, or 30. Each of the 30 days has the same chance of appearing in the display.

Example: Use your calculator to select a random age of a teenage person.
Key in: 13 [RAND] 19 [=]

The calculator will randomly select 13, 14, 15, 16, 17, 18, or 19. Each of the ages has the same chance of appearing in the display.

Some calculators allow you to use the constant function with the random number generator. In the key sequence below, the [STO] key stores the first number in the range of numbers so that [RAND] 6 is the constant function.

Example: Use your calculator to find "rolls of a die" five times.
Key in: [STO] 1 [RAND] 6 [OP$_1$] 1 [OP$_1$]   Sample display: 6

1 [OP$_1$]	5
1 [OP$_1$]	3
1 [OP$_1$]	4
1 [OP$_1$]	3

Games

Games are an important part of *Everyday Mathematics*. Throughout the year, you will be learning games that will help you practice important skills and give you an opportunity to strengthen your understanding of some of the new concepts to which you are introduced.

In the following section of your *Student Reference Book*, you will find the directions for many favorite games from fourth and fifth grade *Everyday Mathematics* and for some new games that are introduced in sixth grade.

Since the numbers in most games are generated randomly, the games can be played over and over without repeating the same problems. We encourage you to create your own variations to these games to make them more interesting and more challenging.

You might want to take your *Student Reference Book* home to play some of your favorites with siblings or adults at home. We hope that you will play often and have fun!

Materials

For many of the games, you will need a deck of number cards. You can use an *Everything Math Deck*, a regular deck of cards, or make your own deck out of index cards. If you use a regular deck of cards, the 2–10 cards represent the numbers 2–10, the aces the number 1, the queens the number 0, the jacks and kings the numbers 11–18, and the jokers the numbers 19 and 20.

For some games, you will also need one or two 6-sided dice. If a game calls for two 6-sided dice to generate numbers up to 12, roll both dice and add the numbers that come up. Or you can use a 12-sided die instead, if one is available.

If a game requires using counters of two colors, you can use pennies instead and let "heads" stand for one color and "tails" for the other color.

Sometimes you will have to make a game board or a set of cards that are not number cards with which to play. The instructions for doing this are included with the game directions. Some of the games require a Master game board or card deck. These are available from your teacher.

Practicing Skills

To become good at anything, such as playing an instrument, playing soccer, or spelling words, you need to spend time practicing. Practice isn't always fun, but it is necessary if you want to acquire a skill. The advantage of playing mathematics games is that games give you a chance to practice math skills in a way that is usually more enjoyable than doing a page of problems. Use the table on the next page to help you choose games that address the skills you need to practice.

Name That Number

Materials: *Everything Math Deck* or ordinary deck of playing cards, previously marked with a permanent marker, as follows:

• The 2 through 10 cards represent the numbers 2 through 10.

• Aces represent the number 1.

• The Q on queens' face cards represents zero.

• The remaining face cards (kings and jacks) are numbered 11 through 18.

• Jokers, if available, are 19 and 20.

Number of players: 2 or 3

Directions:

Shuffle the cards and deal 5 cards to each player. Then turn over the top card and place it beside the deck. This is the **target number** for the round.

Players try to name the target number by adding, subtracting, multiplying, or dividing the numbers on as many of their cards as possible. A card can only be used once. They write their solutions on a sheet of paper or slate. When both players have made their best solution:

• They set aside the cards they used to name the target number.

• Replace them by drawing new cards from the top of the deck.

• Put the old target number on the bottom of the deck.

• Turn over a new target number, and play another hand.

Play continues until there are not enough cards left to replace both players' cards. The player who set aside more cards wins the game.

> *Example:*
>
> Players' numbers: 7, 5, 8, 2, 10
>
> Target number: 16
>
> Some possible solutions:
>
> $7 * 2 + 10 - 8 = 16$ *(four cards used)*
>
> $8/2 + 10 + 7 - 5$ *(all five cards used)*

Addition Top-It

Materials: 1 deck of number cards 1–10

Number of players: 2–4

Directions: Each player turns over 2 cards and calls out the sum of the 2 numbers.

The player with the highest sum takes all the cards. In case of a tie for the highest sum, each tied player turns over 2 more cards and calls out the sum. The player with the highest sum takes all the cards from both plays.

Answers can be checked in an Addition Table or on a calculator.

Play continues until there are too few cards left for each player to have another turn. The player who took the most cards wins.

Variation: Each player turns over 3 cards and finds their sum.

Subtraction Top-It

Each player turns over 3 cards, finds the sum of any two of the numbers, then finds the difference between the sum and the third number.

> *Example:*
>
> A 4, 8, and 3 are turned over. There are 3 combinations that will result in a positive number.
>
> $4 + 8 = 12; 12 - 3 = 9$
>
> $3 + 8 = 11; 11 - 4 = 7$
>
> $3 + 4 = 7; 8 - 7 = 1$

Multiplication Top-It

The rules are the same as for *Addition Top-It*, except that players find the product of the numbers instead of the sum.

The 3-card variation involves finding the product of 2-digit by 1-digit numbers.

Division Top-It

Each player turns over 3 cards and uses them to generate division problems, as follows.
• Choose 2 cards to form the dividend.
• Use the remaining card as the divisor.

Divide and drop the remainder. The player with the largest quotient wins a round.

Advanced version: Turn over 4 cards and choose three of them to form a 3-digit number. Divide it by the remaining number.

Top-It Games (continued)

Addition Top-It with Positive and Negative Numbers

57

Materials: 1 deck of number cards

> When using a deck of playing cards instead of an *Everything Math Deck*, use the 2–10 cards to represent these numbers, the aces to represent the number 1, and the queens to represent zero. Mark the jacks, kings, and jokers (10 cards total) to represent the numbers 11–20.

Number of players: 2–4

Object: To collect the most cards.

Directions:

Black cards (spades and clubs) show positive numbers and blue cards (*Everything Math Deck*) or red cards (hearts and diamonds) negative numbers.

1. Shuffle the cards.

2. Each player turns over 2 cards and calls out the sum of the 2 numbers.

3. The player with the highest sum takes all the cards. In case of a tie for the highest sum, each tied player turns over 2 more cards and calls out the sum. The player with the highest sum takes all the cards from both plays.

4. Answers can be checked with a calculator.

Play continues until there are too few cards left for each player to have another turn. The player who took the most cards wins.

> *Example:*
>
> Player A turns over a red 5 and a black 7. Score: $-5 + 7 = 2$
>
> Player B turns over a red 3 and a red 4. Score: $-3 + (-4) = -7$
>
> 2 is greater than -7, so Player A wins the round.

Variation: Each player turns over 3 cards and finds the sum.

Subtraction Top-It with Positive and Negative Numbers

58

Each player turns over 2 cards, one at a time, and subtracts the second number from the first number.

> *Example:*
>
> Player A turns over a black 2 first, then a red 3. Score: $2 - (-3) = 5$
>
> Player B turns over a red 5 first, then a red 7. Score: $-5 - (-7) = 2$
>
> 5 is greater than 2, so Player A wins the round.

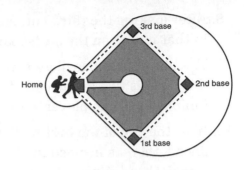

2 Factor Game

Materials: 4 regular dice, 4 pennies, a calculator

Number of players: 2

Directions: Take turns being the "pitcher" and the "batter."

1. Draw a diamond and label "home plate," "1st base," "2nd base," and "3rd base."

2. Make a score sheet that looks like the following:

Inning		1	2	3	4	5	6	7	Total
Team 1	outs								
	runs								
Team 2	outs								
	runs								

3. At the start of the inning, the batter puts a penny on home plate.

4. The pitcher rolls the 4 dice. The batter separates them into 2 pairs, adds the numbers in each pair, multiplies the sums, and tells the answer. The pitcher checks the answer on a calculator.

Example:

Suppose the numbers 2, 3, 5, and 6 come up. They could be separated as follows:

$2 + 3 = 5$	$2 + 5 = 7$	$2 + 6 = 8$
$5 + 6 = 11$	$3 + 6 = 9$	$3 + 5 = 8$
$5 * 11 = 55$	$7 * 9 = 63$	$8 * 8 = 64$

5. An incorrect solution is a strike, and another pitch (dice roll) is thrown. Three strikes make an out.

If the solution is correct, the batter looks up the product in the Hitting Table at the right. If it is a hit, the batter moves all pennies the number of bases shown in the table.

Hitting Table
2 to 12 Facts

1 to 24	Out
25 to 49	Single (1 base)
50 to 64	Double (2 bases)
66 to 77	Triple (3 bases)
80 to 144	Home Run (4 bases)

6. A run is scored each time a penny crosses home plate. If a play is not a hit, it is an out.

7. A player remains the batter for 3 outs. Then players switch roles. The inning is over when both players have made 3 outs.

8. After making the third out, a batter records the number of runs scored in that inning on the scoreboard.

9. The player who has more runs at the end of 4 innings wins the game. If the game is tied at the end of 4 innings, play continues into extra innings until one player wins.

10. If, at the end of the first half of the last inning, the second player is ahead, there is no need to play the second half of the inning. The player who is ahead wins.

3 Factors Game

The pitcher rolls 3 dice. The batter multiplies the three numbers and uses the 3 Factors Hitting Table to determine hits and outs.

Hitting Table 3 Factors	
1 to 54	Out
60 to 90	Single
96 to 120	Double
125 to 150	Triple
180 to 216	Home Run

World Series

Choose 2 teams of players as in real baseball. Make up a batting order. The first team to win 4 games wins the World Series.

For a shorter Series, play the best 3 out of 5 games.

Materials: a calculator for each player

Number of players: 1 or 2

Directions:

The √ key is used to generate the numbers you will be dividing. It is not used for any other part of the game.

1. Each player chooses a number and enters it on the calculator.

2. Each player presses the √ key. If the number on a player's calculator display has fewer than 3 digits, the player should repeat Steps 1 and 2.

3. Each player uses the final digit in the calculator display as a 1-digit number, and uses the two digits before the final digit as a 2-digit number.

4. Each player divides the 2-digit number by the 1-digit number and records the result. (This result is the quotient. Remainders are ignored.) Players calculate mentally or on paper, not on the calculator.

5. The players press √ and repeat Steps 3 and 4 until the sum of a player's quotients is 100 or more. The winner is the first player to reach at least 100.

Example:

	Quotient	Score
First turn: Enter 5678 and press √ .		
On a 10-digit display, the result is 7 5 . 3 5 2 5 0 <u>4 9</u> <u>4</u>. Divide 49 by 4. The quotient is 12 with a remainder of 1.	12	12
Second turn: Without clearing the calculator, press √ .		
The result is 8 . 6 8 0 5 8 2 <u>0 6</u> <u>2</u>. Divide 06, or 6 by 2. The quotient is 3.	3	15
Third turn: Without clearing the calculator, press √ .		
The result is 2 . 9 4 6 2 8 2 <u>7 5</u> <u>3</u>. Divide 75 by 3. The quotient is 25.	25	40

Continue until one player has a total score of 100 or more.

If there is only one player, the object of the game is to reach 100 or more in as few turns as possible.

Frac-Tac-Toe

2-4-5-10 Game

Materials:

- *Cards:* a deck of number cards, 4 each of the numbers 0–10
- *Game Board:* Ask your teacher for one of the *Frac-Tac-Toe* Game Boards.
- *Number-Card Board:* Ask your teacher for one of the *Frac-Tac-Toe* Card Boards, or make one of your own.
- *Markers:* counters of 2 colors or pennies

Number of players: 2

Set-up:

Separate the cards into two piles on the Card Board—a numerator pile and a denominator pile. For a *2-4-5-10* game, place two each of the 2, 4, 5, and 10 cards in the denominator pile. The remaining cards are placed on the numerator pile.

Shuffle the cards in each pile. Place the piles facedown in the left-hand spaces. When the numerator pile is completely used, reshuffle that pile and place it facedown in the left-hand space. Whenever the denominator pile is completely used, it is simply turned over and placed facedown in the left-hand space. The denominator pile is never reshuffled.

Directions:

If pennies are used, then one player uses the heads side of the coin and the other player the tails side.

Players take turns. Player 1 turns over the top card from each pile to form a fraction (numerator card over denominator card).

Player 1 then tries to match the fraction shown by the cards with one of the grid squares on the game board. If a match is found, the player covers that grid square with his or her marker; the turn is over. If no match is found, the player's turn is over. Then Player 2 does the same thing, using the same game board.

Players may use either a calculator or the Table of Decimal Equivalents for Fractions on page 336 at the back of this book to convert the fraction shown by the cards to a decimal.

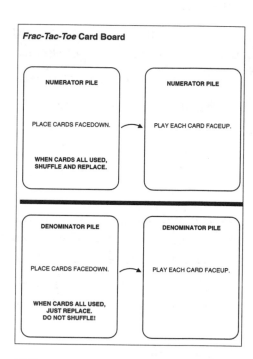

Frac-Tac-Toe Card Board

NUMERATOR PILE	NUMERATOR PILE
PLACE CARDS FACEDOWN.	PLAY EACH CARD FACEUP.
WHEN CARDS ALL USED, SHUFFLE AND REPLACE.	

DENOMINATOR PILE	DENOMINATOR PILE
PLACE CARDS FACEDOWN.	PLAY EACH CARD FACEUP.
WHEN CARDS ALL USED, JUST REPLACE. DO NOT SHUFFLE!	

2-4-5-10 Frac-Tac-Toe

If you use a standard deck of cards:
Use Queens as zeros (0).
Use Aces as ones (1).
Discard Jacks and Kings.

If you use an *Everything Math Deck*, discard cards greater than 10.

Numerator Pile — All remaining cards

Denominator Pile — Two each of 2, 4, 5, and 10 cards

Use different color counters or coins as markers. If you use coins, one player is "heads" and the other player is "tails."

> 1.0	0 or 1	> 2.0	0 or 1	> 1.0
0.1	0.2	0.25	0.3	0.4
> 1.5	0.5	> 1.5	0.5	>1.5
0.6	0.7	0.75	0.8	0.9
> 1.0	0 or 1	> 2.0	0 or 1	> 1.0
0 or 1	0.25	> 1.5	0.6	0 or 1
0.1	> 1.0	0.5	> 1.0	0.8
> 2.0	0.3	> 1.5	0.7	> 2.0
0.2	> 1.0	0.5	> 1.0	0.9
0 or 1	0.4	> 1.5	0.75	0 or 1

Examples:

The cards show the fraction $\frac{4}{5}$. The player may mark the 0.8 square, unless that square has already been marked.

The cards show the fraction $\frac{0}{5}$. The player may mark any one of the four squares labeled "0 or 1" that has not already been marked.

The cards show the fraction $\frac{4}{2}$. The player may mark any square labeled "> 1.0" or "> 1.5" that has not been previously marked. The player may not mark a square labeled "> 2.0," because $\frac{4}{2}$ is equal to, but not greater than, 2.0.

Scoring: The first player covering 3 squares in a row in any direction (horizontal, vertical, diagonal) is the winner.

Variations:

• Play with the 2-4-5-8-10 or the 3-6-9 game boards.

• *The Bingo Version:* The whole class plays the game together. Use a Bingo game board and fill in any numbers you wish in the empty squares. The caller turns over the number cards and names the fractions. Each player plays for himself or herself.

Fraction Action, Fraction Friction

Materials: calculator

Make one set of 16 *Fraction Action, Fraction Friction* cards. The suggested set includes a card for each of the following fractions (for several fractions there are 2 cards): $\frac{1}{2}, \frac{1}{3}, \frac{2}{3}, \frac{1}{4}, \frac{3}{4}, \frac{1}{6}, \frac{1}{6}, \frac{5}{6}, \frac{1}{12}, \frac{1}{12}, \frac{5}{12}, \frac{5}{12}, \frac{7}{12}, \frac{7}{12}, \frac{11}{12}, \frac{11}{12}$.

Number of players: 2 or 3

Object of the game: To gather a set of fraction cards with a sum as close as possible to 2, without going over.

Directions:

Shuffle the *Fraction Action, Fraction Friction* cards. Deal one card to each player. The player with the fraction closest to $\frac{1}{2}$ begins the game.

Players return their cards to the desk. Shuffle the deck again. Place the pile facedown between the players.

Players take turns. At each turn:

1. The player takes a card from the top of the pile and places it faceup on the playing surface.

2. At each turn, the player must announce one of the following:

   "Action!"
   This means that the player wants an additional card. The player believes that the sum of the cards is not close enough to 2 to win the hand and that with an additional card, there is a good chance that the sum of the cards will be even closer to 2, without becoming greater than 2.

   "Friction!"
   This means that the player does not want an additional card. The player believes that the sum of the cards is close enough to 2 to win the hand and that with an additional card, there is a good chance that the sum of the cards will be greater than 2.

Play continues until all players have announced, "Friction!" or have a set of cards whose sum is greater than 2. The player whose sum is closest to 2 without going over is the winner of the hand. Players may check each other's sums on their calculators.

Reshuffle the cards and begin again. The winner of the game is the first player to win 5 hands.

Materials: number cards, 4 each of the numbers 0 through 9

Number of players: 2

Directions:

Shuffle the cards and place the deck facedown on the playing surface. Each player has a scorecard on which to record his or her results.

In each round:

- Player A draws the top card from the deck and writes that number on any one of the three blanks on the scorecard. It need not be the first blank—it can be any one of them.

- Player B draws the next card from the deck and writes the number on one of his or her blanks.

- Players take turns doing this two more times. The player with the larger number wins the round.

Game 1

Round 1   **Score**

0. ___ ___ ___   _____

Round 2

0. ___ ___ ___   _____

Round 3

0. ___ ___ ___   _____

Round 4

0. ___ ___ ___   _____

                    Total:
                    _____

Scoring: The winner's score for a round is the difference between the two players' scores. The loser scores 0 points for the round.

> **Example:**
>
> Player A: 0.6 5 4
> Player B: 0.7 5 3
>
> Player B has the larger number and wins the round. Since 0.753 − 0.654 = 0.099, Player B scores 0.099 points for the round. Player A scores 0 points.

Players take turns starting a round. At the end of 4 rounds, they find their total scores. The player with the larger total score wins the game.

Spoon Scramble

Materials: 3 spoons

36 | 134
52 | 135

Make a deck of 16 Spoon Scramble cards. The suggested set contains one card for each of the following expressions.

$\frac{1}{4}$ of 24;	$\frac{3}{4} * 8$;	50% of 12;	$0.10 * 60$;
$\frac{1}{3}$ of 21;	$3\frac{1}{2} * 2$;	25% of 28;	$0.10 * 70$;
$\frac{1}{5}$ of 40;	$2 * \frac{16}{4}$;	1% of 800;	$0.10 * 80$;
$\frac{3}{4}$ of 12;	$4\frac{1}{2} * 2$;	25% of 36;	$0.10 * 90$.

Number of players: 4

Object of the game: To be the first player to avoid getting all the letters in the word SPOONS.

Directions:

1. Place the spoons in the center of the table.

2. Pick a player to be the dealer. The dealer shuffles and deals the cards facedown (4 to each player).

3. Players look at their cards. If a player has 4 cards of equal value, proceed to Step 5 below. Otherwise, each player chooses a card to discard and passes it, facedown, to the player on the left.

4. Each player picks up the new card and chooses a card to pass to the next player. The passing of the cards should proceed as quickly as possible.

5. As soon as a player has 4 cards of equal value, the player places the cards faceup on the table and grabs a spoon.

6. The other players then try to grab one of the remaining spoons.

7. The player left without a spoon in each round is assigned a letter from the word SPOONS, starting with the first letter. If a player incorrectly claims to have 4 cards of equal value, that player receives a letter instead of the player left without a spoon.

8. Players put the spoons back in the center of the table. The dealer shuffles and deals the cards. A new round begins (Step 3 above).

9. Play continues until 3 players get all the letters in the word SPOONS. The player who does not have all the letters is the winner.

Variations:

• For 3 players: Eliminate one set of 4 equivalent *Spoon Scramble* cards and one spoon.

• Players can make their own deck of *Spoon Scramble* cards. Each player writes 4 computation problems with equivalent answers on 4 index cards. Check to be sure different players have chosen different values.

Materials: 1 deck of cards with 4 each of the numbers 0 through 9
(If you are using regular playing cards, aces count as 1 and queens as 0.);
4 index cards labeled 0.1, 1, 10, and 100;
2 counters or coins per player (to use as decimal points);
calculator

Number of players: 2

Object of the game: To have the most cards at the end of the game.

Directions:

1. One player shuffles the number cards and deals 4 cards facedown to
   each player.

2. The other player shuffles the index cards, places them facedown, and
   turns over the top card. The number that appears (0.1, 1, 10, or 100) is
   the Target Number.

3. Using 4 number cards and 2 decimal-point counters, each player forms
   two numbers, each with two digits and a decimal point:
   - Each player tries to form numbers whose product is as close as
     possible to the Target Number.
   - The decimal point can go anywhere in a number—for example:

4. Players compute the product of their numbers on a calculator.

5. The player whose product is closer to the Target Number wins all
   8 number cards.

6. Four new number cards are dealt to each player, and a new Target
   Number is turned over.

7. The game ends when all four Target Numbers have been turned over.

8. The player with the most number cards wins the game. In the case of a
   tie, reshuffle the index cards and turn over a Target Number. Play one
   tie-breaking round.

   Example:
   - The index card turned over is 10, so the Target Number is 10.
   - Briana is dealt 1, 4, 8, and 8. She forms the numbers 8.8 and 1.4.
   - Evelyn is dealt 2, 3, 6, and 9. She forms the numbers 2.6 and 3.9.
   - Briana's product is 12.32 and Evelyn's is 10.14.
   - Evelyn's product is closer to 10. She wins the round and the cards.

Scientific Notation Toss

Materials: 2 six-sided dice

Number of players: 2

Object of the game: To create the largest number, written in scientific notation.

Directions:

Each player rolls 2 dice and uses one number to name a power of 10 (such as 10^2 or 10^4) and the other number to name its multiplier. Each player does this 3 times and writes each result in scientific notation.

Next, the players convert the numbers from scientific notation to standard notation and order the numbers from largest to smallest.

Players compare lists. The player who has the largest number wins. In case of a tie, they roll a fourth time.

Example:

Player 1 rolls:	2 and 4	5 and 3	1 and 6
writes:	$2 * 10^4$	$3 * 10^5$	$1 * 10^6$
	$= 2 * 10,000$	$= 3 * 100,000$	$= 1 * 1,000,000$
	$= 20,000$	$= 300,000$	$= 1,000,000$
orders:	1,000,000	300,000	20,000

Player 2 rolls:	5 and 5	2 and 1	4 and 3
writes:	$5 * 10^5$	$1 * 10^2$	$3 * 10^4$
	$= 5 * 100,000$	$= 1 * 100$	$= 3 * 10,000$
	$= 500,000$	$= 100$	$= 30,000$
orders:	500,000	30,000	100

1,000,000 is the highest number, so Player 1 wins.

Advanced Scientific Notation Toss

Use two 12-sided dice (or use 4 six-sided dice and add the results on pairs of dice).

Materials: 1 calculator with a constant function for both players

Number of players: 2

Object of the game: To guess a mystery number in as few tries as possible.

Directions:

1. Player A chooses a mystery number less than 100.

2. Suppose the mystery number is 65. Player A secretly keys in one of the following keying sequences:

    • If the calculator does not have a [K] key or an [OP$_1$] key, key in 65 [÷] 65 [=].
    • If the calculator does have a [K] key, key in 65 [÷] 65 [K] [=].
    • If the calculator has an [OP$_1$] key, key in [÷] 65 [OP$_1$] 65 [OP$_1$]. (Do not press the [=] key.)

    The number 1 should appear in the display. (Player A should substitute his or her mystery number for 65 in one of the above keying sequences.)

3. Player B guesses the mystery number and, **without clearing the calculator**, enters the guess and [=], unless the calculator has an [OP$_1$] key. If the calculator has an [OP$_1$] key, press [OP$_1$] instead of [=]. (Do not press the [=] key.)

    • If the calculator shows a number less than 1, then the guess is too low.
    • If it shows a number greater than 1, then the guess is too high.
    • If it shows 1, then Player B guessed the mystery number.

4. Player B continues to enter guesses, **without clearing the calculator**, until the result is 1. Player A keeps track of the number of guesses.

5. When Player B has guessed the mystery number, players trade roles and follow Steps 1–4. The player who guesses the mystery number in the fewest number of guesses wins the round.

    Example:

    Player A enters the mystery number 65.

Player B enters:	55 [=]	Calculator shows:	0.846153...	Too small
	70 [=]		1.076923...	Too big
	65 [=]		1	Just right!

Scoring: Play 5 rounds that do not end in a tie. The player who wins more rounds wins the game.

Another way: Play 5 rounds and keep track of the number of guesses for each round. The player with the smaller total number of guesses wins the game.

Advanced version: Allow mystery numbers up to 1000.

Estimation Squeeze

Number of players: 2

Materials: calculator, paper, pencil

Directions: Pick a number less then 600 that is not a perfect square (not the square of a whole number). Record this target number.

Players take turns. At each turn a player:

1. Estimates the square root of the target number and enters this estimate on the calculator.

2. Finds the square of the estimate with the calculator and records it. (Use the [x^2] key or the multiplication key.)

Perfect Squares		
1	81	289
4	100	324
9	121	361
16	144	400
25	169	441
36	196	484
49	225	529
64	256	576

The first player who makes an estimate whose square is within 0.1 of the target number wins the game. For example, if the target number is 139, the square of the estimate must be greater than 138.9 and less than 139.1.

Note: The [$\sqrt{\ }$] key on the calculator may not be used. This key provides the best estimate of a square root that the calculator can calculate.

Example:

Target Number: 139

	Estimate	Square of Estimate	
Player 1	12	144	too large
Player 2	11	121	too small
Player 1	11.5	132.25	too small
Player 2	11.8	139.24	too large
Player 1	11.75	138.0625	too small
Player 2	11.79	139.0041	less than 139.1

Player 2 wins.

Buzz

Materials: none

Number of players: 5–10

Directions:

1. Players sit in a circle.

2. Choose a leader. The leader names any whole number from 3–9. This number is the BUZZ number. The leader also chooses the STOP number. This STOP number should be at least 30.

3. The player to the left of the leader begins the game by saying "one." Play continues clockwise with each player saying either the next whole number or "BUZZ."

   A player must say BUZZ instead of the next number in the count if:

   • The number is the BUZZ number;

   • The number is a multiple of the BUZZ number; or

   • The number contains the BUZZ number as one of its digits.

   Example: The BUZZ number is 4. Play should proceed as follows:

   > 1, 2, 3, BUZZ, 5, 6, 7, BUZZ, 9, 10, 11, BUZZ, 13, BUZZ, 15, and so on.

   > If a player makes an error, the next player must start again with 1.

   > Play continues until the STOP number is reached.

   > For the next round, the player to the right of the leader becomes the new leader.

Bizz-Buzz

Bizz-Buzz is played like *Buzz,* except the leader names two numbers: a BUZZ number and a BIZZ number. Players say:

   • BUZZ instead of the number if the number is the BUZZ number or a multiple of the BUZZ number.
   • BIZZ instead of the number if the number is the BIZZ number or a multiple of the BIZZ number.

   • BIZZ-BUZZ instead of the number if the number is a multiple of both the BUZZ number and the BIZZ number.

   Example:

   > The BUZZ number is 6, and the BIZZ number is 3. Play should proceed as follows:
   > 1, 2, BIZZ, 4,5, BIZZ-BUZZ, 7, 8, BIZZ, 10, 11, BIZZ-BUZZ, 13, 14, BIZZ, 16, and so on.

Note that the numbers 6 and 12 are replaced by the word "BIZZ-BUZZ" since 6 and 12 are multiples of both 6 and 3.

Factor Captor

Materials: 48 counters the size of a coin, scratch paper, calculator
Ask your teacher for a *Factor Captor* grid—either Grid 1 or Grid 2 (beginning or advanced).

Number of players: 2

Directions:

To start the first round, Player 1 chooses a 2-digit number on the number grid, covers it with a counter, and records the number on the scratch paper. This is Player 1's score for the round.

Player 2 covers all of the factors of Player 1's number, finds the sum of the factors, and records it on the scratch paper. This is Player 2's score for the round. **A factor may only be covered once during a round.**

If Player 2 missed any factors, Player 1 can cover them with counters and add them to his or her score.

In the next round, players switch roles. Player 2 chooses a number that is not covered by a counter; Player 1 covers all factors of that number.

Any number that is covered by a counter is no longer available and may not be used again.

The first player in a round may not cover a number less than 10, unless no other numbers are available.

Play continues with players trading roles in each round, until all numbers on the grid have been covered. Players then use their calculators to find their total scores. The player with the higher total score wins the game.

> **Example:**
>
> Round 1:
> Player 1 covers 27. Player 1's score: 27 points.
> Player 2 covers 1, 3, and 9. Player 2's score 1 + 3 + 9 = 13 points.
>
> Round 2:
> Player 2 covers 18. Player 2's score: 18 points.
> Player 1 covers 2, 3, and 6. Player 1's score: 2 + 3 + 6 = 11 points.
> Player 2 covers 9 with a counter, because 9 is also a factor of 18.
> Player 2 adds 9 points to his or her score.

Factor Captor Grid 1

1	2	2	2	2	2
2	3	3	3	3	3
3	4	4	4	4	5
5	5	5	6	6	7
7	8	8	9	9	10
10	11	12	13	14	15
16	18	20	21	22	24
25	26	27	28	30	32

Factor Captor Grid 2 (Advanced Level)

1	2	2	2	2	2	3
3	3	3	3	4	4	4
4	5	5	5	5	6	6
6	7	7	8	8	9	9
10	10	11	12	13	14	15
16	17	18	19	20	21	22
23	24	25	26	27	28	30
32	33	34	35	36	38	39
40	42	44	45	46	48	49
50	51	52	54	55	56	60

Materials: 1 six-sided die; penny or other counter; calculator
Ask your teacher for an *Exponent Ball* game board.

Number of players: 2

Directions:

The game is similar to U.S. football.

1. Players decide who goes first. The first player puts the ball (counter) on one of the 20-yard lines. The player's goal is to reach the goal line, 80 yards away.

2. A turn consists of four chances to advance the counter to the goal line and score.

3. The first three chances must be runs on the ground. To run, the player rolls the die twice. The first roll names the base, and the second roll names the exponent. For example, rolls of 5 and 4 name the number "5 to the fourth power."

4. The player calculates the value of the rolls.

5. Use Table 1 on the game board page to find how far to move the ball forward (+) or backward (−).

6. If the player does not score in the first three chances, the player may choose to either run or kick on the fourth chance. The player must first announce "run" or "kick."

   • To kick, the player rolls the die once and multiplies the result by 10. The result is the distance the ball travels (Table 2 on the game board page).

7. If the ball reaches the goal line on a run, the player scores 7 points. If the ball reaches the goal line on a kick, the player scores 3 points.

8. If the ball does not reach the goal line in four chances, there is no score and the turn ends. The second player starts where the first player stopped and moves toward the opposite goal line.

9. If the first player scores, the second player puts the ball on the other 20-yard line and moves toward the opposite goal line.

10. Players take turns. A round consists of 4 turns for each player. The player with the most points wins. In the case of a tie at the end of a round, play continues until one player scores.

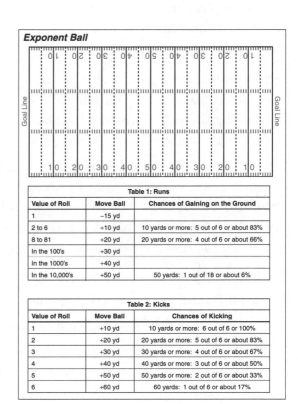

Exponent Ball

Table 1: Runs		
Value of Roll	Move Ball	Chances of Gaining on the Ground
1	−15 yd	
2 to 6	+10 yd	10 yards or more: 5 out of 6 or about 83%
8 to 81	+20 yd	20 yards or more: 4 out of 6 or about 66%
In the 100's	+30 yd	
In the 1000's	+40 yd	
In the 10,000's	+50 yd	50 yards: 1 out of 18 or about 6%

Table 2: Kicks		
Value of Roll	Move Ball	Chances of Kicking
1	+10 yd	10 yards or more: 6 out of 6 or 100%
2	+20 yd	20 yards or more: 5 out of 6 or about 83%
3	+30 yd	30 yards or more: 4 out of 6 or about 67%
4	+40 yd	40 yards or more: 3 out of 6 or about 50%
5	+50 yd	50 yards or more: 2 out of 6 or about 33%
6	+60 yd	60 yards: 1 out of 6 or about 17%

Credits/Debits Game

Materials: 1 deck of playing cards or *Everything Math Deck*; 1 penny with red dot on the tails side
Ask your teacher for a recording sheet or make one that looks like the one shown at the right.

Number of players: 2

Pretend that you are an accountant for a new business. Your job is to keep track of the company's "bottom line." You will do this by recording the debits and credits that are reported to you. Credits add to your bottom line. Debits subtract from your bottom line.

Red Alerts: Because this is a new business, the accounting system is not perfected yet. At times, credits or debits are reported incorrectly. You are informed of such errors by a notice called a "Red Alert." When you receive a "Red Alert," you must subtract the incorrect debit or credit from the bottom line.

Credits/Debits **Recording Sheet**

	Start	Change		End, and next start
		Addition or Subtraction	Credit or Debit	
1	+$10			
2				
3				
4				
5				
6				
7				
8				
9				
10				

Directions:

1. Shuffle the deck and lay it facedown between you and your partner.

2. The black cards are the "credits" and the blue or red cards are the "debits."

3. The heads side of the coin tells you to add a credit or debit to the bottom line. The red side of the coin signals a "Red Alert." You must subtract a credit or debit from the bottom line.

4. Each player begins with a bottom line of $10.

5. Take turns. When it is your turn:
   • Flip the coin. This tells you whether to add or subtract.
   • Draw a card. The card tells you what amount in dollars (positive or negative) to add or subtract from the bottom line.
   • Record the result in the table.

6. After 10 turns or at the end of the playing time, whichever comes first, the partner in the best financial position wins the round.

Materials: Spreadsheet Scramble game board

Number of Players: 2

Object of the Game: To get the most points.

Directions:

1. Player 1 uses the positive numbers 1, 2, 3, 4, 5, 6. Player 2 uses the negative numbers –1, –2, –3, –4, –5, –6.

2. Player 1 begins the game. Players take turns writing one of their numbers in a cell within the 4-by-3 rectangle outlined on the spreadsheet. Once a player has written a number, that number cannot be used again.

	A	B	C	D	E	F
1						Total
2						
3						
4						
5	Total					

3. After all 12 numbers have been used, fill in "Total" cells F2, F3, and F4 by adding each row. For example, F2 = B2 + C2 + D2 + E2. Fill in "Total" cells B5, C5, D5, and E5 by adding each column. For example, C5 = C2 + C3 + C4.

4. Seven cells show row and column totals: F2, F3, F4, B5, C5, D5, and E5. Player 1 gets 1 point for each of these cells that contains a positive number. Player 2 gets 1 point for each of these cells that contains a negative number. Neither player gets a point for 0. The player with the most points wins.

Examples:

Game 1:

Player 1 gets 1 point each for cells F3, F4, and C5.

Player 2 gets 1 point each for F2 and E5.

Player 1 wins the game, 3 points to 2 points.

	A	B	C	D	E	F
1						Total
2		–1	–6	3	–5	–9
3		4	2	–4	6	+8
4		–3	5	1	–2	+1
5	Total	0	+1	0	–1	

Game 2:

Player 1 gets 1 point each for F2, F4, and C5.

Player 2 gets 1 point each for F3, B5, and E5.

The game is a tie, 3 points to 3 points.

	A	B	C	D	E	F
1						Total
2		–4	6	4	–5	+1
3		–1	–3	–6	–2	–12
4		3	5	2	1	+11
5	Total	–2	+8	0	–6	

Materials: 4 pennies or other small counters; 1 six-sided die; pencil; scratch paper; calculator
Ask your teacher for 32 *Algebra Election* Problem Cards and an Electoral Vote Map.

Number of players: 2 teams, each with 2 players

Object of the game: Players move their counters on a map of the United States. For each state, or the District of Columbia (DC), a player lands on, the player tries to win that state's electoral votes by solving a problem. The first team to collect 270 or more votes wins the election. Winning-team members become president and vice president.

Directions:

1. Each player puts a counter in Iowa.

2. One member of each team rolls the die. The team with the higher roll goes first.

3. Turns alternate between teams and partners:
   Team 1, Player 1; Team 2, Player 1; Team 1, Player 2; Team 2, Player 2.

4. Shuffle the *Algebra Election* Problem Cards and place them facedown in a pile.

5. The first player rolls the die. The result tells how many moves the player must make from the current state. Each new state counts as one move. Moves can be in any direction as long as they pass between states that share a common border.
   Exceptions: Players can get to and from Alaska by way of Washington, and to and from Hawaii by way of California. Once a player has been in a state, the player cannot return to that state on the same turn.

6. The player makes the indicated number of moves and puts the counter in the last state landed on. The map names how many electoral votes the state has.

7. The player takes the top Problem Card. The state's number of electoral votes is substituted for x in the problem(s) on the card. The player solves the problem(s) and offers an answer. The other team checks the answer with a calculator.

8. If the answer is correct, the player's team wins the state's electoral votes. They do the following:

   • Write the state's name and its electoral votes on scratch paper.
   • Write their first initials in pencil on the state to show that they have won it.

Algebra Election Cards, Set 1

What is the value of n? $-20 + x = n$ $-100 + (-x) = n$	What is the value of n? $20 + (-x) = n$ $-20 - (-x) = n$	Which is greater: x^2 or 10^3? x^3 or 10^4?	Which is less: $\frac{x^3}{10}$ or $(x + 10)^2$? $10 * x^2$ or $(x + 10)^2$?
Complete: $x * 10^6 = $ _____ million $x * 10^9 = $ _____ billion $x * 10^{12} = $	What is the value of n? $n = ((5 * x) - 4) / 2$	Suppose you earn x dollars per hour. Complete the table. Time | Earnings 1 hr | $ 2 hr | $ 4 hr | $ 10 hr | $	A boulder dropped off a cliff falls approximately $16 * x^2$ feet in x seconds. How many feet is that?
Find: x squared x to the fourth power $1/x$	Find n. (Hint: n could be a negative number.) $1000 - n = x$ $1000 + n = -x$	Find n. (Hint: n could be a negative number.) $n + 10 = x$ $n - 10 = x$	Find n. $n = (2 * x) / 10$ $n + 1 = (2 * x)$	What number is this? $x * 10^2$ $x * 10^5$
Insert parentheses in $10 * x - 10$ so that its value is greater than 0 and less than 100.	$T = B - (2 * \frac{H}{1000})$ If $B = 80$ and $H = 100x$, what does T equal?	Tell whether each is true or false. $10 * x > 100$ $\frac{1}{2} * x * 100 < 10^3$ $x^3 * 1000 > 4 * 10^4$

Algebra Election Cards, Set 2

What is n? $5 + 2 * x = n + x$	$x + \triangle = 200$ oz. $1 \triangle$ weighs _____ ounces	Insert parentheses so that the equation is true. $10 * x + 4 = $ $10 * x + 40$	$A (0,30)$ $B (80,30)$ Is point (x,x) above, below, or on the line through points A and B?
Tell which is correct for each: $<$, $=$, or $>$. x __ $=$ __ $>$ 30 $- x$ x __ $=$ __ $>$ 20 $- x$ x __ $=$ __ $>$ 10 $- x$	Name a number n such that $x - n$ is a negative number greater than -10.	Suppose you have 10 ⊞ markers and $2 * x$ ⊟ markers. What is your balance?	Suppose you have x ⊞ markers and 40 ⊟ markers. What is your balance?
$B (30,60)$ $A (30,0)$ Is point (x,x) to the left of, to the right of, or on the line through points A and B?	What is the value of n? $10 + (-x) = n$ $-10 - (-x) = n$	What is the median of 4, 8, 12, 13, and x?	If $(2 * x) + n = 100$, what is the value of n?
Is $1/x$ greater than, less than, or equal to $\frac{1}{10}$?	Subtract. $x - 100 = ?$ $x - (-100) = ?$	Add. $-25 + x = ?$ $x + 3 - 10 = ?$	Suppose you travel x miles per hour. Complete the table. Time | Distance 1 hr | 2 hr | 4 hr | 10 hr |

Once a state is won, it is out of play. The opposing team may land on the state, but they cannot get its votes.

9. If the partners do not solve the problem(s) correctly, the state remains open. Any player may land on it and try to win its votes in a later turn.

10. The next player rolls the die and moves her or his counter.

11. The first team to get at least 270 votes wins the election.

Electoral Vote Map

WA Washington 11		MT Montana 3	ND North Dakota 3	Minnesota MN 10				Vermont*	ME Maine 4
OR Oregon 7	ID Idaho 4	WY Wyoming 3	SD South Dakota 3	WI Wisconsin 11	MI Michigan 18		NY New York 33	VT 3	NH 3	New Hampshire*
NV Nevada 4	UT Utah 5	CO Colorado 8	NE Nebraska 5	IA Iowa 7	IL Illinois 22	IN Indiana 12	OH Ohio 21	PA Pennsylvania 23	MA	Massachusetts* 12
CA California 54			KS Kansas 6	MO Missouri 11		KY Kentucky 8	WV West Virginia 5	VA Virginia 13	CT	RI Rhode Island* 4
AZ Arizona 8	NM New Mexico 5	OK Oklahoma 8	AR Arkansas 6	TN 11 Tennessee	NC North Carolina 14		Connecticut* 8	NJ	New Jersey* 15
			MS Mississippi 7	AL Alabama 9	GA Georgia 13	SC South Carolina 8	DE Delaware* 3		
		TX Texas 32	LA Louisiana 9		FL Florida 25		Maryland* 10	DC District of Columbia* 3	

AK Alaska 3

HI Hawaii 4

*If your marker does not fit on the state, put your marker on the state name.

Notes

- In the rules, "state" means "state or District of Columbia (DC)."

- Partners may explain the problem to each other. Each player, however, has to answer the problem on her or his own.

- If a player does not want to answer a card, the player can say "Pass," and draw another card. A player may declare "Pass" twice during each round (32 cards).

- Some Problem Cards have several problems. In order to win a state's votes, the player must answer all questions correctly.

- It is helpful to have a strategy. Partners should look at the map to see which states have the most votes, and then work together to win those states.

- When all of the Problem Cards have been used, shuffle and use them again.

- Each player begins a turn from the last state she or he landed on.

- Some people who have played the game suggest the following:

    1. Agree on a time limit for answering problems.

    2. Give 1 extra point if the player can name the capital of the state landed on.

A shorter version of the game can be played by going through all 32 cards just once. The team with the most votes is then declared the winner.

Solution Search

Materials: 1 set of *Solution Search* cards; 1 deck of number cards

When using a deck of playing cards instead of an *Everything Math Deck*, use the 2–10 cards to represent these numbers, the aces to represent the number 1, and the queens to represent zero. Mark the jacks, kings, and jokers (10 cards total) to represent the numbers 11–20.

Number of players: 3–4

Object: To be the first player to discard all of his or her cards.

Directions:

Shuffle the *Solution Search* cards and place them facedown in the center of the playing surface.

Shuffle the deck of playing cards and deal 8 cards to each player. Place the remainder of the deck facedown in the center of the playing surface.

A round is played as follows:

1. Player 1 turns over the top *Solution Search* card. For example, Player 1 may turn over $x > 9$. Player 1 then does one of the following.

   - Discards a card that is a solution to the inequality.

   - If the player does not have a card that is a solution, he or she must continue to draw from the deck of playing cards until a possible solution is drawn. The player then discards this card.

$x > 9$	$y^2 < 5$	$m < 3.5$	$q * 2 > 20$
$b < 6$	$5 \neq s$	$100 / k > 25$	$(9 * z) + 2 > 65$
$49 \leq p^2$	$r/2 \geq 5$	$w - 3 < 2$	$-2 + a \geq 5$
$\sqrt{25} \leq t$	$10 < 50/d$	$c * 7 \leq 14$	$81 > f^2$

Solution Search cards

2. Play continues in this same way in a clockwise direction, with each player discarding a solution card. The round is over when each player has had a turn.

3. Player 2 starts the next round by turning over the top *Solution Search* card. The round proceeds as above.

4. When no more *Solution Search* cards remain, without shuffling, turn the pile facedown and take the top *Solution Search* card.

5. The winner is the first player to discard all of his or her cards.

Variation:

Twos and 7s are special cards. Twos are WILD. A player may choose to play a 2 card with its given value of 2 or may assign any value he or she wishes to the 2 card. The value of the 7 card is always 7. However, if a player plays the 7 card, the next player loses his or her turn.

Materials: Ask your teacher for 1 set of 16 polygons and 1 set of 16 Property cards.

Numbers of players: 2 (or 2 teams of 2)

Directions:

1. Players spread out the polygons between them.

2. Either player shuffles the Property cards and sorts them facedown into two piles, ANGLE cards and SIDE cards. (The cards are labeled on the back.)

3. Players decide who will play first.

4. Player 1 draws the top card from each pile of Property Cards.

5. Player 1 takes all of the polygons that have *both* of the properties on these cards. For example, if Player 1 has "All angles are right angles" and "All sides are the same length," Player 1 may take all of the squares (polygons A and H). The player has "won" these polygons.

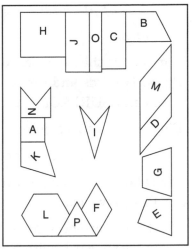

The 16 polygons

6. If no polygon has both properties, Player 1 takes one additional Property card—either an ANGLE or a SIDE card. The player looks for polygons that have this property and one of the properties already drawn and takes the polygons.

7. When Player 1 has taken all of the polygons that match the Property cards, it is Player 2's turn to draw Property cards and take polygons.

8. When all the Property cards have been drawn, players shuffle them, sort them facedown into two piles, and continue playing.

9. If a player does not take a polygon that he or she could have taken, the other player can take it.

10. Players take turns until there are fewer than three polygons left. Then the game ends. The player with the most polygons is the winner.

Property Cards

	Angle cards			
	There is only one right angle.	There are one or more right angles.	All angles are right angles.	There are no right angles.
	There is at least one acute angle.	At least one angle is more than 90°.	All angles are right angles.	There are no right angles.

	Side cards			
	All opposite sides are parallel.	Only one pair of sides is parallel.	There are no parallel sides.	All sides are the same length.
	All opposite sides are parallel.	Some sides have the same length.	All opposite sides have the same length.	**Wild Card:** Pick your own side property.

3-D Shape Sort

Materials: Ask your teacher for 1 set of 12 Shape cards and 1 set of Property cards.

Number of players: 2 (or 2 teams of 2)

Directions:

Spread out the Shape cards on the playing surface, faceup. Shuffle the Property cards and sort them into two facedown piles, VERTEX/EDGE cards and SURFACE cards.

Players take turns doing the following:

1. Draw the top card from both piles of Property cards.

2. Take all the Shape cards that have both of the properties shown on the Property cards.

3. If there are no shapes with both properties, draw one additional Property card—either a VERTEX/EDGE card or a SURFACE card. Look for shapes that have the new property and one of the properties drawn before. Take any Shape cards that match.

4. When all the Property cards have been drawn, shuffle the cards, sort them again into two facedown piles, and continue playing.

5. At the end of a turn, if a player has not taken a Shape card he or she could have taken, the other player can take it.

6. The game ends when there are fewer than three Shape cards left. The player with more Shape cards wins.

Shape Cards

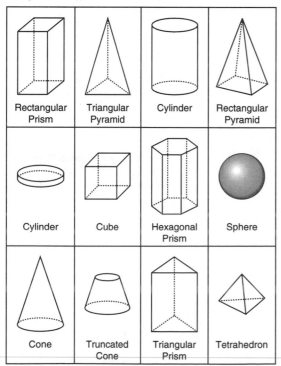

Rectangular Prism	Triangular Pyramid	Cylinder	Rectangular Pyramid
Cylinder	Cube	Hexagonal Prism	Sphere
Cone	Truncated Cone	Triangular Prism	Tetrahedron

Property Cards

Vertex/ Edge cards	I have an even number of vertices.	I have no vertices.	I have at least 2 edges that are parallel to each other.	I have an odd number of edges.
	One of my vertices is formed by an even number of edges.	I have at least one curved edge.	I have fewer than 6 vertices.	I have at least 2 edges that are perpendicular to each other.
Surface cards	All of my surfaces are polygons.	I have at least one face (flat surface).	I have at least one curved surface.	All of my faces are triangles.
	All of my faces are regular polygons.	At least one of my faces is a circle.	I have at least one pair of faces that are parallel to each other.	**Wild Card:** Pick your own surface property.

Materials: protractor, straightedge, blank sheets of paper

113 114

Number of players: 2

Directions:

In each round:

1. Player A uses a straightedge to draw an angle on a sheet of paper.

2. Player B estimates the degree measure of the angle.

3. Player A measures the angle with a protractor.

4. Player B's score is the difference between the estimate and the actual measure of the angle.

5. Players trade roles and repeat Steps 1–4.

Players add their scores at the end of 5 rounds. The player with the lower total score wins the game.

Example:

	Player A			Player B		
	Estimate	**Actual**	**Score**	**Estimate**	**Actual**	**Score**
Round 1	120°	108°	12	50°	37°	13
Round 2	75°	86°	11	85°	87°	2
Round 3	40°	44°	4	15°	19°	4
Round 4	60°	69°	9	40°	56°	16
Round 5	135°	123°	12	150°	141°	9
Total score			48			44

Player B has the lower total score. Player B wins the game.

Hidden Treasure

Materials: pencil, red pen or crayon
Each player makes 2 playing grids (on one sheet of graph paper) which have both the horizontal and the vertical axes labeled from 0 to 10.

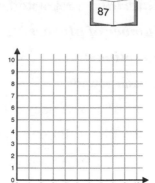

Number of players: 2

Object: Each player "hides" a grid point. Each player tries to "find" the other player's hidden point.

Directions:

1. Each player writes on his or her own copy of the playing grids. They sit so that neither player can see what the other is writing.

2. Using a red pen or crayon, each player secretly marks a grid point on Grid 1. These are the "hidden" points.

3. Player A tries to guess the location of Player B's hidden point by naming an ordered number pair. For example, to name (2,5), Player A might say, "2 comma 5."

4. If Player B's hidden point is at that location, Player A wins the game.

5. If the hidden point is not at that location, Player B marks the guess in pencil on Grid 1. Then Player B counts the least number of "square sides" needed to travel from the hidden point to the guessed point and tells it to Player A.

6. Player A records this number at the guessed location on Grid 2. Player A can use this information to improve the next guess.

7. Player B names an ordered number pair for the location of Player A's hidden point and proceeds as above.

   Example:

   Player B marks the hidden point on Grid 1, in color, at (3,7). Player A marks his or her hidden point on Grid 1, in color, at (2,5).

   Player A guesses that Player B's hidden point is at (1,2) and marks it on Grid 2 in pencil. Player B marks the point (1,2) in pencil on Grid 1 and tells Player A that (1,2) is 7 units away from the hidden point. Player A writes 7 next to point (1,2) on Grid 2.

8. Play continues until a player guesses the location of a hidden point.

Advanced Version: Use a 4-quadrant grid with axes labeled from −7 to 7.

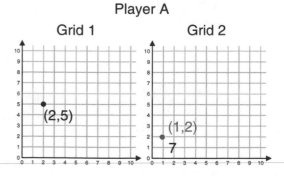

[169]

Materials: 1 deck of number cards (4 each of 0 to 10 and 1 each of 11 to 20); 1 range, median, and mode card for each player; score sheet

Number of players: 2 or 3

Object of the game: To get the most points possible.

Directions:

To play a round:

1. The dealer shuffles the number cards and deals 5 cards facedown to each player.

2. Players arrange their hand from the smallest number to the largest.

3. There are three ways to score points for the hand.

   - **Range:** The player's score is the range of the hand.
     Example:

     | 1 | 4 | 6 | 8 | 12 |

     Total points = 11

   - **Median:** The player's score is the median of the hand.
     Example:

     | 4 | 9 | 13 | 14 | 15 |

     Total points = 13

   - **Mode:** The player must have at least two cards with the same number. The player's score is found by multiplying the mode of the hand by the number of modal cards. If there is more than one mode, the player uses the mode that will produce the most points.
     Example:

     | 1 | 2 | 8 | 8 | 10 |

     Total points = 16

4. Each player decides which landmark will yield the highest score for their hand. The player indicates the choice by placing one of the three landmark cards—range, median, or mode—on the table.

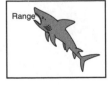 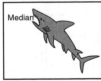 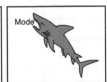

5. Players can try to improve their score by exchanging *up to 3* of their cards for new cards from the deck. However, the landmark card stays the same.

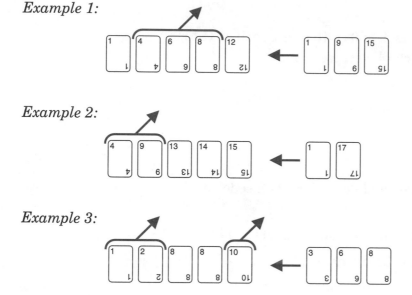

Example 1:

Example 2:

Example 3:

6. Players lay down their hands and record their scores on the score sheet.

7. *Bonus Points*:
Each player calculates the mean of their cards to the nearest tenth. This value is then added to their score.

Repeat steps 1–7 for each round. The winner is the player with the highest total after 5 rounds.

Landmark Shark Score Sheet

		Player One	Player Two	Player Three
Round 1	Points for Hand	14	14	24
	Bonus Points	7.6	12	6.6
	Round 1 Score	21.6	26	30.6
Round 2	Points for Hand			
	Bonus Points			
	Round 2 Score			
Round 3	Points for Hand			
	Bonus Points			
	Round 3 Score			
Round 4	Points for Hand			
	Bonus Points			
	Round 4 Score			
Round 5	Points for Hand			
	Bonus Points			
	Round 5 Score			
Total Score for 5 Rounds				

Projects are an interesting and enjoyable way of exploring ideas that are related to the mathematics you are studying this year. In the following section of this *Student Reference Book*, you will find directions for doing a number of projects. Some of these you can do on your own or with a partner; others are class projects that will involve everyone in your class. Your teacher will give you directions for the class projects. A brief description of each project is is given below.

A Recall Survey of Drinks

A **recall survey** is a survey used to collect information about past behavior, habits, or activities. Typically, *individual* information gathered in such a survey is not precise. However, estimates based on *combined* survey data are very worthwhile.

For example, the United States Department of Agriculture conducts nationwide food consumption recall surveys. Data are collected by interviewing persons who know the most about the food their households eat. A food list is used to help recall kinds, quantities, and costs of foods used during the 7 days prior to the interview.

The newspaper article below reports data that was collected in a food recall survey.

What kids are drinking

For years, experts lauded milk's nutritional value, but now they are questioning its role in the diet of children who suffer from allergies, sinus, and intestinal problems. Children are drinking less milk, but the popularity of juices and soft drinks is increasing.

Source: U.S. Dept. of Agriculture
Chicago Tribune

▶ **What children drink**
Average amount drunk by 6- to 11-year-olds per year.

Milk
1978 46.4 gallons
1994 38.7 gallons

Apple and grape juices
1978 1.4 gallons
1994 3.5 gallons

Soft drinks
1978 10.6 gallons
1994 20.0 gallons

▶ **What teenagers drink**
Average amount drunk by 12- to 19-year-olds per year.

Milk
1978 49.6 gallons
1994 32.9 gallons

Apple and grape juices
1978 0.8 gallons
1994 2.7 gallons

Soft drinks
1978 20.6 gallons
1994 62.5 gallons

You can analyze the newspaper article to answer related questions, and to make interesting comparisons.

Examples:

- Are children and teens drinking less milk than 20 years ago?

  Yes, children are drinking about 8 gallons less, and teens about 17 gallons less than they did 20 years ago.

- In 1994, children drank about *twice as much* milk as soft drinks.

- Teens drank about *2 gallons more* of apple and grape juices in 1994 than they did in 1978.

Collect and Analyze Recall Survey Data for Your Class

Your class will conduct a recall survey of drinks.

1. Each student will report his or her estimates for the amounts of milk, soft drink, and apple or grape juice drunk on the previous day. A student may collect data for more than one day.

2. Your teacher will record each student's three estimates for one day in a column of the Drink Survey Table shown below. If a student does not drink one of the items during the previous day, a 0 will be entered for that item.

Drink Survey Table

Recall Survey of Previous Day's Drinks

	1	2	3	4	5	6	7	8	9	10	11	12	13	14	15	16	17	18	19	20	21	22	23
Milk (8 oz glass)																							
Soft Drinks (12 oz can)																							
Apple/Grape Juice (8 oz glass)																							

	24	25	26	27	28	29	30	31	32	33	34	35	36	37	38	39	40	41	42	43	44	45	46
Milk (8 oz glass)																							
Soft Drinks (12 oz can)																							
Apple/Grape Juice (8 oz glass)																							

Collect data from at least 30 students before analyzing the data.

3. Each column in the Drink Survey Table has estimates for one student for a single day. After two days of collecting recall data, the Drink Survey Table will probably show drink estimates for 40 to 70 "student-days."

4. Your class will then randomly select 30 columns of data to analyze. Work as a class to find the total number of glasses and cans drunk over those 30 days, for each of the 3 drinks. Then convert the total number of glasses and cans to gallons, and complete the table on journal page 48, which is shown below.

Class Data for a Recall Survey of Drinks		
	For 30 days (1 month)	For 360 days (about 1 year)
Milk	_____ 8-ounce glasses or _____ gallons	_____ gallons
Soft Drinks	_____ 12-ounce cans or _____ gallons	_____ gallons
Apple/Grape Juice	_____ 8-ounce glasses or _____ gallons	_____ gallons

5. Discuss how the class results compare with the results in the newspaper article.

Exploring the Solar System

Space Travel

A life-long dream came true for Mae Jemison in September 1992. She became a space traveler. Mae, who is a doctor and an engineer, spent eight days aboard the space shuttle *Endeavor*. She did experiments while the shuttle orbited the Earth at more than 17,000 miles per hour.

Mae grew up on the south side of Chicago. She told one interviewer, "I'm extremely excited to be on the flight, because it's something that I wanted to do since I was a small child." When she was in elementary school, Mae liked to go to the library. She spent many hours reading about space travel and astronomy. She also read science-fiction books and watched *Star Trek* on television. She thought that someday she would travel in space.

Astronauts usually bring items with them as symbols of their beliefs and interests. Mae brought a poster of the Alvin Ailey American Dance Theater to represent creativity and dance. She also brought small art objects from Africa, because she believes space belongs to all the nations of the world.

Mae Jemison

For centuries people have dreamed of exploring outer space. By the time you are Mae's age, it may be possible to travel to other planets in the Solar System. Some people find this exciting. Others think it would be better to explore the Solar System with machines instead of people.

Throughout the remainder of this project you will use mathematics to learn about the Solar System and the possibility of space travel. You will make a scale model of the Solar System with your classmates. Then you will be asked to decide: Will it be possible to travel to other planets in your lifetime? If so, where might you go and how long might it take to get there?

Source: Warren E. Leary, "A Determined Breaker of Boundaries." *New York Times*, September 13, 1992.

The Solar System

The Solar System consists of the Sun, nine planets and their moons, and a large number of asteroids, comets, and meteors. The Sun is at the center of the Solar System.

Astronomers estimate that the Solar System was formed between 4 and 5 billion years ago. A huge, slowly rotating cloud of particles was pulled together to form the Sun. The planets, moons, and other objects were formed from particles in the outer portion of the cloud.

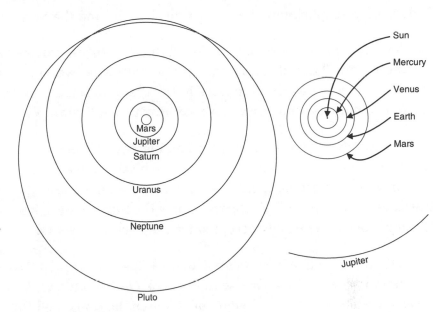

From time to time, you can see Mercury, Venus, Mars, Jupiter, and Saturn in the night sky. For most of history, people thought these were the only planets besides Earth. Then, using increasingly powerful telescopes, astronomers spotted Uranus in 1718, Neptune in 1846, and Pluto in 1930. Neptune and Pluto might never have been found if astronomers were not guided by mathematical predictions which told them where to aim their telescopes.

The four planets closest to the Sun—Mercury, Venus, Earth, and Mars—are called the "rocky dwarfs" because they are small and made mostly of rock. Jupiter, Saturn, Uranus, and Neptune are huge balls of frozen gas and liquid with small solid cores. They are called the "gas giants" or "Jovian planets." They have multiple moons and rings.

Knowledge of the Solar System is growing rapidly. During the past thirty years, all of the planets except Pluto have been visited by one or more space probes. From these expeditions, we have learned that each planet is unique. The planets have different atmospheres, surfaces, and cores.

Movement of the Planets

Today, most people know that Earth revolves around the Sun.

Not long ago, almost everyone believed that the entire universe revolved around Earth. That idea certainly agrees with what we can see with our own eyes: Every day the Sun rises in the east and sets in the west. At night, the Moon, planets, and stars move steadily through the sky.

In the second century A.D., an Egyptian mathematician and astronomer named Claudius Ptolemaeus (Ptolemy) published a book called the *Almagest*. In it he gave a mathematical description of the universe as **geocentric** or Earth-centered. Ptolemy's theory of how the Sun, planets, and stars move through space was widely accepted for the next 1400 years.

In 1543, the Polish astronomer Nicolaus Copernicus (1473–1543) gave a different view of the universe in his book *On the Revolutions of the Celestial Spheres*. After 30 years of research, he concluded that the planets—including Earth—have a **heliocentric** movement: They actually revolve around the Sun. The apparent motion of heavenly bodies through the sky is due primarily to Earth's rotation. This idea had been proposed by Greek scholars as early as the third century B.C., but had been ignored.

Copernicus's theory did not perfectly explain the movement of all the planets that were known at the time, but it led scientists in a new direction. Astronomer Tycho Brahe (1546–1601) gathered large quantities of data in a search for the true laws of motion for the planets. Although Brahe died before he could complete his theory, his assistant, Johannes Kepler (1571–1630), developed mathematical models that correctly explained the observed motion of the planets. Kepler showed that planetary orbits are elliptical (oval) rather than circular. He also demonstrated that the Moon is a satellite of Earth.

In *Everyday Mathematics*, you have developed mathematical models to describe situations, represent relationships, and solve problems. These models have included number sentences and graphs. You are solving problems that are simpler than Kepler's, but you are following the same approach to problem solving that he used. You can read more about problem solving on pages 129 and 130 in the *Student Reference Book*.

Planet Data

The tables on this page and the next page show estimates of diameters, distances from the Sun, and surface temperatures of the planets, rounded to 2 **significant figures**. The data are presented in both customary and metric units. In your explorations, you can choose which units to work with.

The **diameter** of a **sphere** is the length of a line segment that passes through the center of the sphere and has **endpoints** on the sphere. Planets are not quite spheres, so "average diameter" is used in the data tables.

sphere

Planets move around the Sun in orbits that are **ellipses** (ovals), somewhat perturbed by the gravitational pulls of other planets. Except for Mercury and Pluto, the orbits are very nearly circles. Estimates of "average distances" from the Sun are accurate enough for anything done in the *Sixth Grade Everyday Mathematics* Solar System Project.

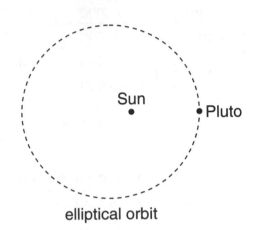

elliptical orbit

Solar System Data Table 1			
	Average Diameter (Miles)	Average Distance from the Sun (Miles)	Surface Temperature (Degrees Fahrenheit)
Mercury	3,000	36,000,000 or $3.6 * 10^7$	−290 to 800
Venus	7,500	67,000,000 or $6.7 * 10^7$	850 to 910
Earth	7,900	93,000,000 or $9.3 * 10^7$	−130 to 140
Mars	4,200	140,000,000 or $1.4 * 10^8$	−190 to 80
Jupiter	89,000	480,000,000 or $4.8 * 10^8$	−240 to −150
Saturn	75,000	890,000,000 or $8.9 * 10^8$	−290 to −150
Uranus	31,000	1,800,000,000 or $1.8 * 10^9$	−330
Neptune	30,000	2,800,000,000 or $2.8 * 10^9$	−310
Pluto	1,600	3,700,000,000 or $3.7 * 10^9$ [†]	−350
Sun	870,000		5,400 to 36,000,000

[†]Since 1979, Pluto has been closer to the Sun than Neptune, at a little less than 2,800,000,000 miles. It will become the most distant planet again in 1999.

Exploring the Solar System (continued)

Solar System Data Table 2			
	Average Diameter (Kilometers)	Average Distance from the Sun (Kilometers)	Surface Temperature (Degrees Celsius)
Mercury	4,900	58,000,000 or $5.8 * 10^7$	−180 to 430
Venus	12,000	110,000,000 or $1.1 * 10^8$	450 to 490
Earth	13,000	150,000,000 or $1.5 * 10^8$	−90 to 60
Mars	6,800	230,000,000 or $2.3 * 10^8$	−120 to 30
Jupiter	140,000	780,000,000 or $7.8 * 10^8$	−150 to −100
Saturn	120,000	1,400,000,000 or $1.4 * 10^9$	−180 to −160
Uranus	51,000	2,900,000,000 or $2.9 * 10^9$	−200
Neptune	49,000	4,500,000,000 or $4.5 * 10^9$	−190
Pluto	2,600	5,900,000,000 or $5.9 * 10^9$ [†]	−210
Sun	1,400,000		3,000 to 20,000,000

[†]Since 1979, Pluto has been closer to the Sun than Neptune, at a little less than 4,500,000,000 kilometers. It will become the most distant planet again in 1999.

Estimates and Comparing Big Numbers

Here is one strategy for comparing big numbers.

Problem   Compare the distance of Earth from the Sun with the distances of Mars and Neptune.

Think   Earth to Sun   150,000,000 km or 150 million km
Mars to Sun   230,000,000 km, or 230 million km
Neptune to Sun   4,500,000,000 km or 4,500 million km

Ask   "About how many 150 millions are in 230 million? In 4500 million?"

Another strategy is to compare distances in scientific notation. It is important to compare like powers of 10. Write equivalent names to make the division easier.

Think   Earth to Sun $1.5 * 10^8$ km or $15 * 10^7$
Mars to Sun $2.3 * 10^8$ km or $23 * 10^7$
Neptune to Sun $4.5 * 10^9$ km or $45 * 10^8$ or $450 * 10^7$

Ask   "About how many 15's in 23? In 450?"

Life on Other Planets

Until recently, scientific studies of the other planets in the Solar System have found no signs of life. Jupiter's large moons have temperatures that could sustain life, but Voyager space probes examined these moons from 1979 to 1981 and found no life. Some scientists speculate that on Mars, small organisms might live underground, where temperatures would be moderate. Also, there are geological signs that Mars had water hundreds of thousands of years ago, which raises the possibility that life existed there in the past.

Just before this book went to the printer, an article in the August 16, 1996, issue of *Science* magazine reported that there may have been life on Mars over 3 billion years ago. The evidence—possibly the remains of bacteria (a tiny, simple form of life)—was in a potato-size rock found in Antarctica in 1984. The rock is thought to have come from Mars after that planet was struck by an asteroid 16 million years ago. There is certain to be considerable argument about this evidence—you may want to find out what has happened since this book was printed.

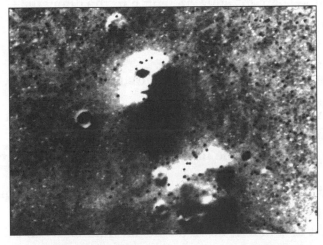

Photographs of the surface of Mars taken by the *Viking I* orbiter in 1976 showed a face-like object. Some people claim that it was built by intelligent beings. Astronomers, however, say that the face is just a combination of sunlight and shadow on eroded landforms.

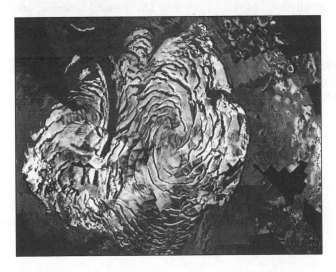

The photograph shows the north pole of Mars, which is covered by water in the form of ice. There might be liquid water under the ice cap. This is one of the regions where missions to Mars will look for signs of life.

Making a Scale Model of Your Planet

To make a 2-dimensional scale model of your planet, your Planet Team needs a pencil, ruler, scissors, tape, compass, and colored construction paper.

If possible, use the chart at the right to select the color(s) of paper for your planet. These are the main colors of the planets as seen from Earth and space probes.

Planet	Color
Mercury	Orange
Venus	Yellow
Earth	Blue, brown, green
Mars	Red
Jupiter	Yellow, red, brown, white
Saturn	Yellow
Uranus	Green
Neptune	Blue
Pluto	Yellow

1. With a ruler, draw a line segment equal in length to the diameter your planet should have in the model. If you are modeling Jupiter or Saturn, you may need to tape two pieces of paper together.

2. Find the **midpoint** (middle) of this line segment and mark a dot there.

3. Use a compass to draw a circle. The center of the circle should be at the midpoint you just marked. Put the point of the compass on the dot. Put the pencil on one endpoint of the line segment, and draw the circle.

If your compass is too small, tie a string around a pencil near the point. Hold the point of the pencil on one endpoint of the line segment. Stretch the string tight and hold it down at the dot (midpoint) on the line segment. Keeping the string tight, swing the pencil around to draw a circle.

4. Cut out and label the circle.

5. Share your work with the other Planet Teams.

Additional Information

More detail can be added to the model by including some or all of the following celestial bodies.

Asteroids These are large pieces of rock too small to be considered planets. They range in size from big boulders to small mountains. Ceres, one of the largest asteroids, has a diameter of 580 miles or 940 kilometers. Most asteroids are in what is known as the Asteroid Belt. The Asteroid Belt lies between Mars and Jupiter, roughly 180 to 270 million miles (290 to 430 million kilometers) from the Sun. To date more than 18,000 asteroids have been identified in this region of the Solar System. They can be represented in the model by small pen dots on pieces of paper or sticky notes.

Moons Mars, Jupiter, Saturn, Uranus, and Neptune each have two or more moons. Mercury and Venus have no moons. The largest moons of Jupiter and Saturn are larger than Mercury and Pluto.

Jupiter has at least 16 moons. The four largest moons and their diameters are the following:

Moons	Diameters	
Ganymede	3200 mi	5300 km
Callisto	2900 mi	4800 km
Io	2200 mi	3600 km
Europa	1900 mi	3100 km

Saturn has at least 18 moons. The largest is Titan; its diameter is 3100 miles (5200 kilometers).

Earth's moon has a diameter of 2200 miles (3750 kilometers). It is slightly less than $\frac{1}{3}$ the size of Earth.

Rings It has been known for a long time that Saturn is surrounded by large, beautiful rings. When the Voyager spacecraft visited Jupiter, Neptune, and Uranus in the 1980's, it discovered that these planets also had rings, although they are considerably smaller and less grand than Saturn's. Saturn has six rings of different colors. The rings are made up of frozen water particles ranging in size from tiny grains to blocks of ice 30 yards in diameter. The rings are only a few miles thick, but they extend out from the planet for 50,000 miles (80,000 kilometers).

Beyond the Solar System

Our Sun is just an ordinary star, one of an estimated 100 billion in the Milky Way galaxy. The nearest star beyond the Solar System, Proxima Centauri, is 25,000,000,000,000 miles from the Sun. That is about 7000 times the average distance from the Sun to Pluto.

The huge distance to Proxima Centauri indicates how extremely large the universe is. To simplify calculations, astronomers usually measure distances beyond the Solar System in **light years**. A light year is the distance light travels in 1 year: about 6 trillion miles ($6 * 10^{12}$ miles), or 9.5 trillion kilometers ($9.5 * 10^{12}$ kilometers).

Proxima Centauri is 4.3 light years away. Some of the visible stars are 20 to 80 light years away, or 5 to 20 times farther than Proxima Centauri. Many of the stars in the Milky Way galaxy are less than 35,000 light years away. Astronomers, however, consider such stars to be relatively near. Andromeda, the galaxy nearest to the Milky Way, is about 2 million light years away.

Four space probes launched in the 1970's, *Pioneer 10* and *11* and *Voyager 1* and *2*, are now heading beyond the Solar System. *Pioneer 10* is the most distant object made by humans. Launched in 1972, it was 5 billion miles from Earth in 1993. It is traveling toward outer space at 40,000 miles per hour.

These probes will send back important information about the outer edges of the Solar System. Then scientists will lose contact with them. The probes, however, may travel through space for hundreds of centuries.

Source: Gerrit Vershuur, "Race to the Sun's Edge," *Air and Space*, April/May 1993.

The **speed of light:**
    about 186,000 miles per second
    about 300,000 kilometers per second

1 **light year:**
    about 5.9 trillion miles ($5.9 * 10^{12}$ mi)
    about 9.5 trillion kilometers ($9.5 * 10^{12}$ km)
    about 63,000 astronomical units

Spaceship Earth

To be a successful space traveler, you must be able to find your way back to Earth. This may not be easy. You do not feel it, but at this moment you are traveling through space at incredible speeds.

Earth spins around like a top. In 24 hours, it makes one complete **rotation.** When the part we live on faces the Sun, we have day. When it faces away from the Sun, we have night.

At the equator, the distance around the Earth is about 25,000 miles. In the middle of the United States, the distance falls to about 21,000 miles. This means that if you live in the middle of the United States, you travel about 21,000 miles every day.

21,000 miles

25,000 miles

At the same time Earth is rotating, it is moving in its orbit around the Sun. In one year, Earth makes one complete **revolution** or trip around the Sun. This trip is approximately 600,000,000 (or $6 * 10^8$) miles long.

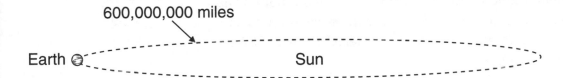

600,000,000 miles

Earth

Sun

Movement of the Planets Around the Sun

Like Earth, all of the planets are in constant motion. Each rotates like a top and revolves around the Sun. Compared with Earth, some planets are fast, while others are quite slow. Understanding the movement of the planets is important for space travel. You need to know where to aim the spaceship.

Solar System Data Table 3			
Planet	Average Speed in Orbit: Miles per Earth day	Time to Revolve Once Around the Sun: Earth Days or Years	Time to Rotate Once: Earth Days or Hours
Mercury	2,600,000	88 days	59 days
Venus	1,900,000	223 days	243 days
Earth	1,600,000	365 days	24 hours
Mars	1,300,000	686 days	25 hours
Jupiter	700,000	12 years	10 hours
Saturn	520,000	29 years	11 hours
Uranus	360,000	84 years	16 hours
Neptune	290,000	165 years	18 hours
Pluto	250,000	249 years	6 days

Source: Lewis, Richard. *The Illustrated Encyclopedia of the Universe.* New York: Harmony Books, 1983.

Minimum Distances

The constant movement of the planets complicates space travel. Since the planets move at different speeds, exact calculations are needed to figure out the direction spaceships should move. Another problem is that the distances between Earth and the other planets are always changing.

Complex mathematical models are used with computers to calculate the relationship of Earth to the other planets, and to plot the data needed to send space probes to other planets. But several fortunate facts make it possible to make rough estimates of some things we might want to know for space travel.

All the planets except Pluto travel in nearly circular orbits with the Sun at the center.

For all the planets except Pluto, those nearly circular orbits are almost in the same plane. This means that when the planets pass each other on the same radius from the Sun, that minimum distance can be calculated from the information in the Solar System Data Tables on pages 231 and 232. This can be seen in the following diagram.

Earth revolves quickly around the Sun compared with all of the planets except Mercury and Venus. This means that at least once a year, Earth and each of the outer planets line up on the same radius from the Sun, at the minimum distance. The times are predictable, too. It is harder to predict when Earth will line up with Mercury and Venus. However, they do line up from time to time. (For Pluto the situation is even more difficult. You might want to take it as a challenge, but it can't be done using only the information in this book.)

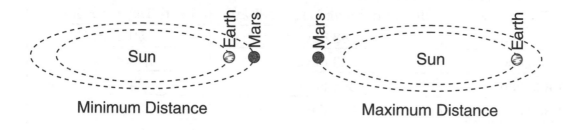

Minimum Distance   Maximum Distance

Moving to Mars

The fourth planet from the Sun has fascinated people for thousands of years. Because of its blood-red color, the Romans named it for their god of war, Mars. The ancient Babylonians called it Nergal, for their god of death; the Greeks called it Ares, for their god of battle.

There has long been speculation about whether life exists on Mars. In 1877, the Italian astronomer Giovanni Schiaparelli reported seeing markings on Mars that he called "canals." The American astronomer Percival Lowell claimed that the canals had been dug by intelligent beings to bring water from polar ice caps to irrigate their crops.

In 1950, Ray Bradbury published *The Martian Chronicles*, a collection of science-fiction short stories that became very popular. In these stories, Earth people colonize and corrupt a peaceful Martian civilization.

Today we know that Mars is a cold, barren planet without intelligent life, although recent discoveries indicate that microscopic life may have existed there long ago. The question of "canals" was settled by pictures from a series of spacecraft that visited Mars. The first was *Mariner 4*, which flew past in 1965. In 1976, *Viking I* and *Viking 2* both landed on the surface of Mars and sent back thousands of images.

Exploration of Mars was delayed when the Mars Observer, a spacecraft sent to make maps, was lost in space in 1993. The U.S. launched two new missions to Mars in 1996. One of these, the Mars Global Surveyor, will observe Mars from an orbit around the planet beginning in September 1997. The other, the Mars Pathfinder, will land on the surface in July 1997 and send out a robot, the 25-pound "Rover Sojourner," to investigate the terrain.

Our increasing knowledge of Mars and of space travel has stimulated people to think seriously about sending people to Mars. They argue that human exploration of Mars would advance our knowledge of the solar system, improve technology, establish a place beyond Earth where humans can survive, and inspire the people of the world.

Opponents claim that such a mission would be too expensive and too dangerous because of long exposure to radiation and zero gravity, and it would require the development of technologies that would not be useful on Earth.

The National Aeronautics and Space Administration (NASA) has developed plans for a human mission to Mars. In one of these plans, a series of spacecraft carrying equipment and supplies are sent to orbit Mars beginning in 2007. A crew of six astronauts is launched in 2009. They descend to the surface of Mars, spend over 500 days there, and return to Earth in 2011.

Sources: Britannica OnLine;
Mars Global Surveyor (http://mgs-www.jpl.nasa.gov/home.html);
Mars Pathfinder (http://mpfwww.jpl.nasa.gov/);
Mars Exploration Strategies (http://www-sn.jsc.nasa.gov/explore/Data/Lib/DOCS/EIC043.HTML)

Predicting Body Sizes

Anthropometry is the study of human body sizes and proportions. An **anthropometrist** is a person who gathers data on the size of the body and its components. Body-size data are useful to engineers, architects, industrial designers, interior designers, clothing manufacturers, and artists. For example:

- Automotive engineers use body-size data in designing vehicles, and to set standards for infant and child safety seats.
- Architects take body-size data into account when designing stairs, planning safe kitchens and bathrooms, and providing access space for wheelchair occupants.
- Clothing manufacturers use body-size data to create sewing patterns.

No two people are exactly alike, not even identical twins. There are big differences in body sizes and proportions depending on age, sex, and ethnic or racial membership.

- There are no "perfect rules" that can be used to predict one body measurement exactly from another body measurement. For example, no rule can exactly predict a man's weight from his height, or his height from his arm length.
- There are "imperfect rules" and "rules of thumb" that can be useful in relating one body measurement to another.

This project investigates two such imperfect rules.

The first rule is sometimes used to predict the height of an adult when the length of the person's tibia is known. The tibia is the shinbone. When the measurements are in inches, the rule is:

Height = 2.6 * Length of Tibia + 25.5

The second rule relates the circumference of a person's neck to the circumference of the person's wrist.

Circumference of Neck = 2 * Circumference of Wrist

As part of this project, you will collect some body-size data for an adult male, an adult female, and yourself.

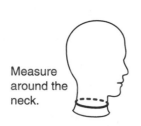

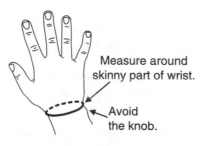

After combining your data with data collected by your classmates, you will evaluate how good the rules are for predicting the body sizes for adults and sixth-grade students.

The First International Paper Airplane Competition

The First International Paper Airplane Competition was held during the winter of 1966–67 and sponsored by *Scientific American* magazine. The 11,851 entries (an estimated 5000 from children), from 28 different countries, were original designs for paper airplanes. These paper airplanes were entered into one or more of the following categories:

- duration aloft (the winning designs spent 9.9 and 10.2 seconds in the air),
- distance flown (the winning designs flew 58 feet, 2 inches and 91 feet, 6 inches),
- aerobatics (stunts performed in flight),
- origami (the traditional Japanese art or technique of folding paper into a variety of decorative or representational forms).

Contestants were permitted to use paper of any weight and size. The smallest entry received, entered in the distance category, measured 0.08 inch by 0.00003 inch. However, this entry was found to be made of foil, not paper. The largest entry received, also entered in the distance category, was 11 feet long. It flew two times its length when tested.

The Leonardo

Scientific American awarded a winner's trophy to two designers, a nonprofessional and a professional, in each category. Nonprofessionals were people not professionally involved in air travel. Professionals were "people employed in the air travel business, people who build non-paper airplanes, and people who subscribe to *Scientific American* because they fly so much."

The winners in each category received a trophy called *The Leonardo*, named after Leonardo da Vinci (1452–1519), whom *Scientific American* refers to as the "Patron Saint of Paper Airplanes."

Da Vinci, known for many accomplishments in the fields of painting and sculpture, was also an architect, engineer, and inventive builder. Studying the flight of birds, da Vinci believed that it would be possible to build a flying apparatus which would enable humans to soar through the air. He designed several wing-flapping machines, suggested the use of rotating wings similar to those of the modern helicopter, and invented the "air screw," similar to the modern propeller, to pull a machine through the air.

Self portrait of Leonardo da Vinci done in red chalk

More information about the First International Paper Airplane Competition, as well as templates and directions for making each of the winning designs, can be found in the book, *The Great International Paper Airplane Book*, by Jerry Mander, George Dippel, and Howard Gossage; Simon and Schuster Publishing, 1971.

A Winning Paper Airplane Design

The design plan shown below was submitted by Louis Schultz, an engineer. Schultz's paper airplane flew 58 feet, 2 inches, and was a winner in the distance category for nonprofessionals. The professional winner in the distance category was Robert Meuser. His paper airplane flew 91 feet, 6 inches, before it hit the rear wall of the testing site.

1. Follow the directions below to make an accurate copy of the design plan on an $8\frac{1}{2}$" by 11" sheet of paper.

   a. Use a ruler to find the midpoints at the top and bottom of the paper. Mark these points. Draw a line connecting the midpoints.

   b. Mark two points that are $\frac{1}{4}$ inch away from the midpoint at the top of the paper.

   c. Use a protractor to make two 45° angles as shown.

   d. Use a protractor to make two 82° angles as shown.

Louis Schultz's Paper Airplane Design Plan

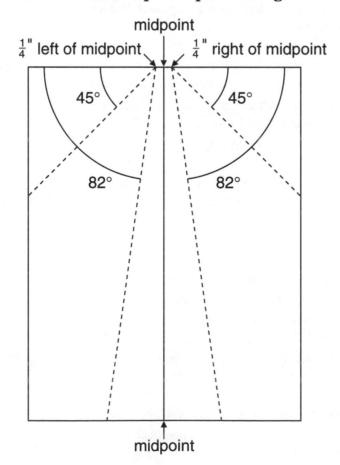

midpoint

$\frac{1}{4}$" left of midpoint $\frac{1}{4}$" right of midpoint

45°   45°

82°   82°

midpoint

A Winning Paper Airplane Design (continued)

2. Assemble the paper airplane as shown below. Be very careful to make precise folds. Make the folds on a table. When making a fold, first press down onto the paper with a finger. Then go over this fold with a pen or a ruler on its side. It is important that you **do not** use your fingernails to make folds. (Using your fingernail causes more than one fold to be made in a small area. This fold will move as you attempt to make the rest of the plane.)

a. Fold the paper back and forth along the center line to get a nice crease. Then unfold.

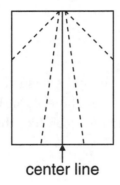

center line

b. Fold corners along the dashed lines as shown. Use a small piece of tape to secure each corner as shown in the sketch.

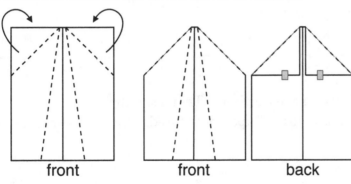

front   front   back

c. With the back side of the paper facing you, fold the right side of the paper toward the center so that the edges highlighted in the sketch meet. Use a small piece of tape to secure the flap in the position shown in the sketch. Do the same to the other side.

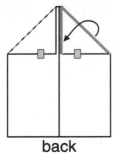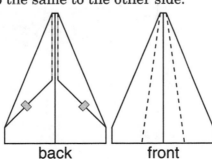

back   back   front

Designing a Paper Airplane (continued)

A Winning Paper Airplane Design (continued)

d. Flip the paper to the front side. Fold in half along the center line so that the front side is now in the inside. Your paper airplane should now look like this.

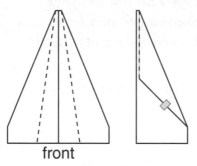

front

e. Take the top flap of the paper and fold it outward along the dashed lines. (Look for these dashed lines on the inside of the plane.) Do the same to the other flap. Your paper airplane should now look like this.

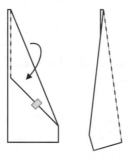

f. First, tape the wings together on top of the airplane. Then tape the bottom as shown, making sure that all loose flaps are secured.

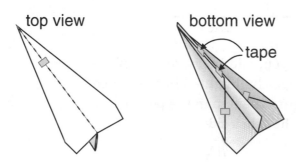

top view
bottom view
tape

Student Reference Book

Air is a real substance, just as water, the earth, and maple syrup are real substances. Because air is a substance, it offers **resistance** or opposition to the movement of objects through it.

Imagine dropping a penny into a bottle of maple syrup. The penny will eventually fall to the bottom of the bottle, but the maple syrup will slow its progress—the maple syrup will offer resistance to the movement of the penny. Air works in much the same way—objects can move through it, but the air offers resistance to the movement of those objects.

Did you know that this resistance can serve a helpful purpose? Try the following experiments to see how resistance can be used to help an object, such as an airplane, move through the air more efficiently.

The "Kite Effect"

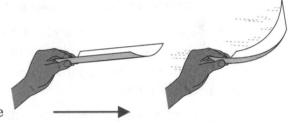

1. Hold one end of an $8\frac{1}{2}$" by 11" sheet of paper as illustrated—forefinger on top, supported by the thumb and second finger on the bottom. Notice that the paper in the illustration is tilted slightly so that the opposite end of the paper is a bit higher than the end that you are holding.

2. *Push* the paper directly forward as illustrated.

You will notice that the end of the paper, opposite the end that you are holding, tilts up. When the tilted surface of the paper pushes against the air, the air pushes back. This partially slows the paper down, and partially lifts it up.

The sheet of paper has some of the characteristics of an airplane wing. The wings of an airplane are set at an angle so that their front edge is higher than their back edge. In this way, the lower surface of the airplane wing uses the air resistance to achieve a small amount of lift.

The "Vacuum Effect"

1. Hold the small end of a 2" by 6" strip of paper between your thumb and forefinger as illustrated—thumb on top. The paper should fall in a curve.

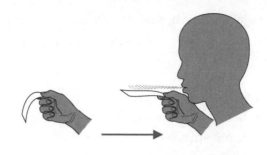

2. Blow over the top of the paper as illustrated.

As you blow over the top of the paper, you will notice that the end of the paper, opposite the end that you are holding, tilts up. Air rushing over the upper surface of the paper causes the air pressure on the upper surface to decrease. When the air pressure on the upper surface becomes less than the air pressure on the lower surface, the higher pressure underneath lifts the paper.

This sheet of paper also has some of the characteristics of an airplane wing. Only the lower surface of an airplane wing is flat; the upper surface is curved or arched. In this way, the upper surface of the airplane wing also uses the air resistance to achieve lift.

Both the "kite effect" and the "vacuum effect" contribute to the total lift of an airplane. However, the "vacuum effect" is responsible for about 80% of it.

Additional Sources of Information About Paper Airplanes

Paper Plane Pilot is a computer program published by MECC. With it, you can study the effect that 4 variables (plane shape, plane weight, launch angle, and launch force) have on paper airplanes. For additional information about obtaining this program, call MECC at 1-800-215-0368.

If you are interested in finding monthly paper airplane designs on the Internet, you can visit the following site: http://pchelp.inc.net/paper_ac.htm. The site allows you to print out directions and templates for folding a variety of planes. As of August of 1996, monthly airplane designs were available from May of 1995 through June of 1996.

If you are interested in available paper airplane software, tips for making and flying planes, and step-by-step directions for folding a variety of planes, you can visit the following site: http://www.cs.man.ac.uk/%7Eyeomansb/planes/tips.html.

Keep in mind that Web sites come and go. The ones cited here may no longer be in existence, but there probably will be many new ones to take their place.

You can find many additional Web sites of interest by simply searching the Internet under the topic "paper airplanes."

Draw a Rectangular Solid

Follow these steps to draw a rectangular solid or box.

Step 1: Draw a horizontal line segment to be the horizon line. Mark a point on the horizon line to be the vanishing point.

Step 2: Use your Geometry Template to draw a rectangle. This will be the front face of the box.

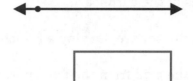

Step 3: Draw line segments from the four vertices of the rectangle to the vanishing point. These are called **vanishing lines**.

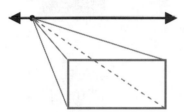

Step 4: Draw a line segment for the edge at the back of the box, parallel to the top edge of the front.

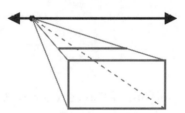

Step 5: Complete the top face of the box.

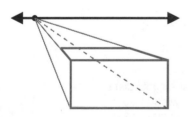

Step 6: Draw a side edge for the back of the box, parallel to the side edge of the front.

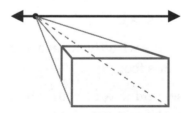

Step 7: Complete the side face of the box.

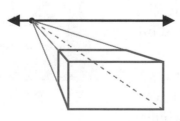

Draw a Person

Materials: piece of cardboard at least $8\frac{1}{2}$ inches by 11 inches, transparency with grid (from your teacher), scissors, masking or transparent tape, Geometry Template, dark-colored transparency marker

Step 1: Near the top of the piece of cardboard, draw a square with sides 6 inches long. Draw it so that its sides are at least 1 inch from the sides of the cardboard.

Step 2: Cut out the square, leaving a 6-inch "window" in the cardboard.

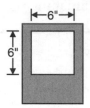

Step 3: Cut out the grid from the transparency. Be sure to cut along the dashed line segments as indicated. You will get a square piece about 7 inches on a side.

Step 4: Tape the grid to the cardboard. The grid should fit completely within the cardboard window.

Step 5: Tape the bottom of the cardboard to a chair back, so that the window is above the chair.

Step 6: Partners take turns drawing each other as follows.

Your partner sits in a chair with her or his legs on a desk or table top.

Place the chair with the attached cardboard 3 to 4 feet in front of your partner's feet.

Sit or kneel and look at your partner through the grid in the window. Adjust your distance away from the window. Your partner should be completely visible, except for the part that is below the desk or table top, and should fill up most of the window.

Try to keep your head in the same position. Use the transparency marker to trace any outline of your partner on the plastic window.

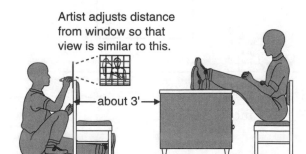

Artist adjusts distance from window so that view is similar to this.

about 3'

What is a Calorie?

Your body needs food to live and grow. It uses the materials in food to produce energy—energy to keep your body warm and moving, and to build and repair muscles and tissues.

The amount of energy a food will produce when it is digested by the body is measured in a unit called the **calorie**. A calorie is *not* a substance in food.

Example:

> A tablespoon of sugar produces about 50 calories of energy when digested.

Calorie information on nutrition labels on food packages assumes that an average adult eats foods that supply about 2000 calories of energy per day. However, the appropriate number of calories will vary, depending on the age and size of the person and on how active the person is. For example, if two persons perform the same physical activity, the heavier person will use more calories than the lighter person because it requires more energy to move the extra body weight. Similarly, an active person expends more energy than a less active person and so needs to take in more calories.

What is a Balanced Diet?

Food contains materials called **fat**, **carbohydrate**, and **protein**.

A person who follows a healthful, **balanced diet** eats foods that supply the recommended balance between fat, carbohydrate, and protein as shown in the graph at the right, and takes in the appropriate number of calories.

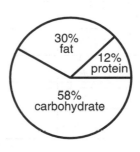

Examples

	Weight	Fat	Carbohydrate	Protein	Calories
1 tbs of oil	14 g	14 g	0 g	0 g	126
1 tbs of sugar	12 g	0 g	12 g	0 g	48
1 large egg white	30 g	trace	trace	4 g	16
1 cup of water	237 g	0 g	0 g	0 g	0

1 cup = 16 tablespoons

1 pound = 16 ounces; 1 pound is about 454 grams; 1 ounce is about 28 grams.

A "trace" indicates an amount less than 0.5 gram.

About How Many Calories Do You Use in a Typical 24-Hour Day?

The calorie-use table on page 251 shows the number of calories per minute and per hour used by the average sixth grader for various activities. In this table, the calorie use is reported

- as calories per minute and
- as calories per hour.

The calorie-use table will help you to estimate the total number of calories you use in a typical day. Make a table like the following or use the table on page 219 in your journal to record your work.

My Activities During a Typical 24-Hour School Day			
Activity	Time Spent in Activity	Calorie Rate (cal/hr or cal/min)	Calories Used for Activity

1. Think of all the things you do during a typical 24-hour school day. Make a list of your activities.

2. Record your estimate of the time you spend on each activity. Check that the times add up to 24 hours.

3. For each activity, refer to the calorie-use table and record the number of calories per hour or per minute for the activity.

4. Calculate the number of calories you use for each activity listed.

5. Add the calories used for each activity to find the total number of calories you use in a typical 24-hour day.

Calorie Use by Average 6th Graders		
Activity	calories/minute	calories/hour
Sleeping	0.7	40
Studying, writing, sitting	1.2	70
Eating, talking, sitting in class	1.2	70
Standing	1.3	80
Dressing & undressing	1.5	90
Walking (slow, at 2 mph)	2.2	130
Walking (brisk, at 3.5 mph)	3.0	180
Housework, gardening	2.0	120
Vacuuming	2.7	160
Raking leaves	3.7	220
Snow shoveling	5.0	300
Bicycling (6 mph)	2.8	170
Bicycling (13 mph)	4.5	270
Bicycling (20 mph)	8.3	500
Running (5 mph)	6.0	360
Running (7.5 mph)	9.3	560
Swimming (20 yards/minute)	3.3	200
Swimming (40 yards/minute)	5.8	350
Basketball & soccer (vigorous)	9.7	580
Volleyball	4.0	240
Aerobic dance (vigorous)	6.0	360
Square dancing	4.0	240

Plan Your Own Lunch

The menu on page 253 lists different food items that you might select for lunch. Calorie information is given for each food.

1. Choose any five items from the menu that you might like to have for lunch. Check these off on the menu.

2. Copy the five items selected from the menu to a table like the one shown below or on page 223 in your journal. Enter the number of calories in the appropriate columns.

Food	Total Calories	Calories from Fat	Calories from Carbohydrate	Calories from Protein
Total				

3. Calculate the total number of calories for each column in the table.

4. Calculate what percent of the total number of calories comes from fat, carbohydrate, and protein calories.

5. Determine whether this is a "healthy" lunch—one in which no more than 30% of calories come from fat, and which comes close to the recommended percents for carbohydrate and protein calories.

6. Plan another lunch in which no more than 30% of calories come from fat, and which comes fairly close to meeting the recommended percents for carbohydrate and protein calories.

Food	Total Calories	Calories from Fat	Calories from Carbohydrate	Calories from Protein
Ham sandwich	265	110	110	45
Turkey sandwich	325	70	155	100
Hamburger	330	135	120	75
Cheeseburger	400	200	110	90
Double burger, cheese, sauce	500	225	175	100
Grilled cheese sandwich	380	220	100	60
Peanut butter & jelly sandwich	380	160	170	50
Chicken nuggets (6)	250	125	65	60
Bagel	165	20	120	25
Bagel with cream cheese	265	105	125	35
Hard-boiled egg	80	55	0	25
French fries (small bag)	250	120	115	15
Apple	100	10	90	0
Carrot	30	0	25	5
Orange	75	0	70	5
Cake (slice)	235	65	160	10
Cashew nuts (1 ounce)	165	115	30	20
Doughnut	205	100	75	25
Blueberry muffin	110	30	70	10
Apple pie (slice)	250	125	115	10
Frozen yogurt cone	100	10	75	15
Orange juice (8 oz)	80	0	75	5
2% milk (8 oz)	145	45	60	40
Skim milk (8 oz)	85	0	50	35
Soft drink (8 oz)	140	0	140	0
Diet soft drink (8 oz)	0	0	0	0

Drawing an Enlargement of a Picture

Use the following procedure to draw an enlargement of your own.
You will need the following materials:

- a picture with simple shapes and lines, such as a comic strip character
- 1-inch grid paper
- ruler
- sharp pencil with eraser
- colored pencils, markers, or crayons

Directions:

Step 1: Use a ruler and pencil to draw a $\frac{1}{2}$-inch square grid pattern onto the picture that you have chosen.

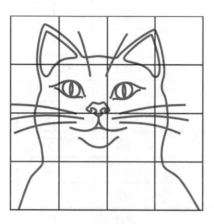

Step 2: Copy the part of the original picture in each grid square onto the corresponding grid square of the 1-inch grid. Notice where each line and shape begins and ends on the original grid and locate its relative position on the 1-inch grid.

Try to reproduce all of the lines and shapes as accurately as you can. This method for drawing the copy is called **sighting**.

Note: Depending on the size of the picture that you chose, you may need to tape together several pieces of one-inch grid paper to create your enlargement.

Step 3: After you have completed the drawing in pencil, you may want to add color to fill in shapes or to darken lines.

If you follow this procedure, you will draw a 2X enlargement of the original picture. Each $\frac{1}{2}$-inch length was doubled. The size-change factor depends on the size of the grid squares on the original picture and the size of the grid onto which you make your drawing.

A West African Mask and the Golden Ratio

Masks have played an important part in the ceremonies of many cultures through the ages. Masks were worn on special occasions—for sacred rituals, initiations, burials, healings, to assure success in hunting or war, or just for entertainment. In the United States, masks are often worn by children as part of their Halloween costumes.

In ancient cultures, masks were commonly used as disguises. The wearer pretended that he or she was someone else—for example, a hero of the past, an animal, a monster, a ghost, or a witch.

The mask shown on this page was made in the Benin Kingdom in western Africa in the early 16th century. It was worn by the Oba, which means "king." The Oba was a sacred figure; many ceremonies took place in his honor.

Artists made masks out of many different kinds of materials—wood, bark, bone, shell, clay, metal, paper, ivory, even skin. The Oba's mask is made out of ivory, iron, and copper.

If you measure the sides of the rectangles that frame some of the features in the mask, you will find that the ratio of length to width is the Golden Ratio, about 1.618 to 1. Notice also that the mask is perfectly symmetric.

Try to create a mask of your own.

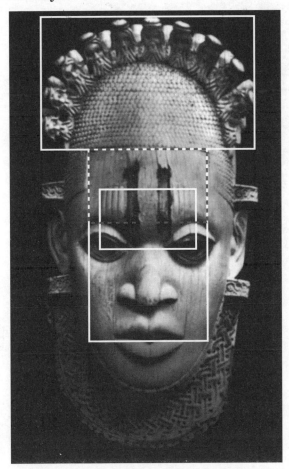

Creating an Escher-Type Translation Tessellation

M. C. Escher (Maurits Cornelius Escher), a graphic artist, was born on June 17, 1898, in Leeuwarden, a small town in the Netherlands. He became famous for his drawings that combined realistic details with optical illusions and distorted perspectives. The drawing at the right, *Hand with Reflecting Sphere*, is a self-portrait of Escher.

In 1936, Escher visited the Alhambra, a Moorish palace in Spain that was built in the thirteenth and fourteenth centuries. He was fascinated by the beautiful tiling patterns, created from simple geometric shapes, that covered the floors and walls.

Escher was inspired by these intricate designs to create tessellations such as those below.

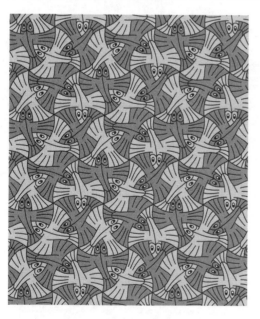
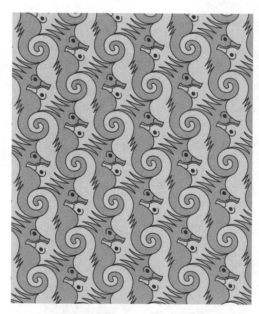

84 85

80 81

Unlike the Islamic artists who decorated the Alhambra, Escher did not limit himself to purely geometric designs. He built tessellations from representations of objects such as birds, fish, reptiles, and humans. Escher used translations (slides), reflections (flips), and rotations (turns) to create unusual and fantastic designs.

Creating an Escher-Type Translation Tessellation (continued)

You will need the following materials:

- sharp pencil
- scissors
- tape
- markers, crayons, or color pencils
- 3-inch by 3-inch square cut from card stock, such as an index card
- large piece of white construction paper

Directions:

Step 1: To create a template for your **translation tessellation**, begin with a square of card stock, 3 inches by 3 inches.

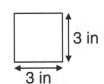

Step 2: Draw a curve from point A to point B.

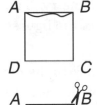

Step 3: Use scissors to cut along curve AB. Tape the cut-out edge of the square so that point A lines up with point D, and point B lines up with point C.

Step 4: Draw a curve from point A to point D.

Step 5: Use scissors to cut along curve AD. Tape the cut-out edge of the square so that point A lines up with point B, and point D lines up with point C.

Step 6: You now have a template for your tessellation. Begin by tracing your template onto the *center* of the construction paper. Continue tracing, interlocking each new tracing with the previous tracing, until you have filled the entire sheet.

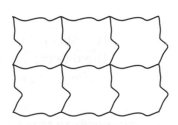

M.C. Escher worked hard to create shapes that not only tessellated, but also looked like birds, reptiles, insects, and other familiar objects. You may want to repeat Steps 1 to 5 several times until you create a recognizable shape.

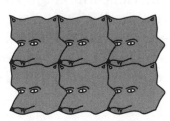

Step 7: Use markers, crayons, or color pencils to decorate your design.

A Point-Symmetry Magic Trick

Set the Stage: Tell a friend that you will be able to guess which playing card, from a set of four, she or he turned upside down while you were not looking.

Materials: Four cards from a regular deck of playing cards. One of the cards should have point symmetry (for example, the 10 of hearts). The other three should not have point symmetry (for example, the ace of hearts).

Performing the Trick:

Step 1: Place four playing cards in a row, faceup.

Example: Notice that only one of the cards, the 10 of hearts, has point symmetry. The other cards do not. Be sure to study the position of the figures on the cards before turning away.

Step 2: Turn your back to the four cards. Tell your friend to rotate one of the cards 180 degrees (turn it upside down).

Step 3: Turn around, study the cards, and tell which card was turned by your friend. If your friend has chosen one of the 3 cards without point symmetry, it will be easy to determine that it was moved. For the cards in the example, you can tell a turned card as follows.

The middle spade is now pointing toward the bottom of the card.

original   180°
position   rotation

The middle diamond is now at the bottom of the card.

original   180°
position   rotation

The stem of the middle club is now at the bottom of the card.

original   180°
position   rotation

If none of the cards without point symmetry has been turned, then the one card with point symmetry must have been turned—in the example, the 10 of hearts.

original   180°
position   rotation

You can perform this trick with any set of playing cards. However, be certain that *exactly one* of the four cards has point symmetry. This may seem like a simple trick, but you know how it works. Many cards look almost the same before and after they have been rotated 180°. So your friend will probably not notice the difference, at least not the first time!

Drawing Shapes with Rotation Symmetry of a Given Order

You will need the following materials:

- sharp pencil
- blank piece of paper
- protractor
- scissors
- index card or other card stock
- compass

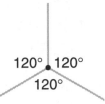

Step 1: On a blank piece of paper, use a sharp pencil to *lightly* draw 3 rays from one point. The rays should be separated by 120°. (The rays form angles of 120°.)

Step 2: Cut out any shape that you wish from an index card. The first time that you try this activity, you might want to work with a simple shape. Once you have learned the procedure, you could try a more complicated shape.

Step 3: Draw a line anywhere through the shape.

Step 4: Push the point of your compass through the shape at any point along the line that you drew. Place the compass point on the paper with the three rays, at the point where the rays intersect. Match the line on the shape with one of the rays.

Step 5: When the shape is lined up properly, remove the compass. Hold the shape in place and trace around it. Replace the compass point and use it to rotate the shape, so that the line on the shape matches up with the next ray. Remove the compass and trace around the shape. Repeat the procedure for the third ray.

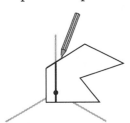
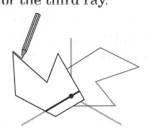

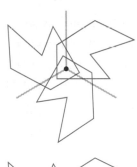

Step 6: Erase any interior lines. The outer edges of the three tracings form a shape with rotation symmetry of order 3. You might want to use tracing paper to copy your shape and check.

Use this procedure to create a shape with a rotation symmetry of order 2. Then try to create a shape with a rotation symmetry of order 5.

A mathematician confided

That a Möbius band is one-sided.

  And you'll get quite a laugh

  If you cut one in half,

For it stays in one piece when divided.

The above limerick was inspired by the work of August Ferdinand Möbius (1790–1868), a German mathematician and astronomer. Möbius examined the properties of one-sided surfaces. One such surface, easily made from a strip of paper, became known as a **Möbius strip** or **Möbius band**. Möbius strips are studied in the branch of mathematics known as topology.

You may think that Möbius strips would be of interest only to mathematicians and magicians. However, they also have practical applications. For example, Möbius strips have been used in the design of drive belts, such as fan belts and conveyor belts.

Friction would wear out an ordinary two-sided belt more quickly on the inside than on the outside.

If a belt with a half-twist (Möbius strip) is used, it wears more evenly and slowly because it only has one side.

Möbius strips are also recognized for their artistic properties. The artist M. C. Escher was intrigued not only by tessellations, but also by Möbius strips. In his work "Möbius Strip II," he depicts nine red ants endlessly crawling along a Möbius strip.

Construct 7 Möbius strips. Follow the directions on page 407 in your journal. Then do the experiments on pages 408 and 409 in your journal.

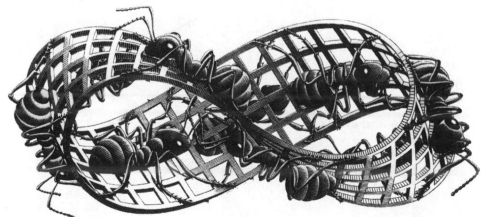

"Möbius Strip II by M.C. Escher. © 1997 Cordon Art - Baarn - Holland. All rights reserved."

Introduction

Two space probes, Voyager 1 and Voyager 2, are now traveling toward outer space. On the chance that life exists beyond the Solar System, each probe carries a gold-coated recording of images and sounds designed to show what life on Earth is like. The recording includes about 90 minutes of music. There is bagpipe music, rock music, and two selections of classical music—the Brandenburg Concerto No. 2 by Johann Sebastian Bach, and the first movement of Ludwig von Beethoven's Fifth Symphony. The music was chosen to demonstrate the intellectual and artistic achievements of human civilization. It was also chosen to show that the people of Earth know how to organize sounds in simple and complex ways to produce music.

In the following projects, you will see that mathematics plays an important role in organizing sounds into music.

1. The Mathematics of Musical Sounds

Motion makes sound. When you speak, pluck a guitar string, hit a drum, or stamp your feet on the ground, you create rapid back-and-forth motions, or **vibrations**. The vibrations produce sound waves in the air, which travel to your ears and move your eardrums back and forth. These vibrations are amplified and carried to the inner ear, where they are turned into electrical signals that travel to your brain.

You can even make sounds without opening your mouth, and you can hear them with your ears covered. Hum without opening your mouth. Can you hear the hum? Now gently cover you ears with your hands and hum. Is the hum louder? Your humming makes your skull vibrate. These vibrations move the little hairs in your inner ear, which turn vibrations into signals to your brain.

High and Low Sounds: Pitch

Some sounds, such as those made by a flute, a crying baby, or a bird, sound "high." Other sounds, such as those made by a big drum, a moose, or thunder, sound "low."

The highness or lowness of a sound is called its **pitch**. The pitch of a sound is related to the rate of the vibrations that produced it.

Typically, things that are shorter, thinner, or more tightly stretched make "higher" sounds because they vibrate more quickly. Things that are longer, thicker, or more loosely stretched make "lower" sounds because they vibrate more slowly.

Materials you need:

- Masters 49–51
- plastic or thin wooden 12-inch ruler

Test this fact by doing the following.

- Place a plastic or thin wooden ruler on your desk or table so that about ten inches stick out over the edge. Hold the ruler firmly on the desk or table with one hand.

- With the other hand, twang the end of the ruler. Notice how quickly it vibrates and the sound it makes.

- Reduce the distance that the ruler hangs over the edge by one-half and twang it again. Then reduce the distance by one-half again and twang the ruler a third time. Look and listen closely. Notice the change in the rate at which it vibrates, and the change in sound.

The pitch of a sound—its highness or lowness—is measured in terms of the vibrations per second of its sound wave. The number of vibrations per second is called the **frequency**.

$$\text{Frequency} = \frac{\text{Number of vibrations}}{\text{Time in which the vibrations occur}}$$

A frequency of 1 vibration per second is called 1 **hertz** (symbol Hz). A sound wave with a frequency of 150 hertz (150 Hz) vibrates 150 times per second.

Example

$$\frac{300 \text{ vibrations}}{2 \text{ seconds}} = 150 \text{ vibrations per second} = 150 \text{ Hz}$$

Low sounds, such as moose's call or thunder, have a low frequency. About 20 vibrations per second creates the lowest sound the average human ear can hear.

High sounds have a high frequency. About 20,000 vibrations per second creates the highest sound the average human ear can hear. The eardrum cannot move any faster.

In most music, the sounds or **notes** range from about 40 vibrations per second to 2000 vibrations per second. The lowest note on a piano has a frequency of about 27 vibrations per second; the highest note has a frequency of about 4200 vibrations per second.

Musical Instruments

Musical instruments produce vibrations of the air in different ways. String instruments, such as a violin, are stroked with a bow or plucked. Drums are hit with sticks. On a clarinet, a reed vibrates; on a trumpet, the player's lips vibrate.

The range of an instrument is the distance from its lowest note (or fewest vibrations per second it can make) to its highest note (or most vibrations per second it can make).

The following chart shows the ranges of some common instruments.

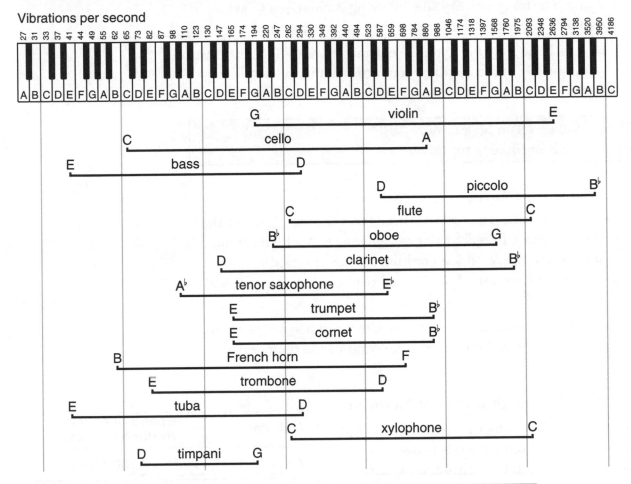

> Complete Music Problem 1 on Master 49.
> Then return here and continue reading.

Loud and Soft Sounds

A sound wave carries information about how high, and how loud, the sound is. The loudness of a sound is determined by how large its vibrations are. When you shout, you move your vocal chords a greater distance than when you whisper. This creates bigger vibrations.

Louder sounds with bigger vibrations cause the eardrum to move back and forth a greater distance.

Soft sounds with smaller vibrations cause the eardrum to move back and forth a smaller distance.

According to some estimates, the faintest sound a human can hear moves the eardrum as little as 1 billionth of a centimeter (0.000000001 cm or $1 * 10^{-9}$ cm).

Very small numbers are hard to understand. It helps to relate them to something you can see or imagine. Try the following comparison to get a sense of how small is 1 billionth of a centimeter.

- The tip of your little finger is about 1 centimeter wide. This distance is about 1 billion times the distance your eardrum moves when it responds to the faintest sound you can hear.

Complete Music Problem 2 on Master 50.
Then return here and continue reading.

The Speed of Sound

Whether they are loud or soft, high or low, sounds travel through air at the same speed. A low whisper will reach your ears just as fast a high scream. This is very important for music. If loud or high sounds traveled faster than soft or low sounds, music would be reduced to chaos before it reached your ears.

Almost all of the sound we hear travels through the air at a speed of about 1100 feet per second. This speed increases somewhat as the temperature increases.

The Speed of Sound through Different Materials

The speed of sound is affected by the material through which the sound travels. Sound travels faster through water, metal, and the ground than through the air.

The speeds shown in the table are approximate. Several factors including the temperature can cause small variations in the speed of sound through a given material. One rule of thumb is that sound can travel through the air at about 1000 feet per second, and through water at about 5000 feet per second.

The fact that sound travels at a constant rate through air affects how musicians are arranged on a stage. Musicians who will be playing or singing at the same time are usually grouped near one another.

Material	Speed of sound through the material
Air	1100 ft/sec
Water	4900 ft/sec
Lucite plastic	8800 ft/sec
Oak wood	14,000 ft/sec
Steel	16,000 ft/sec
Pyrex® glass	18,500 ft/sec

Source: New Grolier's CD ROM Encyclopedia

To see why, complete Music Problem 3 on Master 51.
Then return here and continue reading.

2. The Mathematics of Musical Notes

Music is an organized set of sounds that stir people's minds and emotions. Since sound is made up of vibrations, it is also true that music is an organized set of vibrations. There is a strong mathematical basis to this organization.

The connection between mathematics and music was noticed about 2500 years ago in ancient Greece. The mathematician Pythagoras (or perhaps one of his students) found mathematical relationships between pleasant-sounding combinations of musical notes. When two notes sound good together, there is often a simple ratio between the number of vibrations created by the two notes. This ratio can be described by an "easy" fraction, such as $\frac{1}{2}$.

Materials you need:

- Master 52
- keyboard (optional)

Intervals

In music, an **interval** is the "distance" between two notes. When two notes are sounded one after the other, or together at the same time, they form a musical interval. The interval is the basic building block of music.

- When two or more notes are sounded one after another, they create a **melodic interval**. When two or more notes are sounded at the same time, they create a **harmonic interval**. When three or more notes are played at the same time, they form a **chord**.

Pythagoras was particularly interested in three combinations of musical notes, or intervals. Today musicians know these intervals as the **octave**, the **fifth**, and the **fourth**. It is possible that Pythagoras conducted experiments in order to compare the vibrations created by notes in these intervals.

The Octave

The **octave** is the most basic musical interval. It is like an hour on a clock, an inch on a ruler, or a 10 in counting.

On a piano, the notes played by the white keys are named A, B, C, D, E, F, and G. This series of seven letters, called a scale, is repeated along the keyboard.

An octave spans any eight white keys. It is the interval (or distance) from one note to the next note with the same name—for example, the distance between two consecutive C notes.

When two notes an octave apart are played together, they create a distinct and harmonious sound that is basic in the music of many cultures. This sound can be recognized by most people, even if they do not have musical training.

If there is a piano or other keyboard instrument in the classroom, play two notes an octave apart. Do they sound good together? Then play some combinations that are octaves and some that are not. Can you identify the octaves?

The diagram shows the middle section of a piano and the number of vibrations per second created when each key is played (its frequency).

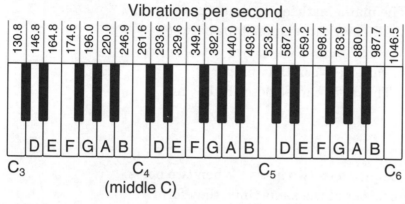

The interval from one A in this diagram to the next A is an octave.

Use this information to uncover the patterns Pythagoras found. Complete Music Problem 4 on Master 52. Then return here and continue reading.

The Fifth and the Fourth

The **fifth** and the **fourth** are two other intervals or combinations of notes that sound particularly good together. Like an octave, they are used extensively by composers.

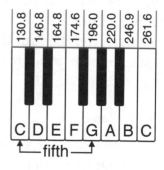

- On a piano, a fifth spans any five white keys, except that a fifth starting on B ends on black key (F sharp).

- On a piano, a fourth spans any four white keys, except that a fourth starting on F ends on a black key (B flat).

Pythagoras learned that if two notes are a fifth apart, or a fourth apart, the rates at which the two notes vibrate can also be compared by simple fractions.

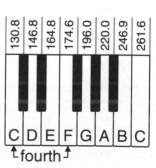

- When two notes a fifth apart are played, the lower note vibrates at a rate that is what fraction of the rate of the higher note? (Use a calculator. Round the resulting decimal to an "easy" fraction.)

- When two notes a fourth apart are played, the lower note vibrates at a rate that is what fraction of the rate of the higher note?

Notes that sound good together have simple mathematical relationships. No one has figured out exactly why this is. Probably some mixture of culture and biology makes us perceive certain combinations to be particularly pleasant and harmonious. Over the centuries, this insight has been used to create new musical instruments and to develop increasingly sophisticated means of organizing sound into music.

Musical Notation

If you create music and want to share it with people far away in time or space, you need a way to record it. Long before the phonograph and tape recorder were invented, musicians developed systems for recording music on paper. These systems of **musical notation** make it possible to give someone instructions for playing a piece of music.

To play a tune, you have to know which pitches to play and in what order to play them. The diagram shows one way of communicating that information. The pattern of evenly spaced horizontal lines is called the **staff**. The curly symbol at the left end of the staff is a **treble clef**. A clef symbol indicates which range of frequencies or pitches to use. The treble clef is used for the right half (the higher pitches) of the piano keyboard.

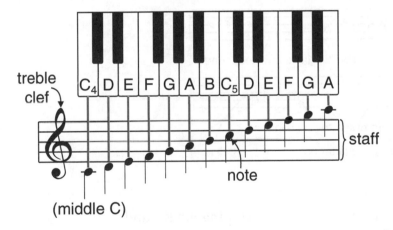

The symbols along the staff are notes. Notes are read from left to right, the same way that you read words in a sentence. The pitch of each note is indicated by where it is placed on the staff. In the diagram, the lowest note is middle C at the left, and the highest note is the A at the far right. The colored lines in the diagram connect each note to the corresponding key on a piano.

Musical notation also represents the rhythm or timing of music. You will learn about rhythm in the next part of the project.

Mathematics and Music (continued)

3. The Mathematics of Musical Time

Composing music involves much more than writing a set of notes that sound good together. Another important consideration is musical time.

A composer needs to consider three aspects of musical time: **rhythm**, **meter**, and **tempo**. Each of these requires mathematical thinking.

You do not need to be a musician to appreciate how mathematics helps organize sound into music. Here is the music for the song "America the Beautiful." The notation conveys a host of mathematical information.

Rhythm

In music, **rhythm** is a regular pattern formed by notes of varying length and emphasis. Rhythm is part of the "beat" or pulse you feel when music is played.

Rhythm makes a piece of music distinct. It's often possible to identify familiar tunes just by hearing their rhythms tapped out.

Try it. Work with a partner. Take turns tapping out well-known tunes, but don't tell each other what they are—for example, "Jingle Bells," "Happy Birthday," "Pop Goes the Weasel," and "Row, Row, Row Your Boat."

Can your partner can recognize the tune? If your partner can, it is because he or she is familiar with its rhythm.

Rhythm is part of dance and speech as well as music. Dance rhythms usually have a steady beat—for example, a waltz rhythm is ONE-two-three, ONE-two-three. Word rhythms are freer. We vary the length of the sounds we make when we talk, as well as their pitch __.his is why when you speak, you don't sound like a robot. In fact, the b__ __ay to sound like a robot is to space all of your words exactly the sar__ __nce apart, and to use the same pitch for each word.

Try it. Read the words to the __ __.e of "America the Beautiful" as a robot might. Hear how unnat__ __ounds. This is the sound of words without a varied rhythm.

Sometimes composers write simple rhythms. Sometimes they create complex rhythms.

Composers use fractions, written in the form of musical symbols, to communicate a tune's rhythm. The symbols tell how long the sound of a note should last, compared with other notes. A **half note** lasts twice as long as a **quarter note**, and four times as long as an eighth note. A half note lasts one-half as long as a **whole note**.

The symbols for these notes are shown below.

♪ Whole note		1 whole note is equivalent to 2 half notes.
♩ or ♩ Half note		1 half note is equivalent to 2 quarter notes.
♩ or ♩ Quarter note		1 quarter note is equivalent to 2 eighth notes.
♪ or ♪ Eighth note		1 eighth note is equivalent to 2 sixteenth notes.
♪ or ♪ Sixteenth note		1 sixteenth note is equivalent to 2 thirty-second notes.
♪ or ♪ Thirty-second note		

In addition to notes representing sounds, a written piece of music usually contains *rests*, which are symbols indicating silence, or no sound.

> Complete Music Problem 5 on Master 53.
> Then return here and continue reading.

Meter

Meter, like rhythm, is part of the "beat" or pulse you feel when music is played. Conductors show it when they move their baton. When you tap your feet to a piece of music, you are tapping its meter.

Music is divided into small units called **measures**. Each measure must contain an equivalent combination of notes (or notes and rests). The meter of a piece tells a composer how to divide the music into measures.

The meter is shown at the start of a piece of music by a symbol called the time signature. The meter for "America the Beautiful" is shown as $\frac{4}{4}$, which is read "four, four." Two other common meters are $\frac{3}{4}$ ("three, four") and $\frac{6}{8}$ ("six, eight").

A **time signature** looks like a fraction, but it is not really a fraction. The top number tells how many beats there are in a measure. In "America the Beautiful" (as in many marches and rock songs), there are four beats per measure. The bottom number tells what kind of note gets one beat.

- 2 indicates that a half ($\frac{1}{2}$) note or its equivalent gets one beat.
- 4 indicates that a quarter ($\frac{1}{4}$) note or its equivalent gets one beat.
- 8 indicates that an eighth ($\frac{1}{8}$) note or its equivalent gets one beat.

The meter of $\frac{4}{4}$ for "America the Beautiful" means that each measure has four beats, and that a quarter note or its equivalent gets one beat. This information tells the composer and performer how long each measure is.

Examples

$\frac{2}{4}$	means each measure needs	Two Quarter Notes (or equivalent)
$\frac{6}{8}$	means each measure needs	Six Eighth Notes (or equivalent)

Using Meter to Figure Out Rhythm

Suppose a composer is hired to turn a poem into a song. The composer might be an advertising jingle writer, a popular songwriter, or a composer of operas.

First, the composer looks at the words, not only to see what the poem is about, but what its rhythms are. (Notice that the notes in "America the Beautiful" follow the rhythm of the words.)

Then the composer selects a meter. If the poem has a fairly regular rhythm, the composer might select a meter of $\frac{4}{4}$. The composer now needs to fill the music with measures that have four quarter notes or their equivalent.

To fill a measure worth four quarter notes, a composer has many options. The composer could use 1 whole note, or 2 half notes, or 4 quarter notes, or 16 sixteenth notes. Other options include 2 quarter notes and 8 sixteenth notes; 1 quarter note, 2 eighth notes, 4 sixteenth notes, and 8 thirty-second notes; and so on. The composer could also include rests.

The choices made by the composer depend on the character of the piece being written.

If the composer wants many short sounds, he or she will use eighth, sixteenth, and thirty-second notes. If longer sounds are desired, then more whole and half notes will be used. If a contrast between long and short sounds is wanted, then a half note might be followed by eighth or sixteenth notes.

There are many ways a composer could fill a measure of music with
4 quarter notes or their equivalent. One way is shown in the example below.

Example

4 quarter notes are equivalent to:

0 Whole	1 Half	0 Quarter	3 Eighth	2 16th	0 32nd
Notes	Notes	Notes	Notes	Notes	Notes

> Complete Music Problem 6 on Masters 54 and 55.
> Then return here and continue reading.

Tempo

Neither rhythm nor meter tells how fast a piece of music should be played
or sung. There is no set length of time for a whole note, half note, or any
other note. The **tempo**—the speed at which the notes are played—is
determined by the performer, the conductor, or the composer. Sometimes
they argue about it.

You can tap the same rhythm (or combination of long and short notes) at a
slow tempo or a fast tempo. The relationship between the different lengths of
sound stays the same. Long notes are still long, and short notes are still short.

Try it. Quickly tap out a familiar tune, such as "London Bridge" or "Happy
Birthday." Then tap it slowly. Notice that in both tempos, it has the same
pattern of long and short sounds.

London Bridge

Traditional

Lon-don Bridge is fal- ling down, fal- ling down, fal-ling down.

Lon-don Bridge is fal- ling down, my fair la - dy.

Here is how tempo works. A time is assigned to a **reference note**. Usually
the reference note is a half note, quarter note, or eighth note. If you want a
slow tempo you might assign a time of 1 second to an eighth note. For a
moderate tempo, you might assign a time of $\frac{1}{2}$ second to a quarter note, and
for a very fast tempo, $\frac{1}{2}$ second to a whole note.

The times of the other notes are determined by their relation to the reference
note. This means that musicians need to be good at "hearing" fractions.

Calculating Tempos

Suppose you want a moderate tempo and make each quarter note take approximately $\frac{1}{2}$ second. That would be 120 beats per minute, which is the tempo indicated for "America the Beautiful" by the notation $\quad \rfloor = 120$.

How long would the other notes take?

> Complete Music Problem 7 on Master 56.
> Then return here and continue reading.

Choosing Tempos

A tempo must be chosen carefully. Suppose you choose a fast tempo; for example, 1/3 second for a quarter note. If the piece has many thirty-second notes, the performers will need to play each thirty-second note in 1/24 second (1/3 sec * 1/8 = 1/24 sec). Can you tap 24 times in one second?

On the other hand, suppose you choose a slow tempo; for example, 1 second for a quarter note. If the piece has many whole notes, the performers will need to be able to hold each whole note for 4 seconds. Can you a sing a single note for 4 seconds ?

Playing Time

The lengths of pieces of music are often listed on the cover or label of a music recording. The length of one song might be given as 1:58 (1 minute 58 seconds), and another as 3:24 (3 minutes 24 seconds).

The time it takes to play a piece is determined by its meter, its tempo, and how many measures there are. The meter determines how many notes are in each measure, and the tempo determines how long each note lasts.

Example

Meter: $\frac{3}{4}$ (each measure contains 3 quarter notes or their equivalent)

Tempo: 1/2 second for a quarter note

Number of measures: 100

Playing time = 3 * 1/2 sec * 100 = 150 sec = 2 min 30 sec

Summing-Up

Numbers and time are basic elements in music. The number of vibrations per second gives a sound its pitch (highness or lowness). The ratio of the rates of vibration gives a certain quality to the sound when notes are played together. Rhythm is a pattern of long and short notes. Meter tells how many notes, and what kind of notes, are in each measure; tempo is the speed at which the measures are played. The human ear and brain are able to organize and enjoy the resulting sounds as music.

4. The Mathematics of Musical Composition

People who compose music like to use patterns.

Composers work with patterns of notes and rhythms in some of the ways that you might work with patterns of numbers or shapes. They experiment. They look for ways to vary the patterns. Some of the patterns in music involve *symmetry* and *transformation*.

Materials you need:

• Masters 57–60

Upside-Down Patterns (Inversions)

One common musical operation turns a pattern of notes upside down. The resulting pattern is called an **inversion** of the original pattern over a line on the musical staff. In geometry, a figure can be turned upside down with a **reflection** over a horizontal line.

original figure

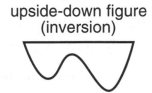

upside-down figure (inversion)

Look at the original pattern of notes below. To turn the original pattern upside down, or **invert** it, you start with the same note, but you reverse the direction to the next note. Where the original pattern goes up, the upside-down or inverted pattern goes down, and vice versa.

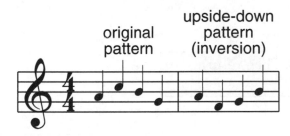

You can also do this with a number pattern. The distance between any two numbers stays the same, but the direction is reversed. For example:

$$10 \quad 15 \quad 13 \quad 17 \qquad \text{inverts to} \qquad 10 \quad 5 \quad 7 \quad 3$$
$$(+5) \quad (-2) \quad (+4) \qquad\qquad\qquad (-5) \quad (+2) \quad (-4)$$

Here is a more complex example. Can you follow the pattern?

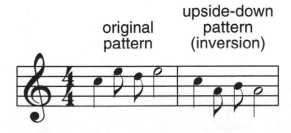

Be a composer. Complete Music Problem 8 on Master 57.
Then return here and continue reading.

Backward Patterns (Retrogrades)

Another common musical operation turns a pattern of notes backward. The patterns are flips or mirror images of each other. The initial set of notes and its flip have line symmetry. The bar between measures is part of the line of symmetry. Composers call backward patterns **retrogrades**. In geometry, flips or mirror images are produced by **reflections**.

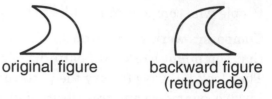

original figure   backward figure (retrograde)

The first note in the backward pattern is the same as the last note in the original pattern.

Here is a number pattern turned backward.

   1 4 7 10 13   becomes   13 10 7 4 1

Here is a music pattern turned backward.

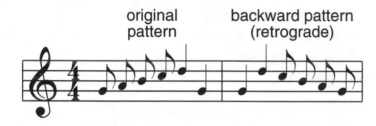

original pattern   backward pattern (retrograde)

> Be a composer. Complete Music Problem 9 on Master 58. Then return here and continue reading.

Slide Patterns (Transpositions)

Another popular way to transform music is keep the pattern of notes the same but to slide its location up or down on the musical staff. The new pattern is called a **transposition**, and the operation is said to **transpose** the original. In geometry, this kind of operation is known as a **translation** or slide.

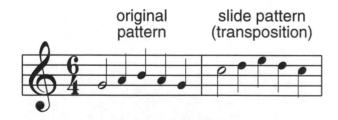

original pattern   slide pattern (transposition)

> Complete Music Problem 10 on Master 58. Then return here and continue reading.

The following pattern of notes is the beginning of " Twinkle, Twinkle, Little Star."

Suppose you want to slide the whole pattern down three steps. You will preserve the pattern, but change the starting place. (This happens often. A singer might transpose a song because it is too high or too low for the singer's voice. Transposition can be easy or quite hard, depending on the piece of music.)

Transposed, "Twinkle, Twinkle, Little Star" would look like this. The pattern of notes is the same, but the notes are two lines or spaces lower.

> Let's put some of these ideas together. Complete Music Problem 11 on Master 59. Then return here and continue reading.

Compose Your Own Piece of Music

Now that you know a little about musical operations, you can try to write your own piece of music.

Imagine that you have been asked to write a short piece of music for the President. The President's daughter will play the piece on the xylophone. This work is called a *commission*, and it is one of the main ways a composer makes a living.

The President has given you the first measure of the piece. It looks like this.

Your job is to turn this first measure into a melody that is four to eight measures long.

Before you begin, do some planning. Artists usually make many decisions before they start writing notes, or putting paint on a canvas, or doing whatever their art requires.

The President has chosen a meter of $\frac{4}{4}$. This means that each measure of music must contain four quarter notes or their equivalent.

The President is also using a typical five-note Chinese scale, called the **pentatonic scale**. (*Penta-* means five. A pentagon is a five-sided figure.) If you have a piano, you can hear the pentatonic scales by playing all the black keys.

Use some of the operations you learned earlier to transform this first measure into a longer piece of music. Your choices include the following:

Vary the pattern.

Invert (reflect) the pattern. (Turn it upside down.)

Retrograde (flip) the pattern. (Turn it backward.)

Transpose the pattern. (Slide it up or down.)

Remember: Each measure of music needs to contain four quarter notes or their equivalent.

Try to use musical notation. The notes you have to work with are positioned on the musical staff as follows.

The values you can use are written like this:

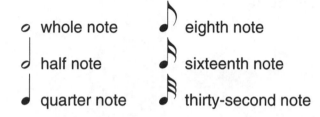

If it is easier, use the following notation. The fraction tells whether a note is a whole note, half note, quarter note, and so on.

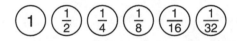

Now write your composition. Complete Music Problem 12 on Master 60. Then return here and continue reading.

Mathematics and Music (continued)

Coda

Composing music is actually more difficult than what you just did. It requires a deep knowledge of music and familiarity with the sounds produced by different combinations of notes and instruments. A composer also needs imagination in order to create beautiful, exciting, or interesting music.

Johann Sebastian Bach (1685–1750) was perhaps the greatest master of the techniques of composition that you just used. Below is the first page of his Brandenburg Concerto No. 2. Recordings of this piece are traveling into outer space on the Voyager space probes as an example of human civilization's intellect and artistry.

Brandenburg Concerto No. 2 in F Major

Mathematics and Poetry

Poetry might not seem to have much to do with mathematics. But you might be surprised. Both poets and mathematicians work within a *system of rules*, follow *patterns*, and make beauty with *abstract forms*.

A poet chooses a form for a poem in order to express meaning through language, just as a mathematician might use a graph or an equation to express relationships.

The form that the poet or mathematician chooses can affect meaning. Here are three poetic forms. You will see that they involve numbers, and that the form contributes to the feeling of the poem.

Haiku

A **haiku** is a poem with 3 lines and 17 syllables. The first line has 5 syllables, the second line has 7 syllables, and the third line has 5 syllables. Haikus originated in Japan, where they are still popular. Some newspapers print haikus about the day's events on their front page.

> In every haiku
> the lines are five, seven, five,
> in every haiku.

This design has a kind of symmetry, with the two shorter lines around the longer middle line. The variation keeps the lines from becoming too rhythmic or song-like.

Traditional haikus try to say something about nature in 17 syllables. The form forces the poet to treat words as precious.

Here are translations of four traditional haikus by Japanese poets.

Wet with morning dew
and splotched with mud, the melon
looks especially cool.

Basho (1644–1694)

Clinging to the bell
he dozes so peacefully,
this new butterfly

Buson (1715–1783)

Those falling blossoms
all return to the branch when
I watch butterflies.

Moritake (1452–1540)

The barnyard rooster
tries to act like a lion
by preening feathers.

Kikaku (1661–1707)

Notice that each haiku has a surface meaning and a deeper meaning as well. Haikus are often about contrasts, such as the beauty of a melon spotted by mud, or the calm of a butterfly just before a bell rings.

The power of haikus comes from compressing content into a small form. Also, the symmetry of the form, and the *asymmetry* (lack of symmetry) of the individual lines, contribute to the poem.

Try These

1. Find several haikus in a book or magazine. Write a paragraph describing their surface meanings and any deeper meanings you see.

2. Try to write a haiku. Notice how it forces you to choose your words with care.

Sonnet

The sonnet is one of the most loved forms of poetry. Sonnets follow strict numerical rules.

- A sonnet must be 14 lines long.

- In English, each line in a sonnet must have 10 syllables.

Sonnets are usually divided into parts. In one type of sonnet, the first 8 lines might state a problem or ask a question. The last 6 lines might solve the problem or answer the question.

In another type of sonnet, there are three parts of 4 lines each, followed by one part of 2 lines.

The lines in a sonnet must rhyme. There are several rhyming patterns, one of which is shown in Sonnet 18 on the following page.

The 14 lines of a sonnet give the poet time to make an argument, but they also force the poet to be careful with words. A line is long enough for a sentence, but sentences can also continue from one line to the next.

The 14 lines also keep the sonnet from becoming too symmetrical. A poem of 16 lines, for example, would be more regular, but possibly less interesting.

Sonnets are not easy to write. Sometimes they are hard to read. Try reading Sonnet 18 on the following page, written by probably the greatest sonnet writer in the English language, William Shakespeare (1564–1616).

Sonnet 18

Shall I compare thee to a summer's day?
Thou art more lovely and more temperate:
Rough winds do shake the darling buds of May,
And summer's lease hath all too short a date:

Sometimes too hot the eye of heaven shines,
And often is his gold complexion dimmed,
By chance or nature's changing course untrimmed:
And every fair from fair sometimes declines,

But thy eternal summer shall not fade,
Nor lose possession of that fair thou ow'st;
Nor shall death brag thou wander'st in his shade,
When in eternal lines to time thou grow'st,

So long as men can breathe or eyes can see,
So long lives this, and this gives life to thee.

Shakespeare is comparing his beloved to summer, and saying she is more beautiful, pleasing, and lasting. He uses the sonnet to convince us of this.

Each group of four lines is called a *quatrain*. In the first quatrain, Shakespeare asks which is more beautiful—summer or his beloved—and begins to answer by showing summer is not perfect.

The second quatrain continues this answer, so that the first eight lines are linked. Shakespeare does not always use the fewest possible words, as a haiku must. For example, he could have referred to "the eye of heaven" in fewer words. (He means the Sun.)

When the third quatrain begins, Shakespeare shifts from summer to his beloved, saying she will never grow old. As in a haiku, he is using contrast. At first this quatrain might seem like a riddle, since everyone grows old. But the riddle is answered in the last two lines, called the *couplet*. The sonnet itself will keep its subject alive.

Like a haiku, this sonnet is about more than one idea. It is a love poem, but it is also about the power of art to keep its subjects alive. The sonnet gives Shakespeare the space he needs to make this argument in "poetic language." The strict design is part of the beauty of the sonnet.

Try These

1. Notice that the last words in the first and third lines of Shakespeare's Sonnet 18 rhyme: "day" and "May." What is the rhyming pattern for the entire sonnet—that is, which lines rhyme?

2. Find a sonnet in a book or magazine. Write a paragraph describing its content and structure.

Free Verse

Many poets in the twentieth century have written in what is called **free verse**. The name is misleading. While a free-verse poem might not follow a set pattern like a haiku or a sonnet, its form has been carefully chosen by the poet.

Artistic forms might be compared to geometric shapes. There are basic shapes—triangles, rectangles, trapezoids, and so on—but there are also unusual or complex shapes, such as a convex nine-sided polygon, which can still be studied and explained with geometry. Poets, painters, and other artists who use unusual or complex forms do not do so because they can't use the basic ones; they use them because the form matches the content they wish to express.

Read this free-verse poem written in 1934.

Poem

As the cat
climbed over
the top of
the jamcloset
first the right
forefoot
carefully
then the hind
stepped down
into the pit of
the empty
flowerpot

William Carlos Williams (1883–1963)

Did you notice the very short lines, and the irregular rhythm and number of syllables? We think of patterns and forms as being "regular," but Williams is actually making a pattern out of irregularity.

Why does he use irregularity? (Have you ever seen a cat climbing over something uneven? The cat does not simply plow through, but takes its time and tests each step carefully. By breaking the poem after every few words, the poet makes us feel the cat's movements.)

Try These

1. Try to write a free-verse poem. Remember, a free-verse poem does not have to follow a set pattern. However, its form should be carefully chosen to help express the ideas and emotions you want to convey.

2. Find a free-verse poem you like in a book or magazine. Write a paragraph describing its content and structure. Are any parts difficult to understand?

Limericks

Limericks are short poems (five lines) with a definite rhyming pattern. They are usually humorous or silly. This one appeared in Unit 10:

> A mathematician confided
> That a Möbius band is one-sided.
> And you'll get quite a laugh
> If you cut one in half,
> For it stays in one piece when divided.

Here is another which *Britannica Online* describes as an old anonymous limerick:

> A tutor who taught on the flute
> Tried to teach two tooters to toot.
>   Said the two to the tutor,
>   "Is it harder to toot, or
> To tutor two tooters to toot?"

Summing-Up

For poets and other artists, form and structure and pattern are not separate from meaning. Since mathematics is so much about form and structure and pattern, we can see similarities between art and mathematics.

Are you starting to feel how a poem's meaning is affected by its design—how many syllables there are in a line, how many lines are grouped together, how repetition and rhyme and strong and weak syllables create patterns?

Are you starting to notice properties that poems share with geometric shapes, such as symmetry and *asymmetry* (lack of symmetry)?

Can you feel that when a poet stretches a sentence across two lines, or changes the rhythm, that the poet is playing with form, just as in mathematics you might transform a geometric shape or vary a pattern?

If you answered "yes," or even "maybe," to these questions, you are on your way to thinking like a poet as well as a mathematician.

> **Try These**
>
> 1. Find out about another form of poetry, such as the ballad, lyric, epic, or ode. What are some examples of this form? Compare the form with one of the forms in this project. How are the two forms similar? Different?
>
> 2. Read about the life and work of a poet—Shakespeare, William Carlos Williams, or someone else, such as William Wordsworth, Emily Dickinson, Robert Frost, or Rita Dove.
>
> 3. Figure out the rhythms and rhyming pattern of limericks. Find other limericks (for example, by Edward Lear), and write some of your own.

absolute value The absolute value of a positive number is the number itself. For example, the absolute value of 3 is 3. The absolute value of a negative number is the opposite of the number. For example, the absolute value of –6 is 6.

abundant number A number for which the sum of all the proper factors is greater than the number itself. For example, 12 is an abundant number because the sum of its proper factors is $1 + 2 + 3 + 4 + 6 = 16$, and 16 is greater than 12. *See also* **deficient number, perfect number,** and **proper factor.**

account balance An amount of money that you have or that you owe.

acre A unit of area equal to 43,560 square feet.

addend *See* **addition.**

addition A mathematical operation based on "putting things together." Numbers being added are called **addends**; the result of addition is called the **sum.** In $12 + 33 = 45$, 12 and 33 are addends, and 45 is the sum. **Subtraction** "undoes" addition: $12 + 33 = 45$; $45 – 12 = 33$, and $45 – 33 = 12$.

addition facts *See* **arithmetic facts.**

additive inverses Two numbers whose sum is 0. The additive inverse of a number is also called its **opposite.** Example: $3 + (–3) = 0$. The additive inverse of 3 is –3, and the additive inverse of –3 is 3.

address In a spreadsheet, a letter and a number used to identify a cell, such as A5.

address box In a spreadsheet, a place where the address of a cell is shown when the cell is selected.

algebraic expression An expression that contains a variable. For example, if Maria is 2 inches taller than Joe, and if the variable M represents Maria's height, then the expression $M – 2$ represents Joe's height.

algorithm A set of step-by-step instructions for doing something— carrying out a computation, solving a problem, and so on.

angle Two rays with a common endpoint. The common endpoint is called the **vertex** of the angle. An **acute** angle has a measure greater than 0° and less than 90°. An **obtuse** angle has a measure greater than 90° and less than 180°. A **right** angle has measure 90°. A **straight** angle has measure 180°. *See also* **reflex angle**.

angle of separation A measure of how far fingers can be spread apart— shown is the angle of separation between a person's thumb and first finger.

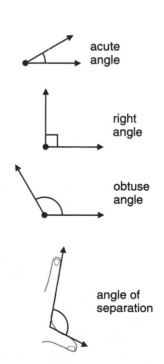

acute angle

right angle

obtuse angle

angle of separation

Glossary

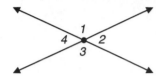

angles, adjacent Two angles with a common side that do not otherwise overlap. In the diagram, angles 1 and 2 are adjacent angles. So are angles 2 and 3, angles 3 and 4, and angles 4 and 1.

angles, opposite *See* **angles, vertical.**

angles, vertical Two intersecting lines form four angles. In the diagram, angles 2 and 4 are vertical angles. They have no sides in common. Their measures are equal. Similarly, angles 1 and 3 are vertical angles.

anthropometry The study of human body sizes and proportions.

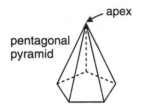

pentagonal pyramid

apex

apex In a pyramid or cone, the vertex opposite the base.

arc Part of a circle, from one point on the circle to another. For example, a **semicircle** is an arc; its endpoints are the endpoints of a diameter of the circle.

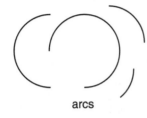

arcs

area The measure of the surface inside a closed boundary. The formula for the area of a rectangle is $A = l * w$ where A represents the area, l the length, and w the width. The formula may also be expressed as $A = b * h$, where b represents the length of the base and h the height of the rectangle.

area model A model for multiplication problems, in which the length and width of a rectangle represent the factors and the area represents the product.

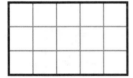

area model for 3 * 5 = 15

arithmetic fact Any of the basic addition and multiplication relationships and the corresponding subtraction and division relationships. There are—

　　100 addition facts, from $0 + 0 = 0$ to $9 + 9 = 18$

　　100 subtraction facts, from $0 - 0 = 0$ to $18 - 9 = 9$

　　100 multiplication facts, from $0 * 0 = 0$ to $9 * 9 = 81$

　　90 division facts, from $0/1 = 0$ to $81/9 = 9$

An **extended fact** is obtained by multiplying some or all numbers in an arithmetic fact by a power of 10; for example, $20 + 30 = 50$, $400 * 6 = 2400$, $500 - 300 = 200$, $240/60 = 4$.

array *See* **rectangular array.**

astronomical unit The average distance from the Earth to the Sun. It is used as a unit of measure to express distances in space.

average *See* **mean.**

axis Either of the two number lines used to form a coordinate grid.

bar graph A graph in which horizontal or vertical bars represent data.

base *See* **exponential notation.**

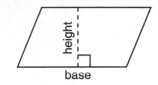

base of a parallelogram One of the sides of a parallelogram; also, the length of this side. The shortest distance between the base and the side opposite the base is the height of the parallelogram.

base of a polygon The side on which the polygon "sits"; the side that is perpendicular to the height of the polygon.

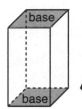

base of a polyhedron The "bottom" face of a polyhedron; the face whose shape is the basis for classifying a prism or pyramid.

base of a rectangle One of the sides of a rectangle; also, the length of this side. The length of the side perpendicular to the base is the height of the rectangle.

base of a 3-dimensional figure One face or a pair of faces on the figure. The height is the length of a line segment drawn perpendicular to a base of the figure that extends from that base to an opposite face or vertex.

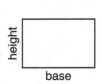
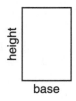

base of a triangle One of the sides of a triangle; also, the length of this side. The shortest distance between the base and the vertex opposite the base is the height of the triangle.

benchmark An important or memorable count or measure that can be used to evaluate the reasonableness of other counts or measures.

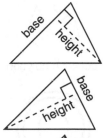

bisect To divide a segment, angle, or figure into two parts of equal measure.

braking distance The distance a car travels from the time the brake pedal is pressed to the time the car comes to a complete stop.

broken-line graph See **line graph.**

calibrate To divide or mark something, such as on a thermometer, with gradations.

calorie A unit for the amount of energy a food will produce when it is digested by the body.

capacity A measure of how much liquid or other pourable substance a container can hold. *See also* **volume.**

cell In a spreadsheet, a box formed where a column and a row intersect. A **column** is a section of cells lined up vertically. A **row** is a section of cells lined up horizontally.

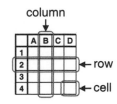

center *See* **circle** or **sphere.**

chance The possibility of an outcome in an uncertain event. For example, in tossing a coin there is an equal chance of getting heads or tails.

circle The set of all points in a plane that are a given distance (the **radius**) from a given point (the **center** of the circle).

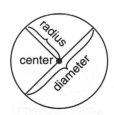

circle graph A graph in which a circle and its interior are divided into parts to represent the parts of a set of data. The circle represents the whole set of data. Also called a **pie graph.**

circumference The distance around a circle or sphere.

column *See* **cell**.

combine like terms *See* **like terms**.

common Shared by two or more numbers. A **common denominator** of two fractions is any nonzero number that is a multiple of the denominators of both fractions. A **common factor** of two numbers is any number that is a factor of both numbers.

compass-and-straightedge construction The drawing of geometric figures using only a compass and straightedge.

complementary angles Two angles whose measures total 90°.

composite number A whole number that has more than two whole-number factors. For example, 10 is a composite number because it has more than two factors: 1, 2, 5, and 10. A composite number is divisible by at least three whole numbers. *See also* **prime number.**

concave polygon

concave (nonconvex) polygon A polygon in which at least one vertex is "pushed in."

concentric circles

concentric circles Circles that have the same center but radii of different lengths.

cone A 3-dimensional shape having a circular base, curved surface, and one vertex.

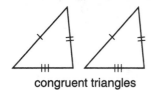

congruent triangles

congruent Two figures that are identical—the same size and shape—are called congruent figures. If you put one on top of the other, they would match exactly. Congruent figures are also said to be *congruent to* each other.

consecutive Following one another in an uninterrupted order. For example, A, B, C, and D are four consecutive letters of the alphabet; 6, 7, 8, 9, and 10 are five consecutive whole numbers.

consecutive angles Two angles that are "next to each other;" they share a common side.

constant A number used over and over with an operation performed on many numbers.

constant term *See* **term**.

contour line A curve on a map through places where a measurement (for example, temperature, elevation, or growing season) is the same.

conversion fact A fact such as 1 yard = 3 feet or 1 gallon = 4 quarts.

convex polygon

convex polygon A polygon in which all vertices are "pushed outward."

coordinate A number used to locate a point on a number line, or either of two numbers used to locate a point on a **coordinate grid**.

coordinate grid A device for locating points in a plane by means of ordered number pairs or **coordinates.** A rectangular coordinate grid is formed by two number lines that intersect at right angles at their 0 points.

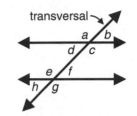

coordinate grid

corresponding angles Any pair of angles in the same relative position in two figures, or in similar locations in relation to a transversal intersecting two lines. In the diagram in the margin, $\angle a$ and $\angle e$, $\angle b$ and $\angle f$, $\angle d$ and $\angle h$, and $\angle c$ and $\angle g$ are corresponding angles. If any two corresponding angles are congruent, then the lines are parallel.

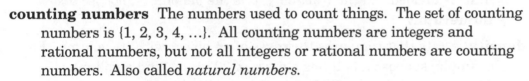

corresponding sides Any pair of sides in the same relative position in two figures. In the diagram in the margin, corresponding sides are marked with the same number of slash marks.

counting numbers The numbers used to count things. The set of counting numbers is {1, 2, 3, 4, ...}. All counting numbers are integers and rational numbers, but not all integers or rational numbers are counting numbers. Also called *natural numbers.*

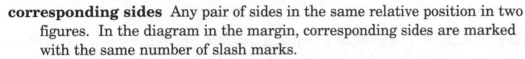

corresponding sides

cover-up method A method for finding the solution of an equation by covering up a part of the equation containing a variable.

cross section A shape formed by the intersection of a plane and a geometric solid.

cube *See* **regular polyhedron.**

cubic centimeter (cm³) A metric unit of volume; the volume of a cube 1 centimeter on a side. 1 cubic centimeter is equal to 1 **milliliter.**

cubic unit A unit used in a volume and capacity measurement.

cubit An ancient unit of length, measured from the point of the elbow to the end of the middle finger, or about 18 inches. The Latin word *cubitum* means "elbow."

curved surface A surface that is rounded rather than flat.

customary system of measurement The measuring system used most often in the United States. Units for linear measure (length, distance) include inch, foot, yard, and mile; units for weight include ounce and pound; units for capacity (amount of liquid or other pourable substance a container can hold) include cup, pint, quart, and gallon.

cylinder A 3-dimensional shape having a curved surface and parallel circular or elliptical bases that are the same size. A can is a common object shaped like a cylinder.

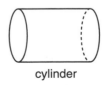

cylinder

data Information gathered by observation, questioning, or measurement.

decimal A number written in **standard notation**, usually one containing a decimal point, as in 2.54. A decimal that ends, such as 2.54, is called a **terminating decimal.** Some decimals continue a pattern without end; for example, 0.333..., or $0.\overline{3}$, which is equal to $\frac{1}{3}$. Such decimals are called **repeating decimals**. A terminating decimal can be thought of as a repeating decimal in which 0 repeats.

deficient number A number for which the sum of all the proper factors is less than the number. For example, 10 is a deficient number because the sum of its proper factors is $1 + 2 + 5 = 8$, and 8 is less than 10. *See also* **abundant number, perfect number,** and **proper factor.**

degree (°) A unit of measure for angles; based on dividing a circle into 360 equal parts. Also, a unit of measure for temperature.

denominator The number of equal parts into which the whole (or ONE or unit) is divided. In the fraction $\frac{a}{b}$, b is the denominator. *See also* **numerator.**

density A rate that compares the mass of an object with its volume. For example, suppose a ball has a mass of 20 grams and a volume of 10 cubic centimeters. To find its density, divide its mass by its volume: $20 \text{ g}/10 \text{ cm}^3 = 2 \text{ g/cm}^3$ (2 grams per cubic centimeter).

diameter A line segment that passes through the center of a circle (or sphere) and has endpoints on the circle (or sphere); also, the length of such a line segment. The diameter of a circle is twice its **radius**. *See also* **circle.**

difference *See* **subtraction.**

digit In the base-10 numeration system, one of the symbols 0, 1, 2, 3, 4, 5, 6, 7, 8, 9. Digits can be used to write any number. For example, the numeral 145 is made up of the digits 1, 4, and 5.

dimension A measure in one direction. For example, length or width.

discount The amount by which the regular price of an item is reduced.

displace To move something from one position to another.

display bar In a spreadsheet, a place where data or formulas entered from the keyboard are shown.

distributive property A property that relates two operations on numbers; usually multiplication and addition, or multiplication and subtraction.

Distributive property of multiplication over addition:
$a * (x + y) = (a * x) + (a * y)$

Distributive property of multiplication over subtraction:
$a * (x - y) = (a * x) - (a * y)$

This property gets its name because it "distributes" the factor outside the parentheses over the two terms within the parentheses.

dividend *See* **division.**

divisibility test A test to determine whether a whole number is divisible by another whole number, without actually doing the division. For example, to tell whether a number is divisible by 3, check whether the sum of its digits is divisible by 3. For example, 51 is divisible by 3 since 5 + 1 = 6, and 6 is divisible by 3.

divisible by One whole number is divisible by another whole number if the result of the division is a whole number (with a remainder of zero). For example, 28 is divisible by 7, because 28 divided by 7 is 4 with a remainder of zero. If a number *n* is divisible by a number *x*, then *x* is a factor of *n*. *See also* **factor of a whole number *n*.**

division A mathematical operation based on "sharing" or "separating into equal parts." The **dividend** is the total before sharing. The **divisor** is the number of equal parts or the number in each equal part. The **quotient** is the result of division. For example, in 28/7 = 4, 28 is the dividend, 7 is the divisor, and 4 is the quotient. If 28 objects are separated into 7 equal parts, there are 4 objects in each part. If 28 objects are separated into parts with 7 in each part, there are 4 equal parts. The number left over when a set of objects is shared equally or separated into equal groups is called the **remainder**. For 28/7, the quotient is 4 and the remainder is 0. For 29/7, the quotient is 4 and the remainder is 1. **Multiplication** "undoes" division: 28/7 = 4, and 4 * 7 = 28.

dividend/divisor = quotient

$\frac{dividend}{divisor}$ = quotient

divisor *See* **division.**

dodecahedron *See* **regular polyhedron.**

edge The line segment where two faces of a polyhedron meet.

elevation The height above sea level.

ellipse A closed, oval, plane figure. An ellipse is the path of a point that moves so that the sum of its distances from two fixed points is constant. Each of the fixed points is called a *focus* of the ellipse.

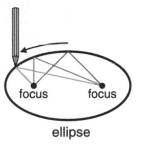
ellipse

endpoint The point at either end of a line segment; also, the point at the end of a ray. Endpoints are used to name line segments; for example, segment *TL* or segment *LT* names a line segment between and including points *T* and *L*. *See also* **ray.**

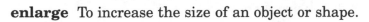

enlarge To increase the size of an object or shape.

equation A mathematical sentence that states the equality of two quantities.

equator An imaginary circle around the Earth halfway between the North Pole and South Pole. *See also* **latitude.**

equidistant marks Marks equally distant from one to the next.

equilateral polygon A polygon in which all sides are the same length.

equivalent Equal in value, but in a different form. For example, $\frac{1}{2}$, 0.5, and 50% are equivalent.

equivalent equations Equations that have the same solution. For example, $2 + x = 4$ and $6 + x = 8$ are equivalent equations; their solution is 2.

equivalent fractions Fractions that have different numerators and denominators but name the same number. For example, $\frac{1}{2}$ and $\frac{4}{8}$ are equivalent fractions.

equivalent ratios Ratios that can be named by equivalent fractions. For example, the ratios 12 to 20, 6 to 10, and 3 to 5 are equivalent ratios, because $\frac{12}{20} = \frac{6}{10} = \frac{3}{5}$.

estimate A calculation of a close, rather than exact, answer; a "ballpark" answer; a number close to another number.

evaluate an algebraic expression To replace each variable in an algebraic expression with a particular number and then calculate the value of the expression.

evaluate a numerical expression To carry out the operations in a numerical expression to find the value of the expression.

even number A whole number such as 2, 4, 6, and so on that can be evenly divided by 2 (divided by 2 with 0 remainder). *See also* **odd number.**

event A happening or occurrence. The tossing of a coin is an event.

exponent *See* **exponential notation.**

exponential notation A shorthand way of representing repeated multiplication of the same factor. For example, 2^3 is exponential notation for $2 * 2 * 2$. The small, raised 3, called the **exponent**, indicates how many times the number 2, called the **base**, is used as a factor.

expression A group of mathematical symbols (numbers, operation signs, variables, grouping symbols) that represents a number (or can represent a number if values are assigned to any variables it contains).

extended fact *See* **arithmetic fact.**

face A flat surface on a 3-dimensional shape.

fact *See* **arithmetic fact.**

fact family A group of addition or multiplication facts together with the related subtraction or division facts. For example, $5 + 6 = 11$, $6 + 5 = 11$, $11 - 5 = 6$, and $11 - 6 = 5$ form a fact family. $5 * 7 = 35$, $7 * 5 = 35$, $35/7 = 5$, and $35/5 = 7$ form another fact family.

factor (noun) A number that is multiplied by another number. Factors may be whole numbers or rational numbers expressed as fractions or decimals. For example, 4, 3, and 2 are factors in the expression $4 * 3 * 2$; 0.5 and 25 are factors in $0.5 * 25$; $\frac{1}{2}$ and 9 are factors in $\frac{1}{2} * 9$; and −2 and −5 are factors in $-2 * (-5)$. *See also* **multiplication**.

factor (verb) To represent a number as a product of factors.

factorial A product of a whole number and all the smaller whole numbers except 0—for example, $3 * 2 * 1$. The exclamation point, !, is used to write factorials. For example:

$3! = 3 * 2 * 1 = 6$ 3! is read as "three factorial."

$4! = 4 * 3 * 2 * 1 = 24$ 4! is read as "four factorial."

For any number N,

$N! = N * (N - 1) * (N - 2) * ... * 1$ $N!$ is read as "N factorial."

factor of a whole number _n_ A whole number, which, when multiplied by another whole number, results in the number n. The whole number n is divisible by its factors. For example, 4 and 7 are factors of 28 because $4 * 7 = 28$, and 28 is divisible by 4 and 7.

factor pair Two whole-number factors of a number n whose product is the number n. A number may have more than one factor pair. For example, the factor pairs for 21 are 1 and 21, and 3 and 7.

factor rainbow A way of showing factor pairs in a list of all the factors of a number. This can be helpful in checking whether a list of factors is correct.

factor string A name for a number written as a product of at least two whole-number factors. For example, a factor string for the number 24 is $2 * 3 * 4$. This factor string has three factors, so its *length* is 3. The number 1 is never part of a factor string. For example, $1 * 2 * 3 * 4$ is not a factor string for 24.

Factors of 24

factor tree A method used to obtain the **prime factorization** of a number. The original number is represented as a product of factors, and each of those factors is represented as a product of factors, and so on, until the factor string consists of prime numbers.

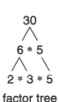

factor tree

fair game A game in which each player has the same chance of winning. If any player has an advantage, or disadvantage (for example, by playing first), then the game is not fair.

fathom A unit used mainly by people who work with boats and ships to measure depths under water and lengths of cables and cords. A fathom is now defined to equal 6 feet.

fifth On a piano, a musical interval spanning any five white keys, except that a fifth starting on B ends on black key (F sharp).

Glossary

triangular
number

square
number

figurate numbers Numbers which can be shown by dots arranged in specific geometric patterns. Rectangular numbers, square numbers, and triangular numbers are examples of figurate numbers.

flowchart A diagram consisting of symbols and arrows to sequentially show a series of steps to complete a task.

formula A general rule for finding the value of something. A formula is often written in abbreviated form with letters, called **variables**. For example, a formula for distance traveled can be written as $d = r * t$, where the variable d stands for distance, r for speed, and t for time.

fourth On a piano, a musical interval spanning any four white keys, except that a fourth starting on F ends on a black key (B flat).

fraction A number in the form $\frac{a}{b}$ or a/b, where a and b are whole numbers and b is not 0. Fractions are used to name part of a whole object or part of a whole collection of objects, or to compare two quantities. A fraction can represent division; for example, $\frac{2}{3}$ can be thought of as 2 divided by 3.

free verse Poetry without a set pattern of rhyme or rhythm. Many poets in the twentieth century have written in free verse.

frequency The number of vibrations per second of a sound wave; more generally, the number of repetitions per unit of time.

friction A surface resistance to motion.

fulcrum A point on a mobile at which a rod is suspended; in general, the point or place around which a lever pivots. *See also* **mobile**.

furlong A unit of distance most commonly used in horse racing. There are 40 furlongs in 5 miles.

general pattern *See* **pattern.**

genus The number of holes in a geometric shape, used to classify shapes in topology; in general, a class or group. Shapes with the same genus are topologically equivalent. *See also* **topology.**

geometric solid A 3-dimensional shape bounded by surfaces. Common geometric solids include the rectangular prism, square pyramid, cylinder, cone, and sphere. Despite its name, a geometric solid is "hollow;" it does not include the points in its interior.

Geometry Template An *Everyday Mathematics* tool that includes a millimeter ruler, a ruler with sixteenth-inch intervals, a half-circle and a full-circle protractor, a percent circle, pattern-block shapes, and other geometric figures. Tiny holes at selected inch and centimeter marks allow the template to serve as a compass.

Golden Ratio A ratio of approximately 1.618 to 1.

Golden Rectangle A rectangle in which the ratio of the length of the longer side to the length of the shorter side is the **Golden Ratio**, or about 1.618 to 1. The shape of a standard index card 5 inches by 3 inches is nearly a Golden Rectangle.

a golden rectangle

great span The distance from the tip of the thumb to the tip of the fourth (little) finger, stretched as far as possible.

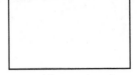

great span

greatest common factor The largest factor that two or more numbers have in common. For example, the common factors of 24 and 36 are 1, 2, 3, 4, 6, and 12. The greatest common factor of 24 and 36 is 12.

grouping symbols Symbols such as parentheses ( ), brackets [ ], or braces { } that indicate the order in which operations in an expression are to be done—for example, $(3 + 4) * [(8 + 2) / 5]$.

haiku A poem with 3 lines and 17 syllables. The first line has 5 syllables, the second line has 7 syllables, and the third line has 5 syllables.

handicap In sports and games, points added to (or subtracted from) a player's score in order to equalize the chances of winning. A handicap may be given to bowlers whose average score is less than 200. Golfers also use a formula based on past performance to calculate their handicap.

height of a parallelogram *See* **base of a parallelogram.**

height of a rectangle *See* **base of a rectangle.**

height of a 3-dimensional figure *See* **base of a 3-dimensional figure.**

height of a triangle *See* **base of a triangle.**

heptagon A polygon with seven sides.

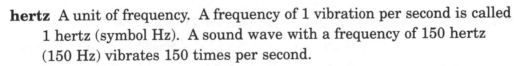

heptagons

hertz A unit of frequency. A frequency of 1 vibration per second is called 1 hertz (symbol Hz). A sound wave with a frequency of 150 hertz (150 Hz) vibrates 150 times per second.

hexagon A polygon with six sides.

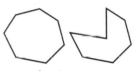

hexagon

horizon (line) Where the Earth and sky appear to meet forming a line.

horizontal Positioned in a left-right orientation.

hypotenuse In a right triangle, the side opposite the right angle.

icon A small picture or diagram, sometimes used to represent quantities. For example, an icon of a stadium might be used to represent 100,000 people on a **pictograph.**

icosahedron *See* **regular polyhedron.**

image A figure that is produced by a **transformation** of another figure. *See also* **preimage.**

improper fraction *See* **top-heavy fraction.**

indirect measurement Methods for determining heights, distances, and other quantities that cannot be measured directly.

inequality A number sentence stating that two quantities are not equal, or might not be equal. Relation symbols for inequalities include $\neq$, $<$, $>$, $\leq$, and $\geq$.

integers The set of integers is $\{... -4, -3, -2, -1, 0, 1, 2, 3, 4, ...\}$. All integers are rational numbers, but not all rational numbers are integers. All counting numbers are integers, but not all integers are counting numbers.

intersect To meet (at a point, line, and so on).

interval A set of numbers between two numbers a and b, possibly including a or b.

In music, the "distance" between two notes. When two or more notes are sounded one after another, they create a **melodic interval**. When two or more notes are sounded at the same time, they create a **harmonic interval**. When three notes or more notes are played at the same time, they form a **chord**.

inversion A musical operation that turns a pattern of notes upside down; compare to a reflection in geometry.

"in the black" A positive account balance. You have more money than you owe.

"in the red" A negative account balance. You owe more money than you have.

inscribed square

inscribed polygon A polygon all of whose vertices are points on a circle or other figure.

integer Any whole number or its opposite; for example, –2, 2, 6, –100.

interior The set of all points in a plane "inside" a closed two-dimensional figure, such as a polygon or circle. Also, the set of all points in space "inside" a closed three-dimensional figure, such as a polyhedron or sphere. The interior is usually not considered to be part of the figure.

irrational numbers Numbers that cannot be written as fractions where both the numerator and denominator are integers and the denominator is not zero. For example, $\sqrt{2}$ and π are irrational numbers.

An irrational number can be represented by a nonterminating, nonrepeating decimal. For example, the decimal for π, 3.141592653..., continues without a repeating pattern. The number 1.10100100010000... is irrational; there is a pattern in the decimal, but it does not repeat.

isometry transformation A transformation such as a translation (slide), reflection (flip), or rotation (turn) that preserves distances between points.

juxtapose To place side by side in an expression to indicate multiplication. For example, $5n$ means $5 * n$, and ab means $a * b$.

key in To press keys on a calculator to enter numbers or perform operations.

key sequence A set of instructions for performing a particular calculation or function with a calculator.

kite A quadrilateral with exactly two pairs of adjacent congruent sides. (A **rhombus** is not a kite.)

kite

label In a spreadsheet, words or numbers used to provide information such as the title of the spreadsheet or the heading for a row or column.

landmark A measure of data. Landmarks include median, mode, maximum, minimum, and range.

latitude The measure of an angle whose vertex is the center of the Earth, used to indicate the location of a place with reference to the **equator.** *See also* **longitude**.

least common denominator The least common multiple of the denominators of every fraction in a given collection of fractions. *See also* **least common multiple**.

least common multiple The smallest number that is a multiple of two or more numbers. For example, some common multiples of 6 and 8 are 24, 48, and 72. 24 is the least common multiple of 6 and 8.

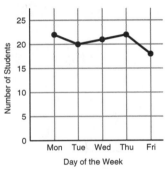

line graph

leg of a right triangle A side of a right triangle that is not the hypotenuse.

life expectancy The number of years in an average person's lifetime.

like terms In an algebraic expression, either the **constant terms**, or any **variable terms** that contain the same variable or variables. For example, $4y$ and $7y$ are like terms in $4y + 7y - z$. To **combine like terms** means to rewrite the sum or difference of like terms as a single term. For example, $5a + 6a$ can be rewritten as $11a$, because $5a + 6a = (5 + 6)a = 11a$. Similarly, $16t - 3t$ can be rewritten as $13t$.

line A straight path that extends infinitely in opposite directions.

line graph (broken-line graph) A graph in which points are connected by a line or line segments to represent data.

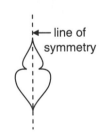

line of symmetry A line through a symmetric figure. Each point in one of the halves of the figure is the same distance from this line as the corresponding point in the other half.

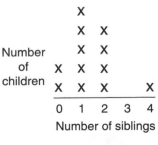

line plot

line plot A sketch of data in which check marks, X's, or other marks above a number line show the frequency of each value.

Glossary

line segment A straight path joining two points, called **endpoints** of the line segment.

line symmetry A figure has line symmetry if a line can be drawn through the figure that divides the figure into two parts so that both parts look exactly alike, but are facing in opposite directions.

liter (L) A metric unit of capacity, equal to the volume of a cube that measures 10 centimeters on a side. $1 \text{ L} = 1000 \text{ mL} = 1000 \text{ cm}^3$. A liter is a little larger than a quart. *See also* **milliliter (mL)**.

longitude A measure (in degrees) of how far east or west of the **prime meridian** a location is on Earth; determined by semicircles of longitude connecting the North Pole and South Pole. *See also* **latitude**.

loop A sequence of steps in a flowchart that is repeated as a result of a previous decision.

magnitude increase A 10-fold increase in a value.

magnitude estimate An estimate of the size of a numerical result— whether it is in the tens, hundreds, thousands, and so on.

map direction symbol A symbol on a map that identifies north, south, east, and west. Sometimes only north is indicated.

map legend A diagram that explains the symbols, markings, and colors on a map. Also called a **map key.**

map scale A rate that compares the distance between two locations on a map with the actual distance between them. The rate is often represented by a labeled line segment, similar to a ruler.

mathematics A study of relationships among numbers, shapes, and patterns. Mathematics is used to count and measure things, to discover similarities and differences, to solve problems, and to learn about and organize the world.

maximum The largest amount; the greatest number in a set of data.

mean A typical or middle value for a set of numbers. It is found by adding the numbers in the set and dividing the sum by the number of numbers. It is often referred to as the **average.**

measure A unit into which a piece of music is divided. Each measure must contain an equivalent combination of notes (or notes and rests). The meter of a piece of music determines how the music is divided into measures.

median The middle value in a set of data when the data are listed in order from smallest to largest (or largest to smallest). If there is an even number of data points, the median is the **mean** of the two middle values.

memory Storage of information for later recall. A calculator's memory stores a value while other operations are performed.

meter In music, part of the "beat" or pulse felt when music is played; determined by the number of beats in a measure, and the kind of note that gets one beat. The meter is shown at the start of a piece of music by a symbol called the time signature.

metric system of measurement A measurement system based on the base-10 numeration system and used in most countries in the world. Units for linear measure (length, distance) include millimeter, centimeter, meter, kilometer; units for mass (weight) include gram and kilogram; units for capacity (amount of liquid or other pourable substance a container can hold) include milliliter and liter.

middle C A note near the middle of the piano keyboard.

midpoint A point halfway between two points.

milliliter (mL) A metric unit of capacity, equal to $\frac{1}{1000}$ of a liter or 1 cubic centimeter.

minimum The smallest amount; the least number in a set of data.

minuend *See* **subtraction.**

mixed number A number that is equal to the sum of a whole number and a fraction. For example $2\frac{1}{4}$, is equal to $2 + \frac{1}{4}$.

mobile A sculpture made of rods and other objects that are suspended by strings or wires. The objects are connected so that the sculpture is balanced and can turn.

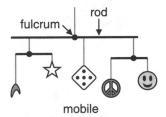

mobile

Möbius strip or **Möbius band** A shape with only one side and one edge; named for mathematician Augustus Ferdinand Möbius.

modal The adjective form of the word *mode.*

mode The value or values that occur most often in a set of data.

Möbius strip

multiple of a number *n* The product of a whole number and the number *n*. For example, the numbers 2, 4, 6, 8, and 10 are all multiples of 2 because $2 * 1 = 2$, $2 * 2 = 4$, $2 * 3 = 6$, and so on.

multiplication A mathematical operation. Numbers being multiplied are called **factors**. The result of multiplication is called the **product**. In $5 * 12 = 60$, 5 and 12 are factors. 60 is the product. **Division** "undoes" multiplication; $60/5 = 12$ and $60/12 = 5$.

multiplication fact *See* **arithmetic fact.**

multiplicative inverses Two numbers whose product is 1. For example, the multiplicative inverse of 5 is $\frac{1}{5}$, and the multiplicative inverse of $\frac{3}{5}$ is $\frac{5}{3}$, or $1\frac{2}{3}$. Multiplicative inverses are also called **reciprocals** of each other.

Glossary

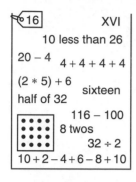

name-collection box

name of tessellation:
4.4.4.4

multiplication property of –1 The property that for any number a, $(-1) * a = a * (-1) = (op)a$, or $-a$.

musical notation A system of recording music on paper. Musical notation makes it possible to give someone instructions for playing a piece of music.

mystery graph, mystery plot An unlabeled graph or plot. The viewer is challenged to figure out a situation it might represent.

name-collection box A box-like diagram containing a number, used for collecting equivalent names for that number.

name of a tessellation A numerical description of a tessellation, which gives, in order beginning with the smallest, the number of sides of the polygons that meet at each vertex point. For example, the name of the tessellation in the margin is 4.4.4.4.

negative number A number less than 0; a number to the left of 0 on a horizontal number line.

negative power of 10 *See* **power of 10.**

negative rational numbers Numbers less than 0 that can be written as a fraction or a terminating or repeating decimal. For example, –4, –0.333..., and $-\frac{4}{5}$ are negative rational numbers.

normal span The distance from the tip of the thumb to the tip of the first (index) finger, stretched as far apart as possible.

Northern Hemisphere The northern half of the Earth, from the equator to the North Pole.

note In music, a sound with a specific frequency; also, a symbol that represents such a sound and its duration. The lowest note on a piano has a frequency of about 27 vibrations per second; the highest note has a frequency of about 4200 vibrations per second. A **half note** lasts twice as long as a **quarter note**, four times as long as an **eighth note**, and one-half as long as a **whole note**.

number-and-word notation A notation consisting of the significant digits of a large number and words for the place value. For example: 27 trillion.

number line A line on which points correspond to numbers.

number model A number sentence that shows how the parts of a number story are related; for example: $5 + 8 = 13$; $27 - 11 = 16$; $3 * 30 = 90$; $56/8 = 7$.

number sentence A sentence that is made up of numerals and a relation symbol ($=$, $<$, $>$, $\neq$, $\leq$, $\geq$). Most number sentences also contain at least one operation symbol. Number sentences may also have grouping symbols, such as parentheses.

numerator In a whole divided into a number of equal parts, the number of equal parts being considered. In the fraction $\frac{a}{b}$, a is the numerator.

octagon An eight-sided polygon.

octagon

octave On a piano, a musical interval spanning any eight white keys; the interval from one note to the next note with the same name—for example, the distance between two consecutive C notes.

odd number A whole number that is not divisible by 2, such as 1, 3, 5, and so on. When an odd number is divided by 2, the remainder is 1. A whole number is either an odd number or an **even number.**

ONE *See* **whole.**

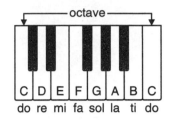

open sentence A number sentence in which one or more variables hold the place of missing numbers.

opposite of a number A number that is the same distance from zero on the number line as the given number, but on the opposite side of zero. The opposite of any number a is written as (op)a or $-a$. If a is a negative number, (op)a or $-a$ will be a positive number. For example, if $a = -5$, then $-a$, or op(a), is (op)$-5 = 5$. *See also* **additive inverses.**

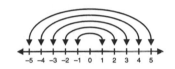

order of operations Rules that tell the order in which operations should be done.

order of rotation symmetry *See* **rotation symmetry**.

ordered number pair Two numbers in a specific order used to locate a point on a coordinate grid. They are usually written inside parentheses: (2,3).

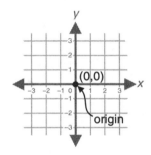

orders of magnitude Powers of ten.

organizing data Arranging and presenting data in a way that makes the data easier to understand.

origin The point where the x-axis and y-axis intersect on a coordinate grid.

outcome The result of an event. Heads and tails are the two outcomes of the event of tossing a coin.

pan balance

pan balance A device used to compare the weights of objects or to weigh objects.

parabola The curve formed by the surface of a right circular cone when it is sliced by a plane which is parallel to a side of the cone. A parabola can also be described as the curve formed by all the points which are the same distance from a line and a point not on that line.

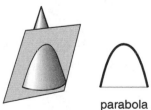
parabola

parallels Lines of latitude.

parallel lines (segments, rays) Lines (segments, rays) that are the same distance apart and never meet.

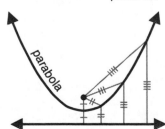

parallelogram

parallelogram A quadrilateral that has two pairs of parallel sides. Pairs of opposite sides of a parallelogram are congruent.

parentheses The symbols ( ) used to group expressions, as in $a(b + c)$. Other grouping symbols include brackets [ ] and braces { }.

part-to-part ratio A ratio which compares a part of the whole to another part of the whole. For example, the statement "There are 8 boys for every 12 girls" expresses a part-to-part ratio.

part-to-whole ratio A ratio which compares a part of the whole to the whole. For example, the statement "8 out of 20 students are boys" expresses a part-to-whole ratio. The statement "12 out of 20 students are girls" also expresses a part-to-whole ratio.

pattern A model, plan, or rule using words or variables to describe a set of shapes or numbers that repeat in a predictable way.

pentagon A polygon with five sides.

pentagon

pentatonic scale A five-note scale. The pentatonic scale can be heard by playing the black keys on a piano.

per capita Per person.

percent (%) Per hundred, or out of a hundred. 1% means $\frac{1}{100}$ or 0.01. For example, "48% of the students in the school are boys" means that out of every 100 students in the school, 48 are boys.

Percent Circle A device on the Geometry Template used to measure or draw figures (such as circle graphs) involving percents.

perfect number A number for which the sum of all the proper factors is equal to the number itself. For example, 6 is a perfect number because the sum of its proper factors is $1 + 2 + 3 = 6$. *See also* **abundant numbers, deficient numbers,** and **proper factors.**

perimeter The distance around a two-dimensional shape. A formula for the perimeter of a rectangle is $P = 2 * (l + w)$, where l represents the length and w the width of the rectangle.

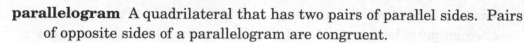

perpendicular lines

perpendicular Two rays, lines, or line segments that form right angles are said to be perpendicular to each other.

perspective A method of drawing that allows an artist to accurately represent a 3-dimensional object on a 2-dimensional surface.

perspective drawing In this type of drawing, parallel lines that move away from the viewer are drawn so that they come together at a vanishing point. The proportions in a perspective drawing are not the same as the proportions of the actual object.

per-unit rate A rate that tells the quantity of items with a given unit for each item of a different unit. Two dollars per gallon, 12 miles per hour, and 4 words per minute are examples of per-unit rates.

pi The ratio of the circumference of a circle to its diameter. Pi is the same for every circle, approximately 3.14. Also written as the Greek letter π.

pictograph A graph constructed with pictures or icons, which make it possible to visualize at a glance the ratios between two counts or measures. Sometimes called **icon** graph.

pitch The highness or lowness of a sound.

place value Determines the value of a digit in a number, written in standard notation, as determined by its position. Each place has a value ten times that of the place to its right and one-tenth the value of the place to its left.

plane A flat surface that extends forever.

point symmetry The property of a figure that can be rotated 180° about a point in such a way that the resulting figure (the image) exactly matches the original figure (the preimage).

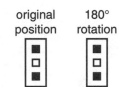

original
position

180°
rotation

polygon A closed figure consisting of line segments (sides) connected endpoint to endpoint.

polyhedron A 3-dimensional shape, all of whose surfaces (faces) are flat. Each face consists of a polygon and the interior of the polygon.

population In data collection, the target audience for a given survey.

population density The number of people living in a given area; usually given as a rate, such as "1000 people per square mile."

positive power of 10 *See* **power of 10.**

positive rational numbers Numbers greater than 0 that can be written as a fraction or a terminating or repeating decimal. For example, 7, $\frac{4}{3}$, 8.125, and 5.111... are positive rational numbers.

power A product of factors that are all the same. For example, $5 * 5 * 5$ (or 125) is called *5 to the third power,* or the *third power of 5,* because 5 is a factor three times. $5 * 5 * 5$ can also be written as 5^3. In general, a power of a number n is a number that can be represented in exponential notation as n^a, where a is any number.

powers key The $[y^x]$ key on a calculator, used to calculate powers. Keying in 4 $[y^x]$ 5 gives the fifth power of 4, or 4^5, which equals 1024.

power of 10 A whole number that can be written as a product using only 10 as a factor; also called a **positive power of 10.** For example, 100 is equal to $10 * 10$ or 10^2. 100 is called *ten squared, the second power of 10,* or *10 to the second power.* A **negative power of 10** is a number that can be written as a product using only 0.1, or 10^{-1}, as a factor. 0.01 is equal to $0.1 * 0.1$, or 10^{-2}. Other powers of 10 include 10^1, or 10, and 10^0, or 1.

precipitation Rain or snow.

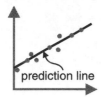

prediction line

prediction line A graph (a picture version) of a formula or rule. For example, the rule for predicting a person's height if you know the length of their tibia is Height = 2.6 * Length of Tibia + 25.5. The prediction line would be drawn through data points for height and length of tibia that satisfy this rule.

preimage A geometric figure that is operated on by a **transformation** to produce another figure. *See also* **image**.

prime factorization A whole number expressed as a product of prime factors. For example, the prime factorization of 24 is 2 * 2 * 2 * 3.

prime meridian An imaginary semicircle on the Earth, connecting the North Pole and South Pole through Greenwich, England. *See also* **longitude.**

prime number A whole number greater than 1 that has exactly two whole-number factors, 1 and itself. For example, 7 is a prime number because its only factors are 1 and 7. A prime number is only divisible by 1 and itself. The first five prime numbers are 2, 3, 5, 7, and 11. *See also* **composite number.**

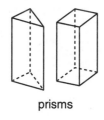

prisms

prism A polyhedron with two parallel faces (called bases) that are the same size and shape. Prisms are classified according to the shape of two parallel bases. The faces of a prism are always bounded by parallelograms, and are often rectangular.

probability A number from 0 to 1 that indicates the likelihood that something (an event) will happen. The closer a probability is to 1, the more likely is it that an event will happen.

product *See* **multiplication.**

profile A general description or view. A profile can be in many different forms, including a graph.

proper factor Any whole-number factor of a number except the number itself. For example, the factors of 10 are 1, 2, 5, and 10. The proper factors of 10 are 1, 2, and 5.

properties of rational numbers *See pages 64-66.*

protractor A tool for measuring or drawing angles. When measuring an angle, the vertex of the angle should be at the center of the protractor and one side aligned with the 0° mark. A half-circle protractor can be used to measure or draw angles up to 180°; a full-circle protractor to measure or draw angles to 360°.

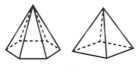

pyramids

pyramid A polyhedron in which one face (the base) is a polygon and the other faces are formed by triangles with a common vertex (the apex). A pyramid is classified according to the shape of its base.

Pythagorean Theorem The following famous theorem: If the legs of a right triangle have lengths a and b, and the hypotenuse has length c, then $a^2 + b^2 = c^2$.

quadrangle or **quadrilateral** A polygon with four sides.

quotient *See* **division.**

radius A line segment from the center of a circle (or sphere) to any point on the circle (or sphere); also, the length of such a line segment.

random Without any pattern or preference.

random number A number that has the same chance of appearing as any other number.

range The difference between the maximum and minimum in a set of data.

rate A comparison of two quantities with unlike units. For example, a speed such as 55 miles per hour compares distance with time.

rate diagram A tool used to solve rate problems.

rate of speed Describes the relationship between the time it takes to travel a distance and the distance traveled in that time.

rate table A means of displaying rate information.

rate unit A unit, used to describe a rate, made up of two different units. For example, miles per hour, dollars per pound, and words per minute are all rate units.

ratio A comparison of two quantities with like units. Ratios can be expressed with fractions, decimals, percents, or words; or they can be written with a colon between the two numbers being compared. For example, if a team wins 3 games out of 5 games played, the ratio of wins to total games is 3/5, 0.6, 60%, 3 to 5, or 3:5 (read "three to five").

rational number Any number that can be represented in the form $\frac{a}{b}$, where a and b are integers and b is not 0. Also, any number that can be represented by a **terminating decimal** or **repeating decimal**. $\frac{2}{3}$, $-\frac{2}{3}$, 0.5, −0.5, and 0.3333... are rational numbers.

ray A straight path that extends infinitely from a point, called its endpoint.

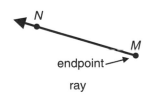

ray

reaction time The amount of time it takes to respond to a stimulus.

reaction-time distance The distance a car travels in the time it takes a driver to react to a situation before actually stepping on the brake pedal.

real number Any rational or irrational number.

recall survey A type of survey used to collect information on past behavior, habits, and activities. Participants in such a survey are asked to recall information from memory.

reciprocal *See* **multiplicative inverses.**

rectangular array

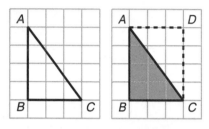

The area of rectangle *ABCD* is
3 units ∗ 4 units = 12 square units.
The area of triangle *ABC* is one half
the area of the rectangle, or
6 square units.

reflex angle

rectangle A parallelogram with four right angles.

rectangular array A rectangular arrangement of objects in rows and columns in which each row has the same number of parts and each column has the same number of parts.

rectangular land survey system A land survey that uses reference lines parallel to the north-south meridians of longitude and the east-west parallels of latitude to divide the land. It outlines pieces of land shaped like rectangles.

rectangular method A method for finding area, in which rectangles are used to surround a figure or parts of a figure. All the areas that are calculated are either areas of rectangles or of triangular halves of rectangular regions.

reduce To make an object or shape smaller.

reference frame A system of numbers, letters, or words to show quantities with reference to a zero point. Examples of reference frames are number lines, time lines, calendars, thermometers, maps, and coordinate systems.

reference note In music, a note used with an indication of time to show tempo; ♩ = 120 represents a tempo of 120 quarter notes per minute, or $\frac{1}{2}$ second per quarter note.

reflection A "flipping" motion of a picture or object so that its image is the opposite of the original (preimage).

reflex angle An angle whose measure is between 180° and 360°.

regular polygon A convex polygon in which all the sides are the same length and all the angles have the same measure.

regular polyhedron A polyhedron with faces that are all **congruent regular polygons**. There are five regular polyhedrons:

tetrahedron:	4 faces, each formed by an equilateral triangle
cube:	6 faces, each formed by a square
octahedron:	8 faces, each formed by an equilateral triangle
dodecahedron:	12 faces, each formed by a regular pentagon
icosahedron:	20 faces, each formed by an equilateral triangle.

tetrahedron   cube   octahedron   dodecahedron   icosahedron

regular tessellation A tessellation made up of only one kind of regular polygon.

relation symbol A symbol used to express the relationship between two quantities. The symbols used in number sentences are: = for "is equal to," ≠ for "is not equal to," < for "is less than," > for "is greater than," ≤ for "is less than or equal to," ≥ for "is greater than or equal to."

remainder *See* **division.**

repeating decimal A decimal which has one digit, or a group of digits, that is repeated without end. For example, 0.3333... and 0.147147... are repeating decimals. *See* **decimal.**

retrograde A musical operation that turns a pattern of notes backward; compares to a reflection in geometry.

revolution Movement in a circle or a curve around some point.

rhombus A parallelogram whose sides are all the same length. The angles are usually not right angles, but they may be right angles.

rhythm In music and poetry, a regular pattern formed by sounds of varying length and emphasis. Rhythm is part of the "beat" or pulse felt when music is played.

right triangle A triangle that has a right angle.

rotation A turn around a center point or axis.

rhombus

right triangle

rotation symmetry Property of a figure that can be rotated around a point in such a way that the resulting figure (the image) exactly matches the original figure (the preimage). The rotation must be more than 0 degrees, but less than 360 degrees. If a figure has rotation symmetry, its **order of rotation symmetry** is the number of different ways it can be rotated to match itself exactly. "No rotation" is counted as one of the ways.

rounding Replacing a number with a nearby number that is easier to work with or better reflects the precision of the data. 12,964 rounded to the nearest thousand is 13,000.

row *See* **cell.**

rubber-sheet geometry *See* **topology.**

sample A subset of a population used to represent the whole population.

scale The ratio of the distance on a map, globe, or drawing to the actual distance.

scale drawing An accurate picture of an object in which all parts are drawn to the same scale. If an actual object measured 33 by 22 yards, a scale drawing of it might measure 33 by 22 millimeters.

scale factor A number that names "How many times as many?" or "What fraction of?" one quantity is of another quantity.

scale model A model that represents an object or display in proportions based on a determined scale.

scientific calculator A calculator that displays very large or very small numbers in scientific notation and has powering, square root, change-of-sign, and reciprocal keys.

scientific notation A system for representing numbers in which a number is written as the product of a power of 10 and a number that is at least 1 but less than 10. Scientific notation allows writing big and small numbers with only a few symbols. For example, 4,000,000 in scientific notation is $4 * 10^6$. 0.00001 in scientific notation is $1 * 10^{-5}$.

section (of land) A land unit equal to one square mile, 640 acres or $\frac{1}{36}$ of a township.

sector

sector A region bounded by an arc and two radiuses of a circle. The word *wedge* is sometimes used instead of sector.

semicircle *See* **arc.**

semiregular tessellation A tessellation made up of two or more kinds of regular polygons. In a semiregular tessellation, the angles around any vertex point must be congruent to the angles around any other vertex point.

Sieve of Eratosthenes A method credited to the mathematician Eratosthenes (about 200 B.C.) for identifying prime numbers.

sighting A method that artists use to draw a free-hand copy of a figure.

similar figures Figures that are exactly the same shape but not necessarily the same size.

simplest form A fraction in which the numerator and denominator have no common factor except 1 and the numerator is less than the denominator. Also, a mixed number in which the fraction is in simplest form.

simplify an expression To rewrite the expression by removing parentheses and by combining like terms. For example, $7y + 4 + 5 + 3y$ can be simplified as $10y + 9$ and $3(2y + 5) - y$ can be simplified as $5y + 15$.

simulation An activity in which an object or event is represented by something else.

size change An enlargement or reduction of an original document.

size-change factor A number that tells the amount of enlargement or reduction.

slanted cylinder A cylinder in which the curved surface is not perpendicular to the base.

slanted cylinder

solution of an open sentence A value or values of the variable(s) in an open sentence for which the sentence is true.

solution set The set of all solutions of an equation or inequality.

sonnet A poem with 14 lines, each with 10 syllables. The lines rhyme according to one of several patterns.

Southern Hemisphere The southern half of the Earth, from the equator to the South Pole.

span *See* **normal span** or **great span.**

special case (of a pattern) When values replace the words or variables in a pattern. For example, 6 + 6 = 12 is a special case of the pattern $Y + Y = 2Y$. *See also* **pattern**.

speed A rate that compares distance traveled with the time taken to travel that distance.

sphere The set of all points in space that are a given distance (the **radius** of the sphere) from a given point (the **center** of the sphere). A ball is shaped like a sphere, as is Earth.

spreadsheet A table displayed by a computer program, which is used to perform mathematical operations, evaluate formulas, and relate data quickly. The name comes from ledger worksheets for financial records. Such sheets were often taped together and then spread out for examination.

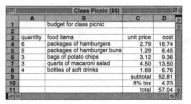

spreadsheet

square array A **rectangular array** with the same number of rows as columns. For example, 16 objects will form a square array with 4 objects in each row and 4 objects in each column.

square array

square number A number that is the product of a whole number multiplied by itself; a whole number to the second power. 25 is a square number, because 25 = 5 * 5. A square number can be represented by a square array.

square of a number The product of a number multiplied by itself; symbolized by a raised 2. For example, $3.5^2 = 3.5 * 3.5 = 12.25$.

square root of a number The square root of a number n is a number which, when multiplied by itself, results in the number n. For example, 4 is a square root of 16, because 4 * 4 = 16. The other square root of 16 is −4 because −4 * (−4) = 16.

square unit A unit used in area measurement.

staff In musical notation, a pattern of evenly spaced horizontal lines on which notes and other information are placed.

standard notation The most familiar way of representing whole numbers, integers, and decimals by writing digits in specified places.

stem-and-leaf plot A display of data in which digits with larger place values are named as stems, and digits with smaller place values are named as leaves.

Stems 10's	Leaves 1's
2	4 4 5 6 7 7
3	1 1 2 2 6 6
4	1 1 3 5 8
5	0 2

stem-and-leaf plot

Glossary

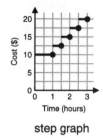

step graph

step graph A graph that looks like steps. Particularly useful when the horizontal axis represents time.

substitute To replace one thing with another; in a formula, to replace letters with numerical values. For example, if $b = 4.5$ and $h = 8.5$, then these values can be substituted in the formula $A = b * h$ to give $A = 4.5 * 8.5$.

subtraction A mathematical operation based on "taking away" or comparing ("how much more?"). The number being subtracted is called the **subtrahend**; the number it is subtracted from is called the **minuend**; the result of subtraction is called the **difference**. In $45 - 12 = 33$, 45 is the minuend, 12 is the subtrahend, and 33 is the difference. **Addition** "undoes" subtraction. $45 - 12 = 33$, and $45 = 12 + 33$.

subtrahend *See* **subtraction.**

supplementary angles Two angles whose measures total $180°$.

surface area A measure of the surface of a 3-dimensional figure.

survey A study that collects data from human respondents. Surveys are used to find out about people's characteristics, behaviors, interests, and so on.

tempo In music, the speed at which notes are played.

term In an algebraic expression or equation, a number or a product of a number and one or more variables. For example, the terms of the expression $5y + 3k - 8$ are $5y$, $3k$, and 8. A **variable term** is a term that contains at least one **variable**. For example, in the equation $4b - 8 = b + 5$, $4b$ and b are variable terms. A **constant term** is a term that does not contain a variable. For example, in the equation $4b - 8 = b + 5$, 8 and 5 are constant terms. *See also* **like terms**.

terminating decimal A decimal which does not repeat. For example, 0.5 and 0.125 are terminating decimals. *See* **decimal.**

tessellation An arrangement of closed shapes that covers a surface completely without overlaps or gaps. *See also* **tile.**

test number A number used to replace a variable in an equation when using the trial-and-error method for finding a solution. Test numbers are useful when trying to "close in" on the exact solution of an equation.

tetrahedron *See* **regular polyhedron.**

theorem A mathematical statement that can be proved to be true (or, sometimes, a statement that is proposed and needs to be proved). For example, the Pythagorean Theorem states that if the legs of a right triangle have lengths a and b, and the hypotenuse has length c, then $a^2 + b^2 = c^2$.

tile A shape used in a tessellation. If only one shape is repeated in a tessellation, the tessellation is called a same-tile tessellation.

tiling Covering a surface with uniform shapes so there are no gaps or overlaps, except possibly gaps around the edges.

time graph A graph that is constructed from a time story and shows what has happened through a progression of time.

time signature A symbol indicating the meter in a piece of music—for example $\frac{3}{4}$. The top number tells how many beats there are in a measure; the bottom number tells what kind of note gets one beat (4 means a quarter note).

top-heavy fraction A fraction that names a number greater than or equal to 1; a fraction whose numerator is equal to or greater than its denominator. Examples of top-heavy fractions are $\frac{7}{3}$, $\frac{5}{5}$, $\frac{9}{7}$, and $\frac{16}{4}$. Also called **improper fraction.**

topological property *See* **topology.**

topological transformation *See* **topology.**

topologically equivalent In topology, a term for shapes that can be transformed into each other with a topological transformation. *See also* **genus**.

topology A modern branch of mathematics that deals, among other things, with the properties of geometric objects that remain the same when the objects are changed by certain operations, such as shrinking, stretching, or twisting. Tearing, breaking, poking holes, and "sticking together" are not permitted. Transformations that follow these rules are called **topological transformations**. Properties of a figure that are not changed by topological transformations are called **topological properties**. Examples of topological properties include the order of points on a curve and the number of holes in a shape (its genus).

township A square land unit 6 miles on each side (area 36 square miles).

transformation An operation on a geometric figure that produces a new figure, called the **image**, from the original figure, called the **preimage**. Transformations are sometimes thought of as "motions" that move a figure from one place to another, and possibly change its size or shape. The study of transformations is called **transformation geometry**.

transformation geometry *See* **transformation**.

translation The motion of "sliding" an object or picture along a straight line.

translation tessellation A tessellation created by translating (sliding) curves from one side of a figure (such as a square) to the opposite side. The resulting figure is then translated to create the interlocking pieces in the tessellation.

translation

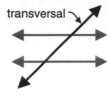

transversal

trapezoid

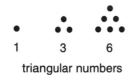

tree diagram

1   3   6

triangular numbers

transposition A musical operation that moves a pattern of notes up or down; compares to a translation in geometry.

transversal A line which intersects two or more other lines.

trapezoid A quadrilateral that has exactly one pair of parallel sides. No two sides need be the same length.

treble clef A symbol at the left end of a musical staff indicating that the notes that follow it are on the right half of the piano keyboard.

tree diagram A tool used to solve probability problems.

trial-and-error method A method for finding the solution of an equation by trying several test numbers.

triangle A polygon with three sides. An **equilateral** triangle has three sides of the same length. An **isosceles** triangle has two sides of the same length. A **scalene** triangle has no sides of the same length.

triangular numbers Figurate numbers that can be shown by a triangular arrangement of dots.

truncate To discard all digits to the right of a particular place.

twin primes Two prime numbers that are separated by just one composite number. For example, 3 and 5 are twin primes, because they are separated by the composite number 4. The numbers 11 and 13 are also twin primes.

unit ONE of something.

unit fraction A fraction whose numerator is 1. For example, $\frac{1}{2}$, $\frac{1}{3}$, $\frac{1}{8}$, $\frac{1}{12}$, and $\frac{1}{20}$ are unit fractions.

unit percent One percent (1%).

unit price The price for one unit of measure; for example $0.50 per ounce.

unit ratio A ratio of some number to 1. Every ratio can be converted to a unit ratio. For example, to convert the ratio of 3 girls to 2 boys to a unit ratio, divide 3 by 2. The unit ratio is 1.5 to 1.

unlike denominators Unequal denominators, as in $\frac{1}{2}$ and $\frac{1}{3}$.

update (revise) a spreadsheet To change one or more numbers in a computer spreadsheet. When a number is changed, the computer recalculates and changes related numbers on the spreadsheet.

vanishing line Line connecting a point on a figure in a perspective drawing with the vanishing point.

vanishing point In a perspective drawing, the point at which parallel lines moving away from the viewer seem to converge. It is located on the horizon line.

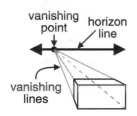

vanishing point   horizon line

vanishing lines

variable A letter or other symbol that represents a number. A variable need not represent one specific number; it can stand for many different values.

variable term *See* **term**.

Venn diagram A picture that uses circles to show relationships between sets.

vertex The point at which the rays of an angle, two sides of a polygon, or the edges of a polyhedron meet.

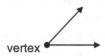

vertex

vertical Positioned in an up-down orientation.

vibration A rapid back-and-forth motion. Sounds are vibrations of the air.

volume The measure of the amount of space occupied by a 3-dimensional shape.

vertices

whole The entire object, collection of objects, or quantity being considered; the ONE, the unit, 100%.

Whole
24 pennies

whole number Any of the numbers 0, 1, 2, 3, 4, and so on.

wind-chill temperature A measure of "how cold" it is, based on a combination of wind speed and air temperature.

Answer Key

Page 2
Sample sentences:
1. The population of Montana in 1990 was about 799,000 people. The school parking lot has space for 75 cars.
2. A bread recipe calls for $1\frac{1}{4}$ cups of wheat flour. The cheapest ticket for the concert is $24.50.
3. The temperature at 6 A.M. was −9°F. The opposite of 5 is −5.

Page 5
1. twenty-seven thousand, three hundred eight
2. ninety-one million, six hundred seventy-two thousand, four hundred fifty
3. six hundred seventy-five billion
4. seven million, four hundred twenty
5. #1: 7000 (7 * 1000); #2: 70,000 (7 * 10,000); #3: 70,000,000,000 (7 * 10,000,000,000); #4: 7,000,000 (7 * 1,000,000)

Page 6
1. 25   2. 27   3. 100,000
4. 8   5. 119,025   6. 20,736

Page 8
1. a. $5 * 10^5$ b. $1 * 10^{10}$ c. $7.5 * 10^8$
   d. $8 * 10^{-5}$ e. $4.5 * 10^{-2}$
2. a. 300,000,000   b. 41,000,000
   c. 70,900,000,000   d. 0.004   e. 0.0906

Page 9
1. 113   2. 364   3. 965   4. 1809   5. 9723

Page 10
1. 37   2. 34   3. 360   4. 15   5. 339

Page 11
1. 37,000   2. 2400   3. 24,000
4. 2100   5. 30,000

Page 12
1. 3227   2. 34,155   3. 5238
4. 3354   5. 4991

Page 13
1. 53   2. 900   3. 3000   4. 60   5. 50

Page 14
1. 42 R1   2. 18 R4   3. 55 R1
4. 138 R4   5. 230 R1

Page 15
1. 68   2. 16 R3   3. 22 R12   4. 71 R7

Page 16
1. 1, 2, 4, 8   2. 1, 3, 9, 27   3. 1, 7, 49
4. 1, 2, 3, 4, 6, 9, 12, 18, 36   5. 1, 13
6. 1, 2, 4, 5, 10, 20, 25, 50, 100

Page 17
divisible by 2: 6270, 526, 13,680
divisible by 3: 105, 6270, 711, 13,680
divisible by 5: 105, 6270, 13,680
divisible by 6: 6270, 13,680
divisible by 9: 711, 13,680
divisible by 10: 6270, 13,680

Page 18
1. $12 = 2 * 2 * 3$ 2. $28 = 2 * 2 * 7$
3. $50 = 2 * 5 * 5$ 4. $36 = 2 * 2 * 3 * 3$
5. $32 = 2 * 2 * 2 * 2 * 2$ 6. $60 = 2 * 2 * 3 * 5$

Page 23
1. $\frac{5}{3}$ 2. $\frac{9}{2}$ 3. $\frac{15}{4}$ 4. $\frac{5}{2}$ 5. $\frac{17}{5}$ 6. $\frac{4}{1}$

Page 24
1. $1\frac{1}{5}$ 2. $2\frac{5}{8}$ 3. 4   4. $5\frac{1}{2}$ 5. $3\frac{3}{4}$ 6. $6\frac{2}{3}$

Page 25
Answers vary for Problems 1–3.
1. $\frac{2}{8}$ 2. $\frac{12}{24}$ 3. $\frac{15}{10}$ 4. $\frac{3}{4}$ 5. $\frac{4}{5}$ 6. $\frac{4}{5}$

Page 26
Answers vary for Problems 1–3.
1. $\frac{2}{4}$ 2. $\frac{6}{8}$ 3. $\frac{10}{12}$ 4. $\frac{3}{4}$ 5. $\frac{2}{3}$ 6. $\frac{5}{6}$

Page 27

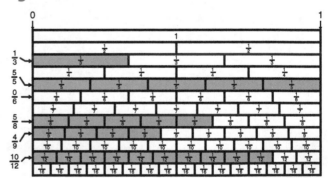

Page 28
1. a. $\frac{1}{2}$ b. $\frac{3}{9}$ c. $\frac{6}{8}$ d. $\frac{5}{8}$ e. $\frac{2}{3}$
2. a. $\frac{1}{10}$ b. $\frac{3}{7}$ c. $\frac{11}{12}$ d. $\frac{5}{9}$

Page 29
1. $\frac{4}{6}$ and $\frac{1}{6}$ 2. $\frac{5}{20}$ and $\frac{8}{20}$ 3. $\frac{3}{10}$ and $\frac{5}{10}$
4. $\frac{15}{20}$ and $\frac{14}{20}$ 5. $\frac{12}{24}$ and $\frac{18}{24}$

Page 30
1. 12 **2.** 20 **3.** 12 **4.** 24 **5.** 18 **6.** 45

Page 31
1. 1 **2.** 2 **3.** 8 **4.** 7 **5.** 6 **6.** 3

Page 32
1. $\frac{2}{3}$ **2.** $\frac{3}{4}$ **3.** $\frac{7}{12}$ **4.** $\frac{1}{12}$ **5.** $\frac{19}{24}$

Page 33
1. 11 **2.** $5\frac{9}{10}$ **3.** $10\frac{1}{12}$ **4.** $22\frac{22}{63}$

Page 35
1. $2\frac{4}{15}$ **2.** $3\frac{3}{8}$ **3.** $2\frac{1}{3}$ **4.** $3\frac{2}{3}$

Page 36
1. $\frac{1}{6}$ **2.** $\frac{3}{20}$ **3.** $\frac{1}{4}$ **4.** 0 **5.** $1\frac{1}{2}$

Page 37
1. $1\frac{1}{2}$ **2.** 24 **3.** $16\frac{1}{5}$ **4.** $9\frac{5}{48}$

Page 39
1. $\frac{12}{5}$, or $2\frac{2}{5}$ **2.** 3 **3.** $\frac{7}{21}$, or $\frac{1}{3}$
4. $\frac{8}{12}$, or $\frac{2}{3}$ **5.** $\frac{28}{10}$ or $2\frac{4}{5}$

Page 42
1. two tenths
2. one and thirty-six hundredths
3. nine hundred forty-eight thousandths
4. nineteen and seven hundredths
5. six thousandths
6. seventy-four and eighty-two thousandths

Page 44
1. a. 0.25 **b.** 0.8 **c.** 2.5 **d.** 0.65 **e.** 0.16
2. a. $\frac{4}{5}$ **b.** $\frac{1}{4}$ **c.** $3\frac{8}{25}$ **d.** $\frac{7}{250}$

Page 45
1. 0.3 **2.** 0.875 **3.** $4.\overline{3}$
4. 0.75 **5.** $1.\overline{7}$ **6.** $0.\overline{285714}$

Page 46
1. 0.125 **2.** $0.\overline{6}$ **3.** $0.41\overline{6}$
4. $08\overline{3}$ **5.** $0.\overline{7}$ **6.** 0.1875

Page 47
1. a. 20% **b.** 70% **c.** 62.5% **d.** 125% **e.** $33\frac{1}{3}$%
2. a. $\frac{3}{5}$ **b.** $\frac{7}{20}$ **c.** $2\frac{1}{2}$

Page 49
1. 2.58 meters
2. a. 9.02 **b.** 21.6 **c.** 11.66 **d.** 4.72

Page 51
1. 345 **2.** 0.0345 **3.** 1600 **4.** 0.509
5. 0.00055 **6.** $5500.00 **7.** 10.8 **8.** 0.327

Page 52
1. 12.88 **2.** 13.392 **3.** 1.5756 **4.** 0.0032

Page 54 .
1. 6.78 **2.** 678 **3.** 0.0054 **4.** $0.29
5. 7750 **6.** 0.004 **7.** 3750 **8.** 20

Page 55
1. 3 **2.** 3.2 **3.** 568 **4.** 15.3

Page 57
1. −15 **2.** 24 **3.** −0.4 **4.** 19 **5.** −18

Page 58
1. −4 **2.** −3 **3.** −10 **4.** 17

Page 59
1. a. −90 **b.** 0 **c.** −270 **d.** −72
2. a. −12 **b.** −6 **c.** 0 **d.** 5

Page 61
1. a. 1, 2, 3, 4 **b.** −1, 0, 1, 2, 3, 4
2. a. yes, $\frac{2}{10}$, $\frac{1}{5}$, or … **b.** yes, $1\frac{1}{6}$
3. a. yes **b.** yes
   c. 1.166…; 1.333…; 1.5 or $1\frac{3}{6}$; 1.666…
4. yes **5.** tan 30°; $\sqrt{2}$; $\sqrt{3}$; $\sqrt{5}$; e; π; $\sqrt{12}$

Page 63
1. Answers vary. Sample answers:
   a. $2 * 5 + 5 = 3 * 5$
   $2 * \frac{1}{2} + \frac{1}{2} = 3 * \frac{1}{2}$
   $2 * (-4) + (-4) = 3 * (-4)$
   b. $4 + (4 + 1) + (4 + 2) = 3 * (4 + 1)$
   $\frac{1}{3} + (\frac{1}{3} + 1) + (\frac{1}{3} + 2) = 3 * (\frac{1}{3} + 1)$
   $6.5 + (6.5 + 1) + (6.5 + 2) = 3 * (6.5 + 1)$
2. a. $a + b = b + a$ **b.** $\frac{x}{y} * \frac{y}{x} = 1$

Page 70

Answers vary. Sample answers:

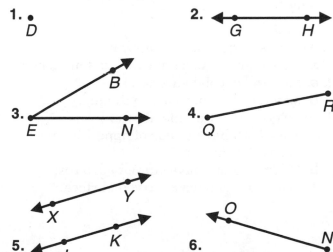

Answer Key

Page 71

1. **a.** same measure **b.** supplementary
   c. supplementary **d.** supplementary
   e. same measure **f.** same measure
2. **a.** 120° **b.** 60° **c.** 120°

Page 72

Answers vary. Sample answers:

1.

2.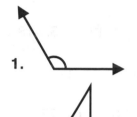

3.

Page 73

1. **a.** triangle, pentagon, heptagon, nonagon
   b. quadrangle or quadrilateral, hexagon, octagon
   c. triangle, pentagon
2. **a.** hexagon **b.** quadrangle or quadrilateral
   c. octagon

Page 74

Answers vary. Sample answers:
1. All sides of a square have the same length; a rectangle has opposite sides of the same length.
2. Trapezoids have exactly one pair of parallel sides; parallelograms have two pairs.
3. All sides of a rhombus have the same length; a kite has only two pairs of sides the same length.

Page 76

1. Answers vary. Sample answers:
   a. cereal box **b.** soup can **c.** tennis ball
2. **a.** all regular polyhedrons
   b. spheres **c.** cones, cylinders
3. Answers vary. Sample answers:
   a. They both have a pair of opposite parallel bases that are flat.
   b. Prisms do not have curved surfaces; cylinders do have a curved surface.

Page 76 (continued)

4. Answers vary. Sample answers:
   a. They both have exactly one base.
   b. Pyramids have all flat surfaces; cones have both flat and curved surfaces.

Page 77

1. Answers vary. Sample answers:
   a. Since prisms and pyramids are polyhedrons, their surfaces are formed by polygons.
   b. Pyramids have one base and an apex; prisms have two opposite, parallel bases.
2. 12

Page 78

C

Page 79

1. side JO = 10 inches
2. side ID = 15 inches

Page 81

1. WHAT   2. A': (6,15)   3. A
              T': (11,11)

Pages 82

1.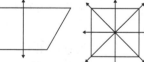

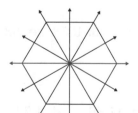 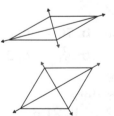

2. A circle has an infinite number of lines of symmetry.

Page 83
Answers vary. Sample answers:

1.   **2.**

Page 87

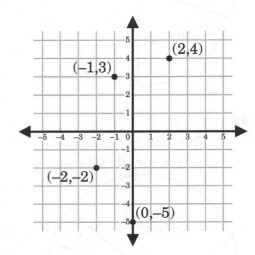

Page 92
1. a. false   **b.** false   **c.** true   **d.** false   **e.** true
2. Sample answer:

Page 93–105
Answers vary.

Page 97
3. equilateral

Page 110
1. a. 200 cm = 2000 mm   **b.** 3500 mL
   c. 5500 m   **d.** 3.2 kg   **e.** 12 mL
2. a. kilogram   **b.** millimeter   **c.** liter
3. a. milligram   **b.** kiloliter
   c. degrees centigrade   **d.** cubic meter

Page 114
1. 45°   **2.** 210°   **3.** about 60°
Answers vary. Sample answers:

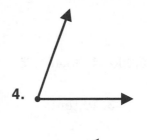

4. **5.**

6.

Page 115
1. a. 2   **b.** 3   **c.** 6   **d.** 10
2. Subtract 2 from the number of sides.
3. 180° * 3 = 540°
4. 135°

Page 116
1. p = 26 feet   **2.** p = 72 yards

Page 117
For calculators with a π key, answer depends on
rounding; approximately 15.70796

Page 118
1. c = 25.1 cm A = 50.3 cm^2
2. c = 18.8 cm A = 28.3 cm^2

Page 119
1. A = 6 units^2 **2.** A = $22\frac{1}{2}$ in^2 **3.** A = 25 m^2

Page 120
1. A = 165 ft^2 **2.** A = 48 in^2 **3.** A = 2.6 cm^2

Page 121
1. A = 6 in^2 **2.** A = 27 cm^2 **3.** A = 1.2 yd^2

Page 123
1. V = 49 yd^3 **2.** V = 1000 cm^3 **3.** V = 288 ft^3

Page 124
1. V = 140 cm^3 **2.** V = 283 ft^3 **3.** V = 113 yd^3

Page 125
1. V = 64 yd^3 **2.** V = 80 cm^3 **3.** V = 100 ft^3

Page 126
1. 33.5 in^3 **2.** 268.1 cm^3

Answer Key

Page 127
1. 340 cm^2 **2.** 48 in^2 **3.** $1\frac{1}{2}$ ft^2

Page 128
94.2 in^2

Page 131
1. 35,500   **2.** 40,000   **3.** 35,000   **4.** 35,481.75

Page 133
1. $3.50   **2.** 3 shirts   **3.** 10 tents

Page 134
1. 5   **2.** 15   **3.** 28   **4.** 12   **5.** 35

Page 135
1. 15   **2.** 15   **3.** 15.12   **4.** 2.65

Page 136
1. 45 counters   **2.** 12 counters

Page 137
$200

Page 138
1. 5 dollars/hour; $5\frac{\text{dollars}}{\text{hour}}$

2. 8 pounds/gallon; $8\frac{\text{pounds}}{\text{gallon}}$

Page 139
1. 5 miles/hour; $\frac{1}{5}$ hour/mile
2. 4 quarts/gallon; $\frac{1}{4}$ gallon/quart

Page 140
1. 15   **2.** $25   **3.** 48¢

Page 142
1. $12 to $20   **2.** $8 to $12   **3.** 1.5 times   **4.** 40%

Page 145
1. a. yes   **b.** no   **c.** 9

Page 146
1. a. no   **b.** yes   **c.** 1

Page 147
3rd grade = about 17%
4th grade = about 22%
5th grade = about 16%

Page 148

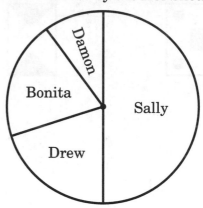

Points Scored by the Hot Shots

Page 149

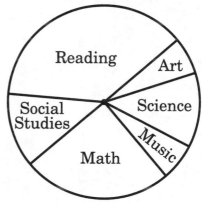

Favorite Subjects
of Sixth Grade Class

Page 150
1. 3, 12, 1/3, 0.5
2. 11, 28, 0, 4
3. multiply "in" by 30

Page 152
About 5000 miles

Page 152
1. 100 students
2. left hand = 18; right hand = 85
3. 3 students

Page 154
1. a. C   **b.** F   **c.** H
2. a. 30°S, 15°W   **b.** 15°N, 15°W
    c. on the Equator, 45°W   **d.** 30°S, 30°E

Page 156
1. A (Audrey's height) = $I - 2$
2. S (Sue's time) = $H * 2$
3. D (Dawn's costs) = $2.00 + (R * $0.50)$

Page 157
1. True **2.** True **3.** False
4. True **5.** False **6.** False

Page 158
1. 12 **2.** 24.1 **3.** 7 **4.** 18 **5.** 10.5 **6.** 0

Page 160
1. 48 square feet
2. 32 square meters
3. 4800 feet
4. a. $V = \frac{1}{3} * (B * h)$
   b. $i = \$1000 * r * t$

Page 161
1. 36 **2.** 21 **3.** 10 **4.** 6

Page 162
1. $4S + 2T = T + 8S$
2. $6B + 2C = 8C + 3B$

Page 163
1. $b < 8$ **2.** $f > 0$
3.

4.

Page 164
1. a. 840 + 240
        1080
   b. 192 − 72
        120
   c. 990 − 66
        924
2. 1531.35 = 1531.35

Page 165
1. $5(12 + 3) - 3 * 12 + 5 = 4(12 - 1)$
        $5(15) - 36 + 5 = 4(11)$
        $75 - 36 + 5 = 44$
        $39 + 5 = 44$
        $44 = 44$

2. a. $x = 4$ **b.** $s = -2$

Page 167
Hits in a Baseball Game
1. Tally Chart

Number of Hits	Number of Students
0	///
1	///
2	////
3	/
4	/

2. Line Plot

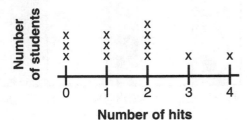

Page 168
Michael Jordan's Scores, 1996 NBA Playoffs
1. Tally Chart of Grouped Data

Number of Points	Number of Times Scored
10–19	/
20–29	~~////~~
30–39	///
40–49	///

2. Stem-and-leaf plot

Stems (100's and 10's)	Leaves (1's)
1	7
2	9 6 8 7 1
3	5 5 5
4	4 6 5

Page 169
minimum: 0 maximum: 4 range: 4
mode: 2 median: 1.5

Answer Key

Page 170
85.4

Page 171

Spending on School Technology

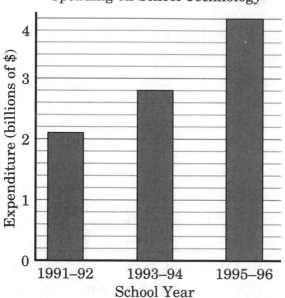

Page 172
1. **a.** $2.00 **b.** $3.50 **c.** $3.50
   d. $8.00 **e.** $6.50
2. 1 mile or less: $2.00;
   additional miles or fraction of a mile: $1.50

Page 173

Average Precipitation for Seattle, Washington

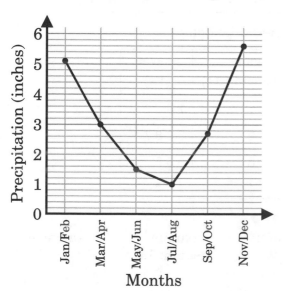

Page 176
1. labels **2.** 4.50 **3.** B1 **4.** 5
5. A4, A5, A6, A7, A8 **6.** D
   C4, C5, C6, C7, C8

Page 179

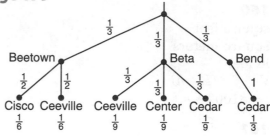

Cisco $\frac{1}{6}$, Ceevile $\frac{1}{6} + \frac{1}{9}$, or $\frac{5}{18}$,

Center $\frac{1}{9}$, Cedar $\frac{1}{9} + \frac{1}{3}$, or $\frac{4}{9}$

Page 259

Order 2: Draw two rays from one point, separated by 180°. (The rays form a line.)

Order 5: Draw five rays from one point, separated by 72°.

Index

Index

Non-Euclidean geometry, 67

Northern Hemisphere, 154

North Pole, 154

Notation
    decimal, 40
    division, 22
    exponential, 6
    fraction, 19, 21
    musical, 267
    percent, 40
    scientific, 3, 7–8, 192, 208
    standard, 3, 8

Number line, 62
    fraction-decimal, 43, 335
    points on, 21
    positive-negative rational, 335

Number model, 16

Number pairs, plotting ordered, 87

Numbers
    composite, 18
    counting, 2, 60
    finding percent of, 135
    history of, 2
    irrational, 19, 60–61
    mixed, 23, 24
    prime, 18
    rational, 2, 60–61, 56–59
    real, 60
    rounding, 131
    scientific notation for large, small, 7
    square, 6
    target, 196, 207
    whole, 2, 3–18, 19, 23

Number sentences, 157–158

Number systems, 2, 60–61

Numerals, 2

Numerator, 21

O

Obtuse angle, 72

Obtuse triangle, 72

Octagon, 73

Octahedron, 76

Octave, in music, 265

Octillions, 5

Open sentence, 158, 163

Operation symbols, 157

Opposite angles, 71

Opposite-change rule, 9

Opposites of Opposites Property, 65

Opposites Properties, 65

Ordered number pair, 87
    game for, 222

Order of operations, 161, 187
    on calculator, 187
    rules for, 334

Order of rotation symmetry, 83

Origin, 87

P

Pan-balance problems and equations, 162

Paper airplane, project, 241–246

Parallel lines, 70, 71, 105
    construction of, 105

Parallelograms, 74
    area of, 120, 340
    classification of, 74
    construction of, 96

Parallels, 154

Parentheses, 158
    in order of operations, 161
    on calculator, 187

Partial-differences method, 10

Partial-products method, 12

Partial-sums method, 9

Part-to-part ratio, 141

Part-to-whole ratio, 141

Pattern-block shapes, 68

Pentagon, 73

Pentatonic scale, in music, 276

Percent circle, 68
    how to use, 147–148

Percents, 43, 47
    on calculators, 185, 186
    converting between fractions and, 47

Index

Index

Spoon Scramble, 206

Spreadsheet Scramble, 215

Spreadsheets, 174–176
    and computers, 175–176
    game for, 215
    history and uses of, 174
    programs for, 175

Square, 74
    area of, 119, 120, 340
    on calculator, 190
    constructing inscribed, 99
    formulas for, 340
    perimeter of, 116, 340

Square array, 6

Square centimeter, 109

Square number, 6

Square roots
    game for, 210
    on calculator, 190

Square units, 111

Staff, in music, 267

Standard, 107, 108

Standard notation, 7–8
    converting to scientific notation, 8

Statistical landmarks, 169

Stem, 168

Stem-and-leaf plot, 168

Step graphs, 172

Straight angle, 72

Straightedge, constructions with, 93–106

Subtraction
    algorithms for, 4, 10
    on calculators, 183
    of decimals, 48-49
    of fractions, 20, 32
    games for, 197, 214
    of mixed numbers, 34–35
    of positive and negative rational numbers, 58
    properties, for rational numbers, 64, 66

Subtraction and Division Properties, 66

Subtraction Top-It, 197–198

Sum of Opposites Property, 65

Supplementary angles, 71

Surface area, 127, 128

Surveys and sampling, 166–173
    bar graphs, 171
    line graphs, 173
    mean, 170
    organizing data in, 167–168
    project for, 226–227
    statistical landmarks, 169
    step graphs, 172

Symbols
    grouping, 157
    math, 157
    in metric system, 110
    operation, 157
    relation, 157

Symmetry, about a line, 82

T

Tally charts, 167, 168

Target numbers, 196, 207

Temperature
    conversions, 341
    metric system for, 109
    solar system, 231–232

Temperature scale, 56

Tempo, in music, 268, 271–272

Ten, powers of, 7, 11, 13, 41
    division by, 53–54
    multiplication of, 50–51

Terminating decimal, 61

Tessellation, 84–85
    project for, 256–257

Tetrahedron, 76

Theorem of Pythagoras, 86

Thousands, 5

3-D Shape Sort, 220

Time
    light years, 236
    metric system for, 109
    units of, 339

Time signature, in music, 270

Top-It games, 197

Tables and Charts

Place-Value Chart

trillions	1000 billions		10^{12}
	100 billions		10^{11}
		10 billions	10^{10}
	1000 millions	billions	10^{9}
		100 millions	10^{8}
		10 millions	10^{7}
millions	1,000,000's		10^{6}
hundred thousands	100,000's		10^{5}
ten thousands	10,000's		10^{4}
thousands	1000's		10^{3}
hundreds	100's		10^{2}
tens	10's		10^{1}
ones	1's		10^{0}
.	.		.
tenths	0.1's		10^{-1}
hundredths	0.01's		10^{-2}
thousandths	0.001's		10^{-3}

Prefixes

uni- . . . . . . one		tera- . . . trillion (10^{12})	
bi- . . . . two		giga- . . . billion (10^{9})	
tri- . . . . three		mega- . . . million (10^{6})	
quad- . . . . four		kilo- . . . . thousand (10^{3})	
penta- . . . . five		hecto- . . . hundred (10^{2})	
hexa- . . . . six		deca- . . . ten (10^{1})	
hepta- . . . . seven		uni- . . . . one (10^{0})	
octa- . . . . . eight		deci- . . . tenth (10^{-1})	
nona- . . . . nine		centi- . . . hundredth (10^{-2})	
deca- . . . . ten		milli- . . . thousandth (10^{-3})	
dodeca- . . twelve		micro- . . millionth (10^{-6})	
icosa- . . . . twenty		nano- . . . billionth (10^{-9})	

Multiplication and Division Table

*, /	1	2	3	4	5	6	7	8	9	10	11	12
1	1	2	3	4	5	6	7	8	9	10	11	12
2	2	4	6	8	10	12	14	16	18	20	22	24
3	3	6	9	12	15	18	21	24	27	30	33	36
4	4	8	12	16	20	24	28	32	36	40	44	48
5	5	10	15	20	25	30	35	40	45	50	55	60
6	6	12	18	24	30	36	42	48	54	60	66	72
7	7	14	21	28	35	42	49	56	63	70	77	84
8	8	16	24	32	40	48	56	64	72	80	88	96
9	9	18	27	36	45	54	63	72	81	90	99	108
10	10	20	30	40	50	60	70	80	90	100	110	120
11	11	22	33	44	55	66	77	88	99	110	121	132
12	12	24	36	48	60	72	84	96	108	120	132	144

Rules for Order of Operations

1. Do operations within parentheses or other grouping symbols before doing anything else.
2. Calculate all powers.
3. Do multiplications or divisions in order, from left to right.
4. Then do additions or subtractions in order, from left to right.

Fraction Stick Chart

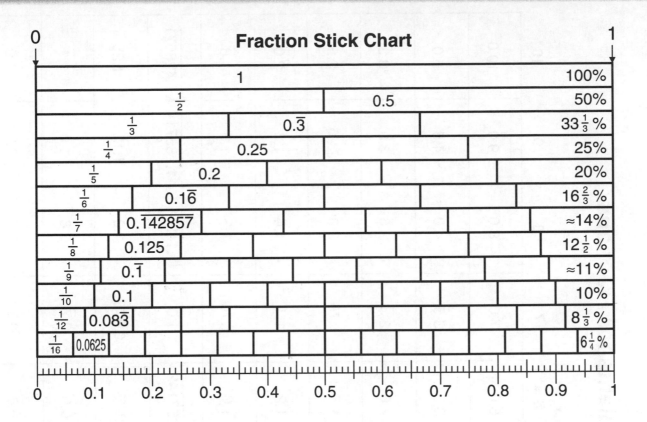

Fraction-Decimal Number Line

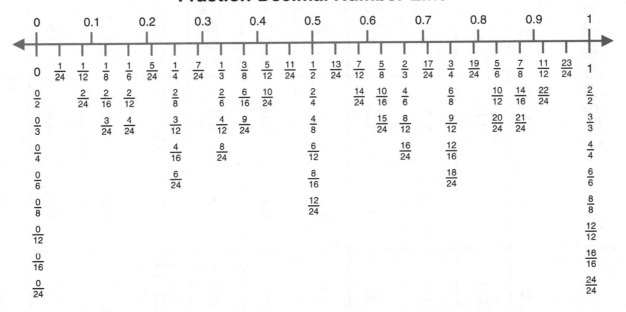

Positive-Negative Rational Number Line

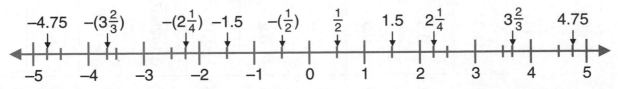

Tables and Charts

Table of Decimal Equivalents for Fractions

Denominator \ Numerator	1	2	3	4	5	6	7	8	9	10
1	1.0	2.0	3.0	4.0	5.0	6.0	7.0	8.0	9.0	10.0
2	0.5	1.0	1.5	2.0	2.5	3.0	3.5	4.0	4.5	5.0
3	$0.\overline{3}$	$0.\overline{6}$	1.0	$1.\overline{3}$	$1.\overline{6}$	2.0	$2.\overline{3}$	$2.\overline{6}$	3.0	$3.\overline{3}$
4	0.25	0.5	0.75	1.0	1.25	1.5	1.75	2.0	2.25	2.5
5	0.2	0.4	0.6	0.8	1.0	1.2	1.4	1.6	1.8	2.0
6	$0.1\overline{6}$	$0.\overline{3}$	0.5	$0.\overline{6}$	$0.8\overline{3}$	1.0	$1.1\overline{6}$	$1.\overline{3}$	1.5	$1.\overline{6}$
7	$0.\overline{142857}$	$0.\overline{285714}$	$0.\overline{428571}$	$0.\overline{571428}$	$0.\overline{714285}$	$0.\overline{857142}$	1.0	$1.\overline{142857}$	$1.\overline{285714}$	$1.\overline{428571}$
8	0.125	0.25	0.375	0.5	0.625	0.75	0.875	1.0	1.125	1.25
9	$0.\overline{1}$	$0.\overline{2}$	$0.\overline{3}$	$0.\overline{4}$	$0.\overline{5}$	$0.\overline{6}$	$0.\overline{7}$	$0.\overline{8}$	1.0	$1.\overline{1}$
10	0.1	0.2	0.3	0.4	0.5	0.6	0.7	0.8	0.9	1.0

Equivalent Fractions, Decimals, and Percents

															Decimal	Percent
$\frac{1}{2}$	$\frac{2}{4}$	$\frac{3}{6}$	$\frac{4}{8}$	$\frac{5}{10}$	$\frac{6}{12}$	$\frac{7}{14}$	$\frac{8}{16}$	$\frac{9}{18}$	$\frac{10}{20}$	$\frac{11}{22}$	$\frac{12}{24}$	$\frac{13}{26}$	$\frac{14}{28}$	$\frac{15}{30}$	0.5	50%
$\frac{1}{3}$	$\frac{2}{6}$	$\frac{3}{9}$	$\frac{4}{12}$	$\frac{5}{15}$	$\frac{6}{18}$	$\frac{7}{21}$	$\frac{8}{24}$	$\frac{9}{27}$	$\frac{10}{30}$	$\frac{11}{33}$	$\frac{12}{36}$	$\frac{13}{39}$	$\frac{14}{42}$	$\frac{15}{45}$	$0.\overline{3}$	$33\frac{1}{3}\%$
$\frac{2}{3}$	$\frac{4}{6}$	$\frac{6}{9}$	$\frac{8}{12}$	$\frac{10}{15}$	$\frac{12}{18}$	$\frac{14}{21}$	$\frac{16}{24}$	$\frac{18}{27}$	$\frac{20}{30}$	$\frac{22}{33}$	$\frac{24}{36}$	$\frac{26}{39}$	$\frac{28}{42}$	$\frac{30}{45}$	$0.\overline{6}$	$66\frac{2}{3}\%$
$\frac{1}{4}$	$\frac{2}{8}$	$\frac{3}{12}$	$\frac{4}{16}$	$\frac{5}{20}$	$\frac{6}{24}$	$\frac{7}{28}$	$\frac{8}{32}$	$\frac{9}{36}$	$\frac{10}{40}$	$\frac{11}{44}$	$\frac{12}{48}$	$\frac{13}{52}$	$\frac{14}{56}$	$\frac{15}{60}$	0.25	25%
$\frac{3}{4}$	$\frac{6}{8}$	$\frac{9}{12}$	$\frac{12}{16}$	$\frac{15}{20}$	$\frac{18}{24}$	$\frac{21}{28}$	$\frac{24}{32}$	$\frac{27}{36}$	$\frac{30}{40}$	$\frac{33}{44}$	$\frac{36}{48}$	$\frac{39}{52}$	$\frac{42}{56}$	$\frac{45}{60}$	0.75	75%
$\frac{1}{5}$	$\frac{2}{10}$	$\frac{3}{15}$	$\frac{4}{20}$	$\frac{5}{25}$	$\frac{6}{30}$	$\frac{7}{35}$	$\frac{8}{40}$	$\frac{9}{45}$	$\frac{10}{50}$	$\frac{11}{55}$	$\frac{12}{60}$	$\frac{13}{65}$	$\frac{14}{70}$	$\frac{15}{75}$	0.2	20%
$\frac{2}{5}$	$\frac{4}{10}$	$\frac{6}{15}$	$\frac{8}{20}$	$\frac{10}{25}$	$\frac{12}{30}$	$\frac{14}{35}$	$\frac{16}{40}$	$\frac{18}{45}$	$\frac{20}{50}$	$\frac{22}{55}$	$\frac{24}{60}$	$\frac{26}{65}$	$\frac{28}{70}$	$\frac{30}{75}$	0.4	40%
$\frac{3}{5}$	$\frac{6}{10}$	$\frac{9}{15}$	$\frac{12}{20}$	$\frac{15}{25}$	$\frac{18}{30}$	$\frac{21}{35}$	$\frac{24}{40}$	$\frac{27}{45}$	$\frac{30}{50}$	$\frac{33}{55}$	$\frac{36}{60}$	$\frac{39}{65}$	$\frac{42}{70}$	$\frac{45}{75}$	0.6	60%
$\frac{4}{5}$	$\frac{8}{10}$	$\frac{12}{15}$	$\frac{16}{20}$	$\frac{20}{25}$	$\frac{24}{30}$	$\frac{28}{35}$	$\frac{32}{40}$	$\frac{36}{45}$	$\frac{40}{50}$	$\frac{44}{55}$	$\frac{48}{60}$	$\frac{52}{65}$	$\frac{56}{70}$	$\frac{60}{75}$	0.8	80%
$\frac{1}{6}$	$\frac{2}{12}$	$\frac{3}{18}$	$\frac{4}{24}$	$\frac{5}{30}$	$\frac{6}{36}$	$\frac{7}{42}$	$\frac{8}{48}$	$\frac{9}{54}$	$\frac{10}{60}$	$\frac{11}{66}$	$\frac{12}{72}$	$\frac{13}{78}$	$\frac{14}{84}$	$\frac{15}{90}$	$0.1\overline{6}$	$16\frac{2}{3}\%$
$\frac{5}{6}$	$\frac{10}{12}$	$\frac{15}{18}$	$\frac{20}{24}$	$\frac{25}{30}$	$\frac{30}{36}$	$\frac{35}{42}$	$\frac{40}{48}$	$\frac{45}{54}$	$\frac{50}{60}$	$\frac{55}{66}$	$\frac{60}{72}$	$\frac{65}{78}$	$\frac{70}{84}$	$\frac{75}{90}$	$0.8\overline{3}$	$83\frac{1}{3}\%$
$\frac{1}{7}$	$\frac{2}{14}$	$\frac{3}{21}$	$\frac{4}{28}$	$\frac{5}{35}$	$\frac{6}{42}$	$\frac{7}{49}$	$\frac{8}{56}$	$\frac{9}{63}$	$\frac{10}{70}$	$\frac{11}{77}$	$\frac{12}{84}$	$\frac{13}{91}$	$\frac{14}{98}$	$\frac{15}{105}$	0.143	14.3%
$\frac{2}{7}$	$\frac{4}{14}$	$\frac{6}{21}$	$\frac{8}{28}$	$\frac{10}{35}$	$\frac{12}{42}$	$\frac{14}{49}$	$\frac{16}{56}$	$\frac{18}{63}$	$\frac{20}{70}$	$\frac{22}{77}$	$\frac{24}{84}$	$\frac{26}{91}$	$\frac{28}{98}$	$\frac{30}{105}$	0.286	28.6%
$\frac{3}{7}$	$\frac{6}{14}$	$\frac{9}{21}$	$\frac{12}{28}$	$\frac{15}{35}$	$\frac{18}{42}$	$\frac{21}{49}$	$\frac{24}{56}$	$\frac{27}{63}$	$\frac{30}{70}$	$\frac{33}{77}$	$\frac{36}{84}$	$\frac{39}{91}$	$\frac{42}{98}$	$\frac{45}{105}$	0.429	42.9%
$\frac{4}{7}$	$\frac{8}{14}$	$\frac{12}{21}$	$\frac{16}{28}$	$\frac{20}{35}$	$\frac{24}{42}$	$\frac{28}{49}$	$\frac{32}{56}$	$\frac{36}{63}$	$\frac{40}{70}$	$\frac{44}{77}$	$\frac{48}{84}$	$\frac{52}{91}$	$\frac{56}{98}$	$\frac{60}{105}$	0.571	57.1%
$\frac{5}{7}$	$\frac{10}{14}$	$\frac{15}{21}$	$\frac{20}{28}$	$\frac{25}{35}$	$\frac{30}{42}$	$\frac{35}{49}$	$\frac{40}{56}$	$\frac{45}{63}$	$\frac{50}{70}$	$\frac{55}{77}$	$\frac{60}{84}$	$\frac{65}{91}$	$\frac{70}{98}$	$\frac{75}{105}$	0.714	71.4%
$\frac{6}{7}$	$\frac{12}{14}$	$\frac{18}{21}$	$\frac{24}{28}$	$\frac{30}{35}$	$\frac{36}{42}$	$\frac{42}{49}$	$\frac{48}{56}$	$\frac{54}{63}$	$\frac{60}{70}$	$\frac{66}{77}$	$\frac{72}{84}$	$\frac{78}{91}$	$\frac{84}{98}$	$\frac{90}{105}$	0.857	85.7%
$\frac{1}{8}$	$\frac{2}{16}$	$\frac{3}{24}$	$\frac{4}{32}$	$\frac{5}{40}$	$\frac{6}{48}$	$\frac{7}{56}$	$\frac{8}{64}$	$\frac{9}{72}$	$\frac{10}{80}$	$\frac{11}{88}$	$\frac{12}{96}$	$\frac{13}{104}$	$\frac{14}{112}$	$\frac{15}{120}$	0.125	$12\frac{1}{2}\%$
$\frac{3}{8}$	$\frac{6}{16}$	$\frac{9}{24}$	$\frac{12}{32}$	$\frac{15}{40}$	$\frac{18}{48}$	$\frac{21}{56}$	$\frac{24}{64}$	$\frac{27}{72}$	$\frac{30}{80}$	$\frac{33}{88}$	$\frac{36}{96}$	$\frac{39}{104}$	$\frac{42}{112}$	$\frac{45}{120}$	0.375	$37\frac{1}{2}\%$
$\frac{5}{8}$	$\frac{10}{16}$	$\frac{15}{24}$	$\frac{20}{32}$	$\frac{25}{40}$	$\frac{30}{48}$	$\frac{35}{56}$	$\frac{40}{64}$	$\frac{45}{72}$	$\frac{50}{80}$	$\frac{55}{88}$	$\frac{60}{96}$	$\frac{65}{104}$	$\frac{70}{112}$	$\frac{75}{120}$	0.625	$62\frac{1}{2}\%$
$\frac{7}{8}$	$\frac{14}{16}$	$\frac{21}{24}$	$\frac{28}{32}$	$\frac{35}{40}$	$\frac{42}{48}$	$\frac{49}{56}$	$\frac{56}{64}$	$\frac{63}{72}$	$\frac{70}{80}$	$\frac{77}{88}$	$\frac{84}{96}$	$\frac{91}{104}$	$\frac{98}{112}$	$\frac{105}{120}$	0.875	$87\frac{1}{2}\%$
$\frac{1}{9}$	$\frac{2}{18}$	$\frac{3}{27}$	$\frac{4}{36}$	$\frac{5}{45}$	$\frac{6}{54}$	$\frac{7}{63}$	$\frac{8}{72}$	$\frac{9}{81}$	$\frac{10}{90}$	$\frac{11}{99}$	$\frac{12}{108}$	$\frac{13}{117}$	$\frac{14}{126}$	$\frac{15}{135}$	$0.\overline{1}$	$11\frac{1}{9}\%$
$\frac{2}{9}$	$\frac{4}{18}$	$\frac{6}{27}$	$\frac{8}{36}$	$\frac{10}{45}$	$\frac{12}{54}$	$\frac{14}{63}$	$\frac{16}{72}$	$\frac{18}{81}$	$\frac{20}{90}$	$\frac{22}{99}$	$\frac{24}{108}$	$\frac{26}{117}$	$\frac{28}{126}$	$\frac{30}{135}$	$0.\overline{2}$	$22\frac{2}{9}\%$
$\frac{4}{9}$	$\frac{8}{18}$	$\frac{12}{27}$	$\frac{16}{36}$	$\frac{20}{45}$	$\frac{24}{54}$	$\frac{28}{63}$	$\frac{32}{72}$	$\frac{36}{81}$	$\frac{40}{90}$	$\frac{44}{99}$	$\frac{48}{108}$	$\frac{52}{117}$	$\frac{56}{126}$	$\frac{60}{135}$	$0.\overline{4}$	$44\frac{4}{9}\%$
$\frac{5}{9}$	$\frac{10}{18}$	$\frac{15}{27}$	$\frac{20}{36}$	$\frac{25}{45}$	$\frac{30}{54}$	$\frac{35}{63}$	$\frac{40}{72}$	$\frac{45}{81}$	$\frac{50}{90}$	$\frac{55}{99}$	$\frac{60}{108}$	$\frac{65}{117}$	$\frac{70}{126}$	$\frac{75}{135}$	$0.\overline{5}$	$55\frac{5}{9}\%$
$\frac{7}{9}$	$\frac{14}{18}$	$\frac{21}{27}$	$\frac{28}{36}$	$\frac{35}{45}$	$\frac{42}{54}$	$\frac{49}{63}$	$\frac{56}{72}$	$\frac{63}{81}$	$\frac{70}{90}$	$\frac{77}{99}$	$\frac{84}{108}$	$\frac{91}{117}$	$\frac{98}{126}$	$\frac{105}{135}$	$0.\overline{7}$	$77\frac{7}{9}\%$
$\frac{8}{9}$	$\frac{16}{18}$	$\frac{24}{27}$	$\frac{32}{36}$	$\frac{40}{45}$	$\frac{48}{54}$	$\frac{56}{63}$	$\frac{64}{72}$	$\frac{72}{81}$	$\frac{80}{90}$	$\frac{88}{99}$	$\frac{96}{108}$	$\frac{104}{117}$	$\frac{112}{126}$	$\frac{120}{135}$	$0.\overline{8}$	$88\frac{8}{9}\%$

Note: The decimals for sevenths have been rounded to the nearest thousandth.

Probability Meter

CERTAIN

Percent	Decimal		Fraction
100%	1.00	EXTREMELY LIKELY	
	0.99		$\frac{99}{100}$
95%	0.95		$\frac{19}{20}$
90%	0.90		$\frac{9}{10}$
	0.875	VERY LIKELY	$\frac{7}{8}$
85%	0.85		
	0.8$\overline{3}$		$\frac{5}{6}$
80%	0.80		$\frac{4}{5}, \frac{8}{10}$
75%	0.75		$\frac{3}{4}, \frac{6}{8}$
70%	0.70	LIKELY	$\frac{7}{10}$
	0.6$\overline{6}$		$\frac{2}{3}$
65%	0.65		
	0.625		$\frac{5}{8}$
60%	0.60		$\frac{3}{5}, \frac{6}{10}$
55%	0.55		
50%	0.50	50–50 CHANCE	$\frac{1}{2}, \frac{2}{4}, \frac{3}{6}, \frac{4}{8}, \frac{5}{10}, \frac{10}{20}, \frac{50}{100}$
45%	0.45		
40%	0.40		$\frac{2}{5}, \frac{4}{10}$
	0.375		$\frac{3}{8}$
35%	0.35		
	0.3$\overline{3}$		$\frac{1}{3}$
30%	0.30	UNLIKELY	$\frac{3}{10}$
25%	0.25		$\frac{1}{4}, \frac{2}{8}$
20%	0.20		$\frac{1}{5}$
	0.1$\overline{6}$	VERY UNLIKELY	$\frac{1}{6}$
15%	0.15		
	0.125		$\frac{1}{8}$
10%	0.10	EXTREMELY UNLIKELY	$\frac{1}{10}$
5%	0.05		$\frac{1}{20}$
1%	0.01		$\frac{1}{100}$
0%	0.00		0

IMPOSSIBLE

Decimal and Percent Equivalents for "Easy" Fractions

"Easy" Fractions	Decimals	Percents
$\frac{1}{2}$	0.50	50%
$\frac{1}{3}$	0.$\overline{3}$	$33\frac{1}{3}\%$
$\frac{2}{3}$	0.$\overline{6}$	$66\frac{2}{3}\%$
$\frac{1}{4}$	0.25	25%
$\frac{3}{4}$	0.75	75%
$\frac{1}{5}$	0.20	20%
$\frac{2}{5}$	0.40	40%
$\frac{3}{5}$	0.60	60%
$\frac{4}{5}$	0.80	80%
$\frac{1}{6}$	0.1$\overline{6}$	$16\frac{2}{3}\%$
$\frac{1}{8}$	0.125	$12\frac{1}{2}\%$
$\frac{3}{8}$	0.375	$37\frac{1}{2}\%$
$\frac{5}{8}$	0.625	$62\frac{1}{2}\%$
$\frac{7}{8}$	0.875	$87\frac{1}{2}\%$
$\frac{1}{10}$	0.10	10%
$\frac{3}{10}$	0.30	30%
$\frac{7}{10}$	0.70	70%
$\frac{9}{10}$	0.90	90%

Metric System

Units of Length
1 kilometer (km)	= 1000 meters (m)
1 meter	= 10 decimeters (dm)
	= 100 centimeters (cm)
	= 1000 millimeters (mm)
1 decimeter	= 10 centimeters
1 centimeter	= 10 millimeters

Units of Area
1 square meter (m^2)	= 100 square decimeters (dm^2)
	= 10,000 square centimeters (cm^2)
1 square decimeter	= 100 square centimeters
1 are (a)	= 100 square meters
1 hectare (ha)	= 100 ares
1 square kilometer	= 100 hectares

Units of Volume
1 cubic meter (m^3)	= 1000 cubic decimeters (dm^3)
	= 1,000,000 cubic centimeters (cm^3)
1 cubic decimeter	= 1000 cubic centimeters

Units of Capacity
1 kiloliter (kL)	= 1000 liters (L)
1 liter	= 1000 milliliters (mL)

Units of Mass
1 metric ton (t)	= 1000 kilograms (kg)
1 kilogram	= 1000 grams (g)
1 gram	= 1000 milligrams (mg)

U.S. Customary System

Units of Length
1 mile (mi)	= 1760 yards (yd)
	= 5280 feet (ft)
1 yard	= 3 feet
	= 36 inches (in)
1 foot	= 12 inches

Units of Area
1 square yard (yd^2)	= 9 square feet (ft^2)
	= 1296 square inches (in^2)
1 square foot	= 144 square inches
1 acre	= 43,560 square feet
1 square mile (mi^2)	= 640 acres

Units of Volume
1 cubic yard (yd^3)	= 27 cubic feet (ft^3)
1 cubic foot	= 1728 cubic inches (in^3)

Units of Capacity
1 gallon (gal)	= 4 quarts (qt)
1 quart	= 2 pints (pt)
1 pint	= 2 cups (c)
1 cup	= 8 fluid ounces (fl. oz)
1 fluid ounce	= 2 tablespoons (tbs)
1 tablespoon	= 3 teaspoons (tsp)

Units of Weight
1 ton (T)	= 2000 pounds (lb)
1 pound	= 16 ounces (oz)

System Equivalents

1 inch is about 2.5 cm (2.54)
1 kilometer is about 0.6 mile (0.621)
1 mile is about 1.6 kilometers (1.609)
1 meter is about 39 inches (39.37)
1 liter is about 1.1 quarts (1.057)
1 ounce is about 28 grams (28.350)
1 kilogram is about 2.2 pounds (2.205)
1 acre is about 2.5 hectares (2.47)

Units of Time

1 century	= 100 years
1 decade	= 10 years
1 year (yr)	= 12 months
	= 52 weeks (plus one or two days)
	= 365 days (366 days in a leap year)
1 month (mo)	= 28, 29, 30, or 31 days
1 week (wk)	= 7 days
1 day (d)	= 24 hours
1 hour (hr)	= 60 minutes
1 minute (min)	= 60 seconds (sec)

The Global Grid

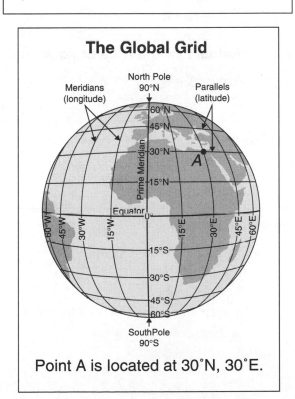

Point A is located at 30°N, 30°E.

Tables and Charts

Formulas	Meaning of Variables
Rectangles • Perimeter: $p = (2 * l) + (2 * w)$ • Area: $A = (b * h)$	p = perimeter; l = length; w = width; A = area; b = length of base; h = height
Squares • Perimeter: $p = 4 * s$ • Area: $A = s^2$	p = perimeter; s = length of side; A = area
Parallelograms • Area: $A = b * h$	A = area; b = length of base; h = height
Triangles • Area: $A = \frac{1}{2} * b * h$	A = area; b = length of base; h = height
Regular Polygons • Perimeter: $p = n * s$	p = perimeter; n = number of sides; s = length of side
Circles • Circumference: $c = \pi * d$, or $c = 2 * \pi * r$ • Area: $A = \pi * r^2$	c = circumference; d = diameter; r = radius; A = area
Pick's Formula for the Area of Polygons • Area: $A = (\frac{1}{2} * P) + I - 1$	A = area; P = number of grid points on polygon; I = number of grid points in the interior
Polyhedrons • Euler's formula: $e = (f + v) - 2$	e = number of edges; f = number of faces; v = number of vertices
Rectangular Prisms • Volume: $V = B * h$, or $V = l * w * h$ • Surface area: $S = 2 * ((l * w) + (l * h) + (w * h))$	V = volume; B = area of base; l = length; w = width; h = height S = surface area

Cubes

- Volume: $V = e^3$
- Surface area: $S = 6 * e^2$

V = volume; e = length of edge
S = Surface area

Cylinders

- Volume: $V = B * h$, or
  $V = \pi * r^2 * h$
- Surface area:
  $S = (2 * \pi * r^2) + ((2 * \pi * r) * h)$

V = volume; B = area of base; h = height;
r = radius of base
S = surface area

Pyramids

- Volume: $V = \frac{1}{3} * B * h$

V = volume; B = area of base; h = height

Cones

- Volume: $V = \frac{1}{3} * B * h$, or
  $V = \frac{1}{3} * \pi * r^2 * h$

V = volume; B = area of base; h = height;
r = radius of base

Spheres

- Volume: $V = \frac{4}{3} * \pi * r^3$

V = volume; r = radius

Temperatures

- Fahrenheit to Celsius conversion:
  $C = \frac{5}{9} * (F - 32°)$
- Celsius to Fahrenheit conversion:
  $F = (\frac{9}{5} * C) + 32°$

C = degrees Celsius; F = degrees Fahrenheit

Distances

- $d = r * t$

d = distance traveled; r = rate of speed;
t = time of travel

Mobiles

- Fulcrum at center:
  $W * D = w * d$
- Fulcrum not at center:
  $(W * D) + (R * L) = w * d$

W = weight of object farthest from fulcrum
D = distance of this object from the fulcrum

w = weight of object closest to fulcrum
d = distance of this object from the fulcrum
R = weight of rod
L = distance from center to fulcrum

Tables and Charts

Everyday Mathematics Geometry Template

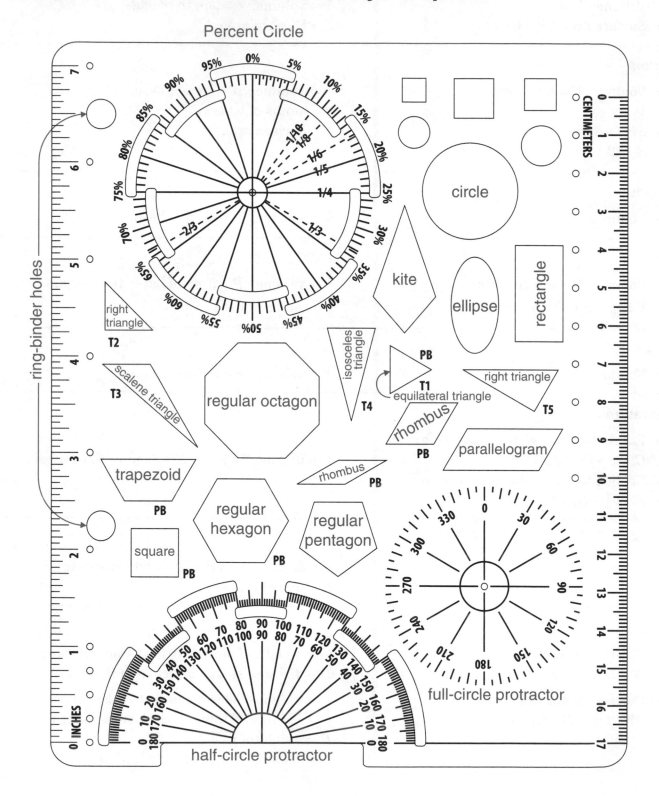

Percent Circle